T H E
Common Sense
of the
Exact Sciences

BY

WILLIAM KINGDON CLIFFORD

EDITED AND WITH A PREFACE BY
KARL PEARSON

NEWLY EDITED

AND WITH AN INTRODUCTION BY
JAMES R. NEWMAN

PREFACE BY
BERTRAND RUSSELL

NEW YORK
DOVER PUBLICATIONS, INC.

This new Dover edition, first
published in 1955, is an unabridged
and unaltered republication of the Knopf edition
published in 1946. It is issued through special arrangement
with Alfred A. Knopf, Inc.

THE

COMMON SENSE

OF THE

EXACT SCIENCES

Remember, then, that [scientific thought] is the guide of action; that the truth which it arrives at is not that which we can ideally contemplate without error, but that which we may act upon without fear; and you cannot fail to see that scientific thought is not an accompaniment or condition of human progress, but human progress itself.

W. K. Clifford

"Aims and Instruments of Scientific Thought"

PREFACE

THE copy of this book which I still possess was given to me by my tutor when I was fifteen years of age. I read it at once, with passionate interest and with an intoxicating delight in intellectual clarification. From that day until I came to write this Preface, I had not looked at the book. Now, having re-read it after fifty-seven years, many of them devoted to the subjects of which it treats, I find that it deserved all the adolescent enthusiasm that I bestowed upon it when I first read it.

Clifford possessed an art of clarity such as belongs only to a very few great men—not the pseudo-clarity of the popularizer, which is achieved by ignoring or glozing over the difficult points, but the clarity that comes of profound and orderly understanding, by virtue of which principles become luminous and deductions look easy. When I first became acquainted with Clifford, it was only three years since I had been struggling with Euclid's theory of proportion—a subject that is now considered too difficult for schoolboys, but which in those days had to be mastered by every budding mathematician. As Euclid treats it, it is a puzzling subject, not only because it is inherently complicated, but because Euclid never mentions his perfectly adequate reasons for not adopting the much simpler arithmetical procedure, of which the fallacies are not obvious until they are pointed out. Clifford, by telling just what is necessary and no more, makes the whole theory as clear as noonday. In this and in other matters the book is invaluable to the schoolboy who, though interested by mathematics, is bewildered, as any intelligent boy must be if he is badly taught.

The later parts of the book, as explained in the original Preface, owe much to Karl Pearson, since Clifford's early death left the manuscript incomplete. Karl Pearson, how-

ever, had so fully assimilated Clifford's way of looking at
mathematics that he was able to carry out his task without
producing in the reader any awareness of discontinuity. The
book can therefore be treated as a whole, and there is no
need to struggle to separate the editor's work from the
author's.

The subject of which the book treats—the basis of pure
mathematics in logic and of applied mathematics in observation—is one in which immense progress has been made
since the time when Clifford wrote, but knowledge of subsequent work only increases the reader's admiration for his
prophetic insight. All that is said on the relation of geometry
to physics is entirely in harmony with Einstein's theory of
gravitation, which was published thirty-six years after Clifford's death. The Book's explicit rejection of "matter" and
"force" as concepts to be used in physics is due to Karl
Pearson, but has some sanction in Clifford's notes and is
clearly in line with his thinking. In this respect, as in many
others, Clifford was ahead of almost all the best thinking of
his time.

Non-Euclidean geometry, in which two straight lines may
enclose a space, or a triangle may have all its angles zero, was
a subject which, though inaugurated by Lobachevsky in
1829, had only just begun to attract the notice of most
geometers in Clifford's day. It was a very exciting and
rather disturbing subject, since it showed that many things
which, since Greek times, had been thought capable of
mathematical proof could in fact be established only by
observation. Clifford himself did important work on this
subject, and read a paper on a branch of it to the British
Association in 1873. But the work remained unpublished,
and might have been forgotten if it had not been mentioned
and carried further by a German mathematician, Felix
Klein, in his *Lectures on Non-Euclidean Geometry*, in which
he states that he felt himself more intimately related to
Clifford than to any other geometer. At the time when I
first read *The Common Sense of the Exact Sciences*, I had only

lately heard of the possibility of geometries that contra-
dicted Euclid; what I read in this book did much to diminish
the bewilderment that I had been feeling. In spite of all the
work that has since been done, hardly anything that Clifford (or Karl Pearson) says on this subject could be bettered
by a writer at the present day. Some other geometrical
topics, however—for instance, the mention of quaternions,
for which apparently the editor is responsible—would be
omitted by most modern authors, since they have not proved
as important or as illuminating as seemed likely at one time.

The opening chapter, on Number, although it says ad-
mirably what, in the seventies, seemed best worth saying,
cannot tell the reader what is now known to be most important, since in this subject the great advances made by
Dedekind, Cantor, and Frege came in the decade immediately following Clifford's death. He was, moreover, a
geometer rather than an analyst, and it was in geometry
that his mathematical intuition appeared at its best.

A taste for mathematics, like a taste for music, can be
generated in some people, but not in others. My brother, to
the end of his life, could not distinguish *God Save the King*
from *Rule, Britannia!* For him even the most admirable
book on harmony and counterpoint would have been totally
useless. In like manner there are people for whom such books
as Clifford's serve no purpose; they are the people who have
no wish to understand the matters of which it treats. But I
think that these could be much fewer than bad instruction
makes them seem. Pupils who have not an unusually strong
natural bent towards mathematics are led to hate the subject
by two shortcomings on the part of their teachers. The
first is that mathematics is not exhibited as the basis of all
our scientific knowledge, both theoretical and practical: the
pupil is not convincingly shown that what we can understand of the world, and what we can do with machines, we
can understand and do in virtue of mathematics. The second
defect is that the difficulties are not approached gradually,
as they should be, and are not minimized by being con-

viii Preface

nected with easily apprehended central principles, so that
the edifice of mathematics is made to look like a collection
of detached hovels rather than a single temple embodying
a unitary plan. It is especially in regard to this second defect that Clifford's book is valuable.

Clifford's book may not only still be read with great profit
by young people interested in mathematics, but should also
be studied with diligent admiration by all who are engaged
in trying to make difficult ideas intelligible. New ideas almost
always appear first in an unnecessarily complicated form,
and are therefore thought harder to master than they are
subsequently found to be. Plato thought the years from
twenty to thirty not too long for acquiring a knowledge of
the mathematics that had been discovered in his day, most
of which in our time any promising student achieves by
the age of thirteen. This acceleration is due to the labours of
many men who have done something of what Clifford did
in this book. As the total amount of human knowledge increases and the journey from childish ignorance to the
frontier of discovery lengthens, it becomes more and more
important to hasten the process and to make the journey
as easy as possible. In each generation some of this work has
to be done afresh, since some old subjects turn out to be un-
important and some new ones important. Plato and Euclid
thought the construction of the regular solids the most important problem in geometry; nowadays this is a mere by-
path. The earliest extant treatise on arithmetic, that of
Ahmes the Egyptian, of about 1700 B.C., is largely concerned
to show how to exhibit fractions as sums of other fractions
having 1 for their numerators, a matter that has since become
totally without interest. The discarding of such useless
traditional problems is one part of what must be done if
instruction is to be sufficiently rapid.

The other thing that must be done—and here Clifford is
supremely excellent—is to discover the point of view from
which a subject is most easily surveyed. A wood in which
the trees are planted in rows looks regular when viewed

along a row from one end of it, but may appear completely
higgledy-piggledy when viewed on a slant. The same sort of
thing is true of a mathematical subject: if you approach it
from the wrong angle, each step will be difficult, you will
be entangled in thickets, and you will get no view of the
whole; but if you start at the right point and advance in the
right direction, the obstacles disappear and progress is easy.
Clifford's survey of elementary Euclidean geometry, beginning with the two axioms that things can be moved without
change of shape, and that the size of things can be increased
or diminished by a change of scale without change of shape,
is just what is needed to make geometry easy to a beginner
without undue sacrifice of logical rigour. And the same
merits remain when he comes, later, to treat of conic sections.

Clifford was much more than a mathematician: he was a
philosopher, of considerable merit in what concerned the
foundations of mathematical knowledge. Moreover, he saw
all knowledge, even the most abstract, as part of the general
life of mankind, and as concerned in the endeavour to make
human existence less petty, less superstitious, and less
miserable. He lived at a time when optimism was not so difficult as it has since become, and when hope for the future
seemed justified by the history of the previous two hundred
years. It was possible, without any blind act of faith, to
believe that the human species would become progressively
more humane, more tolerant, and more enlightened, with
the consequence that war and disease and poverty, and the
other major evils of our existence, would continually diminish. In this beneficent process rational knowledge was
to be the chief agent, and mathematics, as the most completely rational kind of knowledge, was to be in the van.
This faith was Clifford's, and it was mine when I first read
his book; in turning over its pages again, the ghosts of old
hopes rise up to mock me. Over large parts of the earth's
surface the most civilized individuals have suffered perse-
cution, there has been a deliberate lowering of the standard
of comfort, and in the course of combating these evils we

have been compelled to destroy many ancient cities and reduce whole countries, many of them friendly countries, to the
verge of starvation.

In the world in which we find ourselves it is difficult to
believe in the influence of reason on human affairs, or in the
importance to mankind of theoretical knowledge. *Practical*
knowledge, yes, since it enables us to kill our enemies; but
it was not on this account that Clifford valued knowledge,
or that Klein, a German, went out of his way to praise him.
Difficult as it is to maintain the beliefs that inspired the best
men of the nineteenth century, there is, I still think, every
ground for regarding the old virtues of tolerance and en-
lightenment as the basis for the hopes that are possible. If
the men of that time were too optimistic, it is easy for us to
be too pessimistic, for bad periods are no more eternal than
good ones, though while they last they may seem so. I hope
that, in reading this book, readers may imbibe something
of its author's belief in the possibility of excellent things,
and that this may help them to acquire some of the strength
that is needed to fight against the evils of the age in which
we are compelled to live.

Cambridge, 1945   Bertrand Russell

CONTENTS

CHAPTER III. *QUANTITY*

CHAPTER IV. *POSITION*

Contents

Contents xiii

Chapter V. *MOTION*

INTRODUCTION

I

THROUGHOUT the nineteenth century men travelled the roads of science with enormous strides. So numerous were the travellers, so varied and far their journeys, that it is bewildering to attempt to recall the milestones of their progress. In physics: electro-magnetic theory and thermodynamics; in astronomy: the discovery of new planets, the cataloguing of thousands of stars, advances in every part of theoretical astronomy; in chemistry: spectrum analysis, the periodic table, the development of organic chemistry; in biology: theories of evolution and inheritance; in mathematics: group theory, new fields of algebra and analysis, non-Euclidean geometry, foundation studies, a mathematics of infinity—these are among the names which the milestones bear.

If we confine our attention to mathematics two facts stand out. The first is that at no time in the history of mathematics did its contradictory aspects, its diversity and its unity, become more noticeable than in the nineteenth century. While new branches of mathematics emerged, the relationship and interdependence of its existing parts were strengthened, giving to algebra, analysis, and geometry a freedom and generality hitherto inconceivable. The mathematics of the nineteenth century thus brought "scattered but cognate lines of reasoning" together, and, as Merz says,[1] "made them mutually fertile and suggestive."

From the other sciences, which in their forward surge besought the aid of its analytical and descriptive powers, mathematics in the nineteenth century received a powerful impulse; this, the second noteworthy point. The advances

[1] John Theodore Merz: *History of European Thought in the Nineteenth Century*. Fourth edition, Edinburgh and London, 1923.

were so swift and revolutionary that if the mathematics
of the nineteenth century differs markedly from that of the
eighteenth, if it seems strikingly modern and of our time, the
explanation is not far to seek: for the physics, chemistry,
biology, and astronomy of the nineteenth century were also
radically different, also modern and of our time. Nor are
the great movements of our own century belittled by ac-
knowledging their birth in the last.

This stimulus and the search for new links between the
several branches of mathematics are reflected in the papers
of the foremost mathematicians of the century: Gauss,
Riemann, Fourier, Cauchy, Poisson, Hamilton, and many
more. Even those who engaged only in pure research and
like the eminent Jacobi took the view that the principal aim
of mathematics is not "public utility" but, rather, "the
honour of the human spirit," [2] despite their esoteric prefer-
ence, contributed immeasurably to the solution of problems
in physics, astronomy, and chemistry. The "public utility"
of the beautiful structure in function theory erected by
Niels Abel may not have been at once apparent; nor was it
early recognized in the tiny mathematical legacy of Évariste
Galois, killed in a duel at twenty-one. The work of Steiner
and von Staudt in synthetic geometry, of Riemann, Lobachevsky, and Bolyai in non-Euclidean geometry, at first
also seemed remote from the experimental sciences.

But the essence of pure mathematical speculation lies in
the construction of new concepts which, when translated
into symbols, lend themselves to complex operations;
through the operations the concepts are extended in meaning,
their relations developed beyond the boundaries originally
conceived, and again fresh areas of thought are opened.
"All applications of mathematics consist in extending the
empirical knowledge which we possess of a limited number
or region of accessible phenomena into the region of the

[2] ". . . and from this point of view a question about numbers is as important as a question about the system of the world." Quoted by Florian Cajori:
History of Mathematics, p. 413. Second edition, New York, 1919.

unknown and inaccessible." [3] And in this region pure and applied mathematics meet and join forces.

Possessed of mathematical and speculative genius, impelled by a passion for search and inquiry, responsive to the intellectual and social forces that shaped nineteenth-century thought, the author of *The Common Sense of the Exact Sciences* earned a place among the century's distinguished scientists. His best mathematical work lay in geometry, but beyond that he was a citizen of science, ceaselessly endeavouring to strengthen its foundations and organic unity and, by preaching the widest applicability of its methods, to promote the rational and confound the irrational. The gauge and bent of his views are perhaps best shown in a single sentence of an address made at Cambridge when he was twenty-one: "Thought," Clifford said, "is powerless except to make something outside of itself: the thought which conquers the world is not contemplative but active." [4] In a tragically short life of thirty-five years, in a working life of fifteen, he enlarged scientific knowledge by a series of contributions, as beforehanded as they were fertile, as valuable as they were lucid. To the brilliant English astronomer Roger Cotes, Newton paid tribute with the comment: "If he had lived we might have known something." For Clifford, too, this is a fitting epitaph.

II

William Kingdon Clifford was born at Exeter, May 4, 1845. His father, who served as justice of the peace, was well known in town affairs. His mother died when he was young. From her he inherited his restless energy, his genius, perhaps, and, more unfortunately, the predisposition to the disease that so early ended his life.

[3] Merz, op. cit.

[4] *Lectures and Essays* by the late William Kingdon Clifford, F.R.S. Edited by Leslie Stephen and Frederick Pollock. London, 1879. [This is referred to hereinafter as *L & E*; where the quote is from Pollock's Introduction, it is given as *L & E* (P); where the quote is from Clifford's Letters, it is given as *L & E* (Clifford's letters).]

We know nothing of Clifford's childhood. The few stilted anecdotes that survive are of the George Washington cherry-tree school. They tell something of the tellers but nothing of the child. After his early education at Exeter, Clifford at fifteen was sent to King's College in London. There he did well in classical and literary studies as well as in mathematics. Having won a minor scholarship, he left King's in October 1863 to enter Trinity College, Cambridge. The same year that Clifford entered the university he produced a number of original mathematical papers, and his private tutor, Percival Frost, recognizing his gifts, foresaw that he would win a high place among contemporary scientists.

His reputation in his student years stemmed not from his mathematical powers alone. In a rigidly conventional age he was marked by eccentricities of habit, dress, and opinion. His religious views were those of an ardent High-Churchman, and this was not usual in Cambridge at the time. Later in life, influenced by the writings of Darwin and Spencer, Clifford turned violently against organized religion, especially "priestcraft," but at this time, having studied Aquinas, he was "fond of supporting Catholic doctrines by ingenious scientific analogies." [5] What attracted others were "the varied and flexible play of his thought, the boundless range of his human interests and sympathies." [6] Widely read in philosophy, classical literature, and modern history, he challenged his friends by the "daring versatility of his talk." [7] While he often took the unpopular view, even in scientific disputes, he was not eristic in spirit: in debate, as in all activities, he sought the truth. His sincerity and freshness of viewpoint went so naturally together that few of his opponents in argument could take umbrage at his sometimes unlimited enthusiasm; he could give no lasting offence, quite simply, because he meant none.

Frederick Pollock, the eminent jurist, was a student at

[5] Leslie Stephen: article on Clifford, *Dictionary of National Biography*.
[6] *L & E* (P).
[7] Ibid.

Trinity with Clifford. In a tender and reverent biographical note introducing the edition of *Lectures and Essays* that appeared seven years after Clifford's death, Pollock described an incident, at the outset of their friendship, revealing the clarity of Clifford's thought and his talent for imparting knowledge to others.

"In the analytical treatment of statics there occurs a proposition called Ivory's Theorem concerning the attractions of an ellipsoid. The textbooks demonstrate it by a formidable apparatus of co-ordinates and integrals, such as we were wont to call a *grind*. On a certain day in the Long Vacation of 1866, which Clifford and I spent at Cambridge, I was not a little exercised by the theorem in question, as I suppose many students have been before and since. The chain of symbolic proof seemed artificial and dead; it compelled the understanding but failed to satisfy the reason. After reading and learning the proposition one still failed to see what it was all about. Being out for a walk with Clifford, I opened my perplexities to him; I think I can recall the very spot. What he said I do not remember in detail, which is not surprising, as I have had no occasion to remember anything about Ivory's Theorem these twelve years. But I know that as he spoke he appeared not to be working out a question, but simply telling what he saw. Without any diagram of symbolic aid he described the geometrical conditions on which the solution depended, and they seemed to stand out visibly in space. There were no longer consequences to be deduced, but real and evident facts which only required to be seen. And this one instance, fixed in my memory as the first that came to my knowledge, represents both Clifford's theory of what teaching ought to be and his constant way of carrying it out in his discourses and conversation on mathematical and scientific subjects. So whole and complete was the vision that for the time the only strange thing was that anybody should fail to see it in the same way.[8]

Clifford was a member of the well-known club called the Apostles. At its meetings, as in his rooms, he drew around him by his brilliance and charm a group of distinguished contemporaries, who in their discussions—to use his own

expression—"solved the universe with delight" [9] and par-
took generally of the pleasures of good talk and friendly
dialectic.

He belonged also to the Grote Club at Cambridge, which
included among its members the famous economist Alfred
Marshall, Henry Sidgwick, the philosopher, and John Venn,
the logician. Marshall was a great friend of Clifford's and
admired him immensely, although he felt that "He was too
fond of astonishing people." Describing Clifford's participa-
tion in the meetings of the club, Marshall wrote:

"For a year or two (1869) Sidgwick, Mozley, Clifford, Moulton
and myself were the active membrs; and we all attended regu-
larly. Clifford and Moulton had at that time read but little
philosophy; so they kept quiet for the first half hour of the discussion, and listened eagerly to what others and especially Sidgwick,
said. Then they let their tongues loose, and the pace was tre-
mendous." [10]

Whatever Clifford tackled was carried through with a
drive that reflected not merely his eagerness for mastery but
his joy in living things out to the full. He studied French,
German, and Spanish because he thought them necessary
for his work; Arabic, Greek, and Sanskrit because they were
difficult and, because difficult, a challenge; hieroglyphics
because they were a riddle.[11] His justification for learning
the Morse code and shorthand was that he was interested in
all methods of conveying thought, but this was not the only
instance where the little boy in him had to be rationalized.
His athletic achievements seemed to please him even more
than the winning of literary, scientific, and oratorical prizes.
He topped his athletic career hanging by his toes from the
cross-bar on the weathercock of a church steeple, thereby
earning the accolade in the yearbook of his class as "one of
the most daring athletes of the University." [12]

[9] L & E (Clifford's letters).
[10] Essay on Alfred Marshall by John Maynard Keynes: *Essays in Biography.*
London, 1933.
[11] L & E (P).   [12] Ibid.

The catholicity of Clifford's interests and his independence of mind guided his reading even in mathematics. He would not permit himself to be strait-jacketed into the training routine for the competitive examinations known as the tripos. In England more than elsewhere the honours a student wins, or fails to win, at the university tag him for the rest of his life, especially if he follows an academic career. The unfortunate competitive aspect of the tripos has long since been abandoned, but in Clifford's day to finish on top, to be "first wrangler," was coin for the future. To prepare for the competition one placed oneself in the hands of a special coach for a long and unbelievably arduous grind. Months of practice in intricate manipulations were intended to increase the rate at which one could solve, and more especially write out, the solutions of the problems.[13] Tutors and students alike knew that Clifford could be first wrangler if he trained for this intellectual gymnastic. Clifford, too modest to know and caring less, with almost no preparation finished second wrangler. At that level he was in good company: De Morgan, in his time, was fourth; Whewell, Sylvester, Kelvin, and the incomparable Clerk Maxwell were, in their day, all second.

III

In 1868 Clifford was elected to a fellowship at Trinity. While his best mathematical papers were still to come, his output, not voluminous, was steady in quantity—three or four papers a year—in quality, elegant and suggestive. The year of his election also marked his first important lecture, or what was referred to as the "discourse for an enlightened auditory." Great importance attached to popular or semi-popular lectures in the nineteenth century; every scientist, philosopher, and man of letters took to the lecture platform—Huxley, Kelvin, Mach, Helmholtz, Maxwell, Faraday,

[13] A. Macpherson: *Ten British Mathematicians of the Nineteenth Century*, essay on Clifford. New York, 1916.

Davy, to mention at random a few of the scientists—to popularize learning and, often, to impart the first notice of new ideas and discoveries. In this medium for disseminating information, frequently preferred to writing and cultivated as a fine art, Clifford was a master. He spoke with great clarity and enthusiasm and by his evident interest in his audience at once captured their attention. He rarely wrote out his address in advance, and the ease thus achieved, combined with his powers of illustration and his ability to turn the abstract into the concrete, gave his lectures both lucidity and charm, which even the lapse of time and transfer to print do not diminish. A few of the lectures will be considered further on, but there is a brief passage in his first: "Conditions of Mental Development," delivered at the Royal Institution, March 6, 1868, which seems appropriate here. It is Clifford's description of the "twin-characteristics of a man of genius"; it fits the lecturer singularly well: "He is clearly distinct from the people that surround him, that is how you recognize him; but then this very distinction must be such as to bind him still closer to them, extend and intensify his sympathies, make him want their wants, rejoice over their joys, be cast down by their sorrows." [14]

Clifford spent over two years at Cambridge. His mathematical powers, directed mostly to geometry, steadily developed. His work ranged from the more abstruse—"On Syzygetic Relations among the Powers of Linear Quantics," "On the Umbilici of Anallagmatic Surfaces," "On the Space Theory of Matter"—to the simpler "Lectures on Geometry," "given to a Class of Ladies at S. Kensington." He concerned himself increasingly with the work of Lobachevsky, and more particularly Riemann, in non-Euclidean geometry. H. J. Stephen Smith, a noted British geometer of the nineteenth century, who held the Savilian chair at Oxford during the latter part of Clifford's life, points out that while Clifford's predilection for geometry lay deep:

[14] *L & E.*

"to this his favourite science he attributed the widest imaginable scope, and at times regarded it as co-extensive with the whole domain of nature. He was a metaphysician (though he would only have accepted the name subject to an interpretation) as well as a mathematician; and geometry was to him an important factor in the problem of 'solving the universe.' Thus he was a geometer of a type peculiarly his own; and his dealings with the science were characterized by an amount of scepticism and an amount of faith which one would hardly expect to find combined in a mathematician." [15]

Indeed, throughout his work the most arresting facet of Clifford's originality is the manner in which he leavened mathematical thought with the ferment of philosophy.

IV

In 1870 Clifford joined the English eclipse expedition but the ship *Psyche*, carrying the party, was wrecked off Catania. Fortunately all hands were saved and even the instruments were rescued. Clifford took the mishap with his customary good humour. In writing to Lady Pollock from Florence shortly after the shipwreck—only a fragment of the letter is preserved—he says:

"No ink, no paper, no nothing. . . . After that [the shipwreck] somehow to Catania, some in boats and some in holy carts of the country, all over saints in bright shaws—well, if ever a shipwreck was nicely and comfortably managed, without any fuss—but I can't speak calmly about it because I am so angry at the idiots who failed to save the dear ship—alas! my heart's in the waters close by Polyphemus's eye, which we put out. At Catania, orange groves and telescopes; thence to camp at Augusta; Jonadab, son of Rechab, great fun, natives kept off camp by a white cord; 200 always to see us wash in the morning—a performance which never lost its charm—only five seconds totality free from cloud, found polarisation on moon's disc, agree with Pickering, other people

[15] *Mathematical Papers* by William Kingdon Clifford. Edited by Robert Tucker (from the Introduction by H. J. Stephen Smith). London, 1882.

successful. . . . At Rome 2½ days, pictures, statues, Coliseum by moonlight. Both of us sneezed awfully next morning. This morning arrive in Florence—Pitti palace—spent all my money, and shall get stranded between Cologne and Ostend unless I can live on one egg every other day, and thereout suck no small advantage,—be better off in Paris. . . ." [16]

So in the same gay, vividly descriptive vein were most of his letters of travel to the last months of his life, when even to hold the pen meant a fearful effort.

Appointed professor of applied mathematics at University College, London, Clifford left Cambridge in 1871. Among those recommending him for this post, which he occupied until his death, was Clerk Maxwell, who had first learned to value Clifford's talents at the small, more or less informal meetings of the London Mathematical Society, to which both men belonged. Clifford could be shy as well as exuberant or outspoken; and in the company of Sylvester, Maxwell, Smith, and other distinguished mathematicians, members of the society, he rarely rose to speak of his own accord. But the cogency of his remarks when he was called upon was such as to evoke high praise from Maxwell, not given, as Pollock phrases it, to "unmeasured expression of his mind."[17] Maxwell's letter urging the selection of Clifford stressed that his researches did not tend to "the elaboration of abstruse theorems by ingenious calculation, but to the elucidation of scientific ideas by the concentration upon them of clear and steady thought." [18]

Within less than two years after his appointment Clifford delivered several of his best-known lectures and published, among numerous writings, a celebrated paper on biquaternions. This last I pass for the comment of more competent judges with the bare remark that it is a paper on the generalized conceptions of space, a subject to which Clifford made major contributions; the paper stands high in the literature of mathematics. The lectures in which Clifford sets

---

[16] *L & E* (Clifford's letters).   [17] *L & E* (P).   [18] Ibid.

forth his philosophy of science, and more particularly his
analysis of geometry, attract further consideration, being
of wider and less technical interest and epitomizing Clifford's
singular powers.

V

Before the members of the British Association at Brighton,
in 1872, Clifford gave his address: "On the Aims and Instruments of Scientific Thought." [19] He offers at the outset an
admirable definition of scientific thought:

"In the first place, then, what is meant by scientific thought?
You may have heard some of it expressed in the various Sections
this morning. You have probably also heard expressed in the same
places a great deal of unscientific thought; notwithstanding that
it was about mechanical energy, or about hydrocarbons, or about
eocene deposits, or about malacopterygii. For scientific thought
does not mean thought about scientific subjects with long names.
There are no scientific subjects. The subject of science is the
human universe; that is to say, everything that is, or has been, or
may be related to man."

From examples of scientific thought in astronomy, en-
gineering, physics, biology, Clifford then shows that each
step forward in science,

"from past experience to new circumstances, must be made in accordance with an observed uniformity in the order of events. . . .
By the use of this instrument [of uniformity, scientific thought]
gives us information transcending our experience, it enables us to
infer things that we have not seen from things that we have seen;
and the evidence for the truth of that information depends on
our supposing that the uniformity holds good beyond our experience."

Is this uniformity of nature exact—as a wholly mechanical
interpretation of nature would say it must be?

"I suppose there is hardly a physical student (unless he has
specially considered the matter) who would not at once assent to

the statement . . . that if we knew all about it, Nature would
be found universally subject to exact numerical laws. [But there
is a difference between the *theoretical* and the *practical* meaning of
'exact.'] When a grocer weighs you out a certain quantity of
sugar very carefully, and says it is exactly a pound, he means that
the difference between the mass of the sugar and that of the pound
weight he employs is too small to be detected by his scales. If a
chemist had made a special investigation, wishing to be as accurate
as he could, and told you this was exactly a pound of sugar, he
would mean that the mass of the sugar differed from that of a
certain standard piece of platinum by a quantity too small to be
detected by *his* means of weighing, which are a thousandfold more
accurate than the grocer's. But what would a mathematician mean,
if he made the same statement? He would mean this. Suppose
the mass of the standard pound to be represented by a length, say
a foot, measured on a certain line; so that half a pound would be
represented by six inches, and so on. And let the difference between the mass of the sugar and that of the standard pound be
drawn upon the same line to the same scale. Then, if that difference were magnified an infinite number of times, it would still be
invisible.* This is the theoretical meaning of exactness; the practical meaning is only very close approximation; *how* close, depends
upon the circumstances. The knowledge then of an exact law in
the theoretical sense would be equivalent to an infinite observation. I do not say that such knowledge is impossible to man; but
I do say that it would be absolutely different in kind from any
knowledge that we possess at present.

"I shall be told, no doubt, that we do possess a great deal of
knowledge of this kind, in the form of geometry and mechanics;
and that it is just the example of these sciences that has led men
to look for exactness in other quarters. If this had been said to me
in the last century, I should not have known what to reply. But
it happens that at about the beginning of the present century the
foundations of geometry were criticized independently by two
mathematicians, Lobatchewsky [Lobachevsky] and the immortal
Gauss; whose results have been extended and generalized more recently by Riemann and Helmholtz. And the conclusions to which

---

* Here one ought to eliminate the word "infinite," quite meaningless in this
connection, and interpret the passage: "if that difference were magnified as
often as you please—without limit, it would still be invisible." — J.R.N.

these investigations lead us is that, although the assumptions which were very properly made by the ancient geometers are practically exact—that is to say, more exact than experiment can be—for such finite things as we have to deal with, and such portions of space as we can reach; yet the truth of them for very much larger things, or very much smaller things, or parts of space which are at present beyond our reach, is a matter to be decided by experiment, when its powers are considerably increased. I want to make as clear as possible the real state of this question at present, because it is often supposed to be a question of words or metaphysics, whereas it is a very distinct and simple question of fact."

Clifford thus firmly allied himself with Riemann, one of the greatest mathematicians of the century, in the view that geometry as applied to the world of experience is an experimental science and, as physicists today would say, a proper part of physics. Geometry, according to this analysis, remains an exact science but ceases to be a universal one, and between these two, though the difference in practical calculation is inconceivably small, "there is fixed an enormous gulf." For a law is only true universally if it is true of all cases whatever; "and this is what we do not know of any law at all."

Clifford formed this conclusion when much of accredited mathematics and philosophy was against it. His opinions were a challenge to the belief that Euclidean geometry was the perfect description, for all times, of all parts of actual space. Upon the success of this challenge depended the evolution of the new concepts of space, time, energy, and matter underlying modern physics. Clifford's views, from the standpoint of philosophy, also contested the doctrine, advanced in Kant's transcendental æsthetic, that the long-accepted notions of space were immutable because they were a necessary and inherent attribute of our mode of perception or, more simply, were determined by the nature of our minds. To a fuller examination of this problem we shall return when considering Clifford's lectures on the philosophy of the pure sciences.

I cannot leave this lecture without quoting another portion in which Clifford, with his gift for making involved things simple, defines the notion of cause:

"In asking what we mean by this [cause], we have entered upon an appalling task. The word represented by 'cause' has sixty-four meanings in Plato and forty-eight in Aristotle. These were men who liked to know as near as might be what they meant; but how many meanings it has had in the writings of the myriads of people who have not tried to know what they meant by it will, I hope, never be counted. . . . I shall evade the difficulty [of attempting still another definition of my own] by telling you Mr. Grote's opinion. You come to a scarecrow and ask, what is the cause of this? You find that a man made it to frighten the birds. You go away and say to yourself, 'Everything resembles this scarecrow. Everything has a purpose.' And from that day the word 'cause' means for you what Aristotle meant by 'final cause.' Or you go into a hairdresser's shop, and wonder what turns the wheel to which the rotary brush is attached. On investigating other parts of the premises, you find a man working away at a handle. Then you go away and say, 'Everything is like that wheel. If I investigated enough, I should always find a man at a handle.' And the man at the handle, or whatever, corresponds to him, is from henceforth known to you as 'cause.'"

"And so generally. When you have made out any sequence of events to your entire satisfaction, so that you know all about it, the laws involved being so familiar that you seem to see how the beginning must have been followed by the end, then you apply that as a simile to all other events whatever, and your idea of cause is determined by it. Only when a case arises, as it always must, to which the simile will not apply, you do not confess to yourself that it was only a simile and need not apply to everything, but you say, 'The cause of that event is a mystery which must remain forever unknown to me.' On equally just grounds the nervous system of my umbrella is a mystery which must remain forever unknown to me. My umbrella has no nervous system; and the event to which your simile did not apply has no cause in your sense of the word. When we say then that every effect has a cause, we mean that every event is connected with something in a way that might make somebody call that the cause of it. But I, at least,

have never yet seen any single meaning of the word that could be
fairly applied to the *whole* order of nature." [20, 21]

VI

In his book on *The Social Function of Science* J. D. Bernal
points out that in most countries science, since the violent
days of the seventeenth century when a basic philosophy
of the sciences was hammered out, has been able "to get on
perfectly well without philosophy, especially in England
where philosophy, like religion in polite circles, was hardly

[20] The lecture is concluded with these words: "By scientific thought we
mean the application of past experience to new circumstances by means of
an observed order of events. By saying that this order of events is exact we
mean that it is exact enough to correct experiments by, but we do not mean
that it is theoretically or absolutely exact, because we do not know. The process of inference we found to be in itself an assumption of uniformity, and we
found that, as the known exactness of the uniformity became greater, the
stringency of the inferences increased. By saying that the order of events is
reasonable we do not mean that everything has a purpose, or that everything
can be explained, or that everything has a cause; for neither of these is true.
But we mean that to every reasonable question there is an intelligible answer,
which either we or posterity may know *by the exercise of scientific thought.*"

[21] Implicit in Clifford's philosophy of science is a reappraisal of the function
of science: What is the immediate aim of experiment and research? What are
the criteria for a successful hypothesis? Where is the boundary between
philosophy and science? What is the proper task of each? The famous intro-
ductory sentence to Kirchhoff's lecture "Mechanics" embodies the trend of
Clifford's thought: "Mechanics is the science of motion; we define her task: to
describe completely in the simplest manner the motions that take place in
nature." And so for every science, its function being to *describe*, not to *explain*.
To the extent this is true—and it is well to recognize that scientific description,
like any other, implies selecting data, distinguishing between the relevant
and irrelevant, and so cannot be free of explanation in the form of preconceptions, tentative hypotheses and criteria—science partially frees itself of
vexatious and bewildering problems such as choosing between the sixty-four
"causes" of Plato and the forty-eight of Aristotle. There remains to it the more
direct activity of inquiry and experiment, adopting or discarding hypotheses
without too much regard for consequences to philosophical systems, or, for
that matter, common sense. Philosophy may come after to repair the damage;
common sense must lick its wounds and recuperate as best it can. Science, as
Eddington remarks, must not be built like a house that comes tumbling down
when someone takes away a cornerstone; "it should be like an engine with
movable parts."

ever mentioned in connection with science." [22] The spirit of
bold philosophical criticism directed to the foundation and
borderland problems of science, while burgeoning in the
great German universities of the nineteenth century, was
notably withering in the academic centres of England. There
the metaphysical interest had been all but banished from
science.

But the prevailing mores of academicians laid little re-
straint on Clifford. He was among the first in England to call
attention to the philosophical ideas related to the foundations of geometry, bringing them to public notice in the lecture just considered.[23] The next year he translated from the
German the epoch-making paper of Riemann: "On the
Hypotheses Which Lie at the Bases of Geometry." This
work of vast prophecy in mathematics and physics further
inspired and impelled Clifford to his studies in geometry.
Some mathematicians found geometry dull under the sign
of Euclid because they felt themselves imprisoned in the
axioms. If geometry was this perfect logical discipline, its
propositions deduced from a handful of universal postulates
and axioms by rigorous rules of inference, were not all consequences implicit in the axioms? Were not the propositions
already foretold, merely awaiting exfoliation or a mechanical
recital pursuant to formula? How could this exercise challenge
the imagination of the creative scientist? [24] To answer these

[22] J. D. Bernal: *The Social Function of Science* (New York, 1939), p. 230.

[23] In his philosophy of science Clifford held views essentially similar to those
of Clerk Maxwell, Karl Pearson, Ernst Mach, and Hermann Helmholtz. In
some points there was also an affinity to the opinions of that curious nineteenth-
century prophet of "advanced" views in physics, Johann Bernhard Stallo.
Stallo, of German birth, migrated to the United States, settled in Cincinnati
in 1839, and became a teacher, lawyer, judge, and finally United States Am-
bassador to Rome. In this busy and worldly existence he maintained a deep
interest, of early origin, in philosophy and the foundations of science, and his
book *The Concepts and Theories of Modern Physics*, although in almost violent
opposition to the possibility of new-fangled geometries, was filled with trench-
ant and fertile ideas.

[24] "Thus the unknown, or at least the unforeseen, seems to be excluded from
geometry, because whatever may be found out hereafter must be latent in
what is already known. But in the view put forward by Riemann and adopted

questions and better to appreciate the problems on which Clifford focused his speculations it is perhaps desirable to consider for a moment the distinction between geometry as pure and as applied mathematics.[25]

Geometry considered as a pure science of ideal space is an exercise in logic comparable to a game played with formal rules. As in any game, there are pieces or counters (elements: lines, points, etc.), their properties fixed by definition (postulates), their operations prescribed by rules (logical inference). There is no point in asking what the game means; it is essential only that it be consistent and played according to the rules. If the game points some moral or there is discernible in its patterns some similarity to the patterns of physics, politics, or psychoanalysis, the coincidence is interesting, but not necessarily important. The pure logic of games has little to do with the erratic wanderings of nature. And the propositions of pure geometry have nothing to do with the space in the Yale Bowl or around the planet Neptune, with geometric figures on a blackboard, with the path of projectiles or the orbits of electrons.

Geometry considered as applied mathematics is quite another case. The postulates and elements based upon experience purport to describe the space around us and the extensional properties of matter. Pure geometry can no more be wrong than the game of dominoes; like dominoes, also, it cannot be right. Geometry as applied mathematics, on the

---

by Clifford, the essential properties of space have to be regarded as things still unknown, which we may one day hope to find out by closer observation and more patient reflection, and not as axioms to be accepted on the authority of universal experience, or of the inner consciousness." (*Mathematical Papers by William Kingdon Clifford*, edited by Robert Tucker; from the Introduction by H. J. Stephen Smith.)

[25] The basic dichotomy in mathematics is well described in an address of the eminent British mathematician George Cayley to the British Association in 1883: "Mathematics connect themselves on the one side with common life and the physical sciences; on the other side with philosophy in regard to our notions of space and time, and in the questions which have arisen as to the universality and necessity of the truths of mathematics and the foundation of our knowledge of them. . . ."

other hand, can be right or wrong in describing measurable relations. The postulates and propositions of geometry, considered as having physical validity, like the laws of physics or ecology represent an organized body of hypotheses, of tentative and transient judgments subject to modification or abandonment as fresh data may require, so as to yield propositions that more nearly conform to observation.[26]

For two thousand years Euclidean geometry passed as pure and applied geometry. It was judged both a model of human reasoning beyond the contamination of earthly phenomena and a perfect science of nature describing the properties of space with theoretical exactitude. With Euclid's system elevated to an immobile, transcendental heaven, it was thought, not merely that spatial relations within a limited range are thus and so, as Euclid said, but that they must be thus and so, everywhere and for ever.

[26] By focusing attention upon two concepts of space, physical and mathematical, the distinction between applied and pure mathematics reveals itself as follows: Certain *ad hoc* conventions with regard to physical objects and physical operations are granted, for reasons of convenience, a generality beyond any particular set of objects or operations. "They then become, as we say, properties of space. That is what is meant by physical space, which we may define, in brief, as the abstract construct possessing those properties of rigid bodies that are independent of their material content. Physical space is that on which almost the whole of physics is based and it is, of course, the space of everyday affairs." (Lindsay and Margenau: *Foundations of Physics*. New York, 1936.)

". . . On the other hand the spaces or manifolds of pure mathematics are constructed without any reference to physical operations, such as measurement. They possess only those properties expressed in the postulates and axioms of the particular geometry in question, as well as those properties deducible from them.

"It may well be that the postulates are themselves suggested, in part or in whole, by the physical space of our experience, but they are to be regarded as full-grown and independent. If experiments were to show that some, or all, of our ideas about physical space are wrong (as the theory of relativity has in fact done) we would have to rewrite our texts on physics, but not our geometries." (Kasner and Newman: *Mathematics and the Imagination*. New York, 1940.)

For a general discussion of this subject see Enriques: *Historic Development of Logic* (New York, 1929); Cohen and Nagel: *Introduction to Logic and Scientific Method* (New York, 1934); Russell: *The Analysis of Matter* (New York, 1927).

Now, this enthronement was unfortunate in two respects. First, as a description of actual space Euclidean geometry could not pretend to universality: its postulates and theorems having been tested only in a most limited range might not be valid outside that range—in the domain of the very small or of the very large. Second, by turning Euclidean postulates into commandments, the freedom of mathematical inquiry was more effectively throttled than by ecclesiastical ban. For there appeared to be no possibility of constructing new geometries based upon non-Euclidean postulates, such postulates being, clearly, "contrary to nature." Any discussion of space not known to the senses was thus forbidden.

The revolt came in the nineteenth century, the explosive force being the non-Euclidean geometries of Lobachevsky, Bolyai, and Riemann; the powder train, the disputes about the nature of the parallel postulate which Gauss had also studied. The first doubts had been stirred not by experimental evidence but by logical considerations. Inclined to be a Jacobin in re-evaluating the foundations of science, Clifford was an early and ardent disciple of the new doctrines. He saw in them an extension on the widest scale of the importance and influence of geometrical knowledge to every part of physical science. Beyond that, judging geometry as a prototype of intellectual activity, as Clifford observed its branches multiply and its roots go deeper, he was convinced that the method of its emancipation and growth would aid in the development of other phases of speculative thought. His beliefs and his hopes, his deep interest in geometry are fully encompassed in the lectures on "The Philosophy of the Pure Sciences."

VII

The lectures open with an analysis of what our senses really convey to us of the external world. What part of that which we think we see do we actually see? What part of that which we claim our senses tell us do they actually tell us? On brief reflection it becomes clear that just as a story undergoes marked changes as it is retold from one person to the next, just as parts of the original are lost and new parts added until at last it bears little resemblance to the original, so the phenomena of the outside world are told and retold through the senses and then woven by the brain into a fiction, its content a distortion of the objects and events constituting the initial-stimulus.

"On entering this room [says Clifford] and looking rapidly around, what do I see? I see a theatre, with a gallery, and with an arrangement of seats in tiers. [But no, for the] utmost I can possibly see is two distinct curved pictures of a theatre. Upon the two retinas of my eyes there are made pictures of the scene before me, exactly as pictures are made upon the ground glass in a photographer's camera. The sensation of sight which I get comes to me at any rate through those two pictures; and it cannot tell me any more, or contain in itself any more, than is in those two pictures. Now the pictures are not solid; each of them is simply a curved surface variously illuminated at various parts. Whereas, therefore, I think I see a solid scene, having depth, and relief, and distance in it, reflection tells me that I see nothing of the kind; but only (at the most) two distinct surfaces, having no depth and no relief, and only a kind of distance which is quite different from that of the solid figures before me."

Extending his description, Clifford continues:

"I see people sitting upon these seats, people with heads more or less round, with bodies of a certain shape; sitting in various positions. [How much of that is true?] Of course, I cannot see your heads, I can only see your faces. I must have imagined the rest. But just consider what it is that I have imagined. Is it merely that besides what I do see I have added something that I might see by going round to the other side? No, there is more than that. The complete sensation which I have of a human head when I look at one is not merely something which I do not see now, but something which I never could see by any possibility. I have the sensation of a solid object, and not of a series of pictures of a solid object. Although that sensation may be really constructed out of a countless number of possible pictures, yet it is not like any of them. I imagine to myself, and seem to see the other side of things, not as it would look if viewed from beyond them, but as it would look if viewed from here. I seem to see the back of your head, not as it would look if I get behind you, but as if I saw it through your face from the spot where I am standing; and that, you know, is impossible."

What of the composition of our images? We seem to see objects as existing together, but in fact we move our eyes about and "see a succession of small pictures very rapidly changed." Now only a small part of any scene before us can be seen distinctly at once, and so while we really see a panorama, and not the one large picture we imagine, yet looking at the small portion we think we distinctly see the whole.

As to the impressions gained through another of our senses, Clifford observes:

"[Suppose when I came into the room I said:] 'I put my hands on the table, I feel a hard, flat, horizontal surface at rest, covered with cloth.' [That statement will also bear checking. There are three things that really happen:] 'First, there is a definite kind of irritation of certain organs of my skin, called papillæ. It is that irritation that makes me say *cloth*. Secondly, certain of my muscles are in a state of compression, and they tell me that. Thirdly, I make a certain muscular effort which is not followed by motion. This is all that I can really feel; but those three things do not constitute a hard, flat, horizontal surface covered with cloth. As before, I must have imagined the rest.'"

Clifford continues with a characteristic flash of humour:

"Do not suppose that I am advocating any change in our common language about sensation. I do not want anybody to say, for instance, instead of, 'I saw you yesterday on the other side of the street,' 'I saw a series of panoramic pictures in a sort of mosaic, of such a nature that the imaginations I constructed out of them were not wholly unlike the imaginations I have constructed out of similar series of panoramic pictures seen by me on previous occasions when you were present.' This would be clumsy, and it would not be sufficient. And yet I cannot help thinking that in certain assemblies, when some of those who are present are in an exalted state of emotional expectation, and the lights are low, even this roundabout way of putting things might be, to say the least, a salutary exercise."

From this analysis of sense impressions Clifford draws the inference that

"there are really two distinct parts in every sensation that we get. There is a message that comes to us somehow; but this message is not all that we apparently see and hear and feel. In every sensation there is, besides the actual message, something that we imagine and add to the message. This is sometimes expressed by saying that there is a part which comes from the external world and a part which is supplied by the mind. But however we express it, the fact to be remembered is that not the whole of a sensation is immediate experience (where by immediate experience I mean the actual message—whatever it is—that comes to us); but that this experience is supplemented by something else which is not in it. And thus you may see that it is a perfectly real question, 'Where does this supplement come from?'"

Clifford then points out that the spatial aspect of our sensations, the extensional properties of the perceived objects, the relations of distance,

"are always so filled in as to fulfill a code of rules, some called common notions, and some called definitions, and some called postulates, and some assumed without warning, but all somehow contained in Euclid's *Elements of Geometry*."

And these which he calls the "rules [that] are the foundations of the pure sciences of Space and Motion" [27] constitute an important part of the "supplement" by which we fill in our experience.

[27] "Instead of Space and Motion, many people would like to say Space and Time. But in regard to the special matter that we are considering, it seems to me, for reasons which I do not wish to give at present, to be more correct to say that we imagine time by putting together space and motion, than that we imagine motion by putting together space and time." ("The Philosophy of the Pure Sciences." *L & E.*)

There are other rules in accordance with which we fill in our sensations, relating, for example, to continuity, number, uniformity; and some of these rules of supplementation are the foundations of the pure sciences of arithmetic, formal logic, and geometry.[28] As to those of geometry:

"There has been for ages a conviction in the minds of men that these rules about space are true objectively in the exact or theoretical sense, and under all possible circumstances. If two straight lines are drawn perpendicular to the same plane, geometers would have told you for more than two thousand years that these straight lines may be prolonged for ever and ever without getting the least bit nearer to one another or further away from one another; and that they were perfectly certain of this. They knew for certain that the sum of the angles of a triangle, no matter how big or how small it was, or where it was situated, must always be exactly equal to two right angles, neither more nor less. And those who were philosophers as well as geometers knew more than this. They knew not only that the thing was true, but that it could not possibly have been otherwise; that it was necessarily true. And this means, apparently, not merely that I know it must be, but that I know that you must know that it must be."

Concerning these rules of supplementation, Locke, and more especially Hume, gave the explanation

"that the supplement of experience is made up of past experience, together with links which bind together perceptions that have been accustomed to occur together. This fact, that perceptions and feelings which have frequently occurred together get linked,

[28] "The case of arithmetical propositions is perhaps more easily comprehended in this respect. Everybody knows that six things and three things make nine things at all possible times and places; you cannot help seeing not only that they do always without exception make nine things, but that they must do so; and that the world could not have been constructed otherwise. For to those ingenious speculations which suppose that in some other planet there may always be a tenth thing inevitably suggested upon the union of the six and the three, so that they cannot be added together without making ten; to these, I say, it may be replied that the words *number* and *thing*, if used at all, must have different meanings in that planet." ("The Philosophy of the Pure Sciences." *L & E*.)

so that one calls up the other, is called the law of Association, and has been made the basis of scientific Psychology. According to these explanations of Locke and Hume . . . all the knowledge we have that the rules are right, or may be objectively verified, is really derived from experience; only it is *past* experience, which we have had so often and got so accustomed to that it is now really a part of ourselves.

"But Kant, after being staggered for some time by Hume's explanation, at length said, 'It is impossible that all your knowledge can have come from experience. For you know that the axioms of mathematics are absolutely and universally true, and no experience can possibly have told you this. However often you may have found the angles of a triangle amount to two right angles, however accustomed you may have got to this experience, you have no right to know that the angles of every possible triangle are equal to two right angles, nor indeed that those of any one triangle are absolutely and exactly so equal. Now you do know this, and you cannot deny it. You have therefore some knowledge which could not possibly be derived from experience; it must therefore have come in some other way; or there is some other source of knowledge besides experience.'

"At that time there was no answer whatever to this. For men did think that they knew at least the absolute universality if not the necessity of the mathematical axioms. To any one who admitted the necessity, the argument was even stronger; for it was clear that no experience could make any approach to supply knowledge of this quality. But if a man felt absolutely sure that two straight lines perpendicular to the same line would never meet, however far produced, he could not maintain against Kant that all knowledge is derived from experience. He was obliged to admit the existence of knowledge *a priori*, that is, knowledge lying ready in the mind from from the first, antecedent to all experience."

How is it possible to have knowledge of objects antecedent to all experience, *a priori* knowledge? Clifford gives Kant's solution to the problem with the aid of a singularly appropriate analogy:

"If a man had on a pair of green spectacles, he would see everything green. And if he found out this property of his spectacles, he might say with absolute certainty that while he had those spectacles on everything that he saw without exception would be green.

"'Everything that he saw'; that is to say, all objects of sight to him. But here it is clear that the word object is relative; it means a representation that he gets, and has nothing to do with the thing in itself. And the assertion that everything is green would not be an assertion about the things in themselves, but about the representations of them which came to him. The colour of these representations would depend partly on the things outside and partly on his spectacles. It would vary for different things, but there would always be green in it.

"Let us modify this example a little. I know for certain that the colour of every object in the universe is made up of colours that lie within the range of the visible spectrum. This is apparently a universal statement, and yet I know it to be true of things which it is impossible that I should ever see. How is this? Why, simply, that my eyes are only affected by light which lies within the range of the visible spectrum. Now I say that this case is only a little modified from the previous one. The green glass lets in a certain range of light; the range is very little increased when you take it away. Only in the second case it happens that we are all actually wearing very nearly the same spectacles. That universal statement which I made is true not only of objects as they appear to me, but also of objects as they appear to you. It is a statement about objects; that is, about certain representations which we perceive. It may therefore so far have its origin in the things of which these are representations, or it may have its origin in us. And we happen to know that in this case it is not a statement about external things, but about our eyes.

"Admitting, then, that the objects of our sensations are representations made to us; that their character must therefore be partly dependent upon our own character; what properties of these objects should we naturally suppose to have this origin, to be derived from the constitution of our minds? Why, clearly, those which are necessary and universal; for only such properties can be so derived, and there is no other way in which they can be known to be universal.

"Accordingly, Kant supposes that Space and Time are necessary forms of perception, imposed upon it by the perceiving mind; that things are in space and time as they appear to us, and not in themselves; and that consequently the statement that all things exist in space and time is a statement about the nature of our perception and not about the things perceived. . . . And it is just because these statements *are* about me [just as the statement about the colours of things was really a statement about the eyes of the observer and not about the things themselves] that I know them to be not only universally, but always necessarily true about the objects I perceive; for it is always the same *me* that perceives them—or at any rate it is a *me* possessing always the same faculties of representation.

"Now observe what it is that this theory does with general statements; what is the means by which it gets rid of them—for it does get rid of them. It makes them into particular statements. Instead of being statements about all possible places and times and things, they are made out to be statements about me, and about other men in so far as they have the same faculties that I have."

Clifford then shows why the method by which Kant attempted to answer the question: "Are there any properties of objects in general which are really due to me and to the ways in which I perceive them, and which do not belong to the things themselves?" was inadequate. For just as in the case of the man with the green spectacles, the way to clinch the argument that he *necessarily* saw everything green because of his spectacles would be "to take him to a looking glass and show him that these spectacles were actually upon his nose," the answer to the question Kant set out to answer

"must be sought not in the subjective method, in the conviction of universality and necessity, but in the physiological method, in the study of the physical facts that accompany sensation, and of the physical properties of the nervous system. The materials for this valid criticism of knowledge did not exist in Kant's time. I believe that they do exist at present to such an extent at least as to indicate the nature of the results which that criticism is to furnish."

After considering opinions of Berkeley, Hume, Whewell, Mill,[29] and Spencer as to how concepts of every kind are related to experience, Clifford continues:

"It seems to me that the Kantian dilemma about universal propositions is just as valid now, in spite of these explanations, as it was in his time. How am I to know that the angles of a triangle are exactly equal to two right angles under all possible circumstances; not only in those regions of space where the solar system has been, but everywhere else? The accumulated experience of all my ancestors for a hundred and fifty million years is no more competent to tell me *that* than my own experience of the last five minutes. Either I have some source of knowledge other than experience, and I must admit the existence of *a priori* truths, independent of experience; or I cannot know that any universal statement is true. Now the doctrine of evolution itself forbids me to admit any transcendental source of knowledge; so that I am driven to conclude in regard to every apparently universal statement, either that it is not really universal, but a particular statement about my nervous system, about my apparatus of thought; or that I do now know that it is true. And to this conclusion, by a detailed examination of various apparently universal statements, I shall in subsequent lectures endeavour to lead you."

Clifford then goes on to show that while Kant's arguments for the universality of geometric truths were valid against

[29] "One broad result of non-Euclidean geometry, even in its earliest form, was that the geometry of actual space is, at least in part, an empirical study, not a branch of pure mathematics. It may be said that empiricists, such as J. S. Mill, always based geometry upon empirical observation. But they did the same with arithmetic, in which they were certainly mistaken. No one before the non-Euclideans perceived that arithmetic and geometry stand on a quite different footing, the former being continuous with pure logic and independent of experience, the latter being continuous with physics and dependent upon physical data. Geometry can, it is true, be still studied as a branch of pure mathematics, but it is then hypothetical, and cannot claim that its initial hypothesis (which replace the axioms) are true in fact, since this is a question outside the scope of pure mathematics. The geometry which is required by the engineer or the astronomer is not a branch of pure mathematics, but a branch of physics. Indeed, in the hands of Einstein geometry has become identical with the whole of the general part of theoretical physics: the two are united in the general theory of relativity." (Bertrand Russell: *The Analysis of Matter*, London, 1927.)

Hume they failed against the thesis of the non-Euclideans:
(a) the axioms of traditional geometry "are convenient
assumptions and not *a priori* necessities of thought or perception"; (b) there are possible any number of *a priori* pos-
tulational systems, in addition to the Euclidean, defining
different kinds of ideal space; (c) the geometry of our world
space is a matter of experience, and as that is enlarged, the
refinement of our geometry must continue.

VIII

Perhaps the two greatest nineteenth-century advances of
thought were made by mathematics and biology. While the
first deposed, as sole authority, a system regnant almost
since the beginning of science, biology took man from his
pedestal of isolation and assigned him a place in the Linnæan
table. "While Huxley, the Duke of Argyll and the bishops
were exciting themselves and the world about Darwin and
the Book of Genesis," [30] the non-Euclideans reaffirmed, as
consolation for their annihilating scepticism in demonstrat-
ing the tentative character of human judgments even in
mathematics, the almost unlimited freedom of man's
thought. In this adventure of ideas, Clifford by temperament and speculative powers felt himself at home. How he
appraised the work of Lobachevsky, almost lyrically, is re-
vealed in the following passage:

"What Vesalius was to Galen, what Copernicus was to Ptolemy,
that was Lobatchewsky to Euclid. There is, indeed, a somewhat
instructive parallel between the last two cases. Copernicus and
Lobatchewsky were both of Slavic origin. Each of them has
brought about a revolution in scientific ideas so great that it can
only be compared with that wrought by the other. And the reason
of the transcendent importance of these two changes is that they
are changes in the conception of the Cosmos. Before the time of
Copernicus, men knew all about the Universe. They could tell you

[30] Sir William Dampier: *A History of Science and Its Relations with Philosophy and Religion.* Cambridge, England, 1936.

in the schools, pat off by heart, all that it was, and what it had been, and what it would be. There was the flat earth, with the blue vault of heaven resting on it like the dome of a cathedral, and the bright cold stars stuck into it; while the sun and planets moved in crystal spheres between. Or, among the better informed, the earth was a globe in the centre of the universe, heaven a sphere concentric with it; intermediate machinery as before. At any rate, if there was anything beyond heaven, it was a void space that needed no further description. The history of all this could be traced back to a certain definite time, when it began; behind that was a changeless eternity that needed no further history. Its future could be predicted in general terms as far forward as a certain epoch, about the precise determination of which there were, indeed, differences among the learned. But after that would come again a changeless eternity, which was fully accounted for and described. But in any case the Universe was a known thing. Now the enormous effect of the Copernican system, and of the astronomical discoveries that have followed it, is that, in place of this knowledge of a little, which was called knowledge of the Universe, of Eternity and Immensity, we have now got knowledge of a great deal more; but we only call it the knowledge of Here and Now. We can tell a great deal about the solar system; but, after all, it is our house, and not the city. We can tell something about the star-system to which our sun belongs; but, after all, it is our star-system, and not the Universe. We are talking about Here with the consciousness of a There beyond it, which we may know some time, but do not at all know now. . . . This, then, was the change effected by Copernicus in the idea of the Universe. But there was left another to be made. For the laws of space and motion . . . implied an infinite space and infinite duration, about whose properties as space and time everything was accurately known. The very constitution of those parts of it which are at an infinite distance from us, 'geometry upon the plane at infinity,' is just as well known, if the Euclidean assumptions are true, as the geometry of any portion of this room. . . . So that here we have real knowledge of something at least that concerns the Cosmos; something that is true throughout the Immensities and the Eternities. That something Lobatchewsky and his successors have taken away. The geometer of today knows nothing about the nature of actually existing space at an infinite distance; he knows nothing about the properties of this present space in a past or future eternity. He knows, indeed, that the laws assumed by Euclid are true with an accuracy that no direct experiment can approach . . . but he knows this as of Here and Now; beyond his range is a There and Then of which he knows nothing at present, but may ultimately come to know more. So, you see, there is a real parallel between the work of. Copernicus and his successors on the one hand, and the work of Lobatchewsky and his successors on the other. . . ."

Completing his theme, Clifford analyses the four fundamental postulates upon which the ordinary Euclidean conception of space is based. What is their necessary order and classification? Which postulates are true independently of the others? By adopting the contraries of certain of the postulates, what new geometries can be developed?

The first postulate states that space is continuous, without breaks or gaps of any kind. But continuity, Clifford argues, is an impression gathered from our senses. And with respect to space our senses may be deceiving us as thoroughly as when they tell us that water is continuous, that a moving picture has no breaks or gaps. In such instances science corrects our impressions so that we recognize the "continuous" medium or phenomenon as consisting of separate little pieces, so closely joined or following upon one another so quickly in time that we are unable to perceive the discontinuity and separateness. The instruments of physics and chemistry further reveal the breaks, the atomicity, of smooth, compact objects wholly unbroken in appearance. What proof have we that space is not of the same nature, smooth in appearance but actually criss-crossed, say, by a lacework of tiny fissures. The Euclidean postulate of continuous space therefore waits upon experience. While, as Clifford admits, observation has not yet disclosed instances of a discontinuous space, there is no certainty, nor even a likelihood, that it will never do so. Continuous space is not one of the "eternities"; it is not necessarily and universally true.

The second postulate relates to "the flatness of space in its smallest parts." Many attempts have been made to define this concept simply. But it is not a simple idea, especially in relation to space.[31] The matter is certainly put more easily by analogy, in two dimensions. Clifford gives the example for a curved surface:

". . . If you perceive a portion of the surface of a very large sphere, such as the earth, it appears to you to be flat. If, then, you take a sphere of say a foot diameter, and magnify it more and more, you will find that the more you magnify it the flatter it gets. . . . Any curved surface which is such that the more you magnify it the flatter it gets, is said to possess the property of elementary flatness."

H. J. S. Smith in his Introduction to Clifford's *Mathematical Papers* offers what is perhaps the most intuitable extension of the concept to space of three dimensions: A space which is flat in its smallest parts is so constituted "that if anywhere in it we take three points very near to one another and join them by the shortest lines that can possibly be drawn, the triangular figure so formed will lie very nearly in a plane. . . .

The universality of this postulate Clifford also doubts. For as he says:

"we have merely to point to the example of polished surfaces. The smoothest surface that can be made is the one most completely covered with the minutest ruts and furrows. Yet geometrical constructions can be made with extreme accuracy upon such a surface, on the supposition that it is an exact plane. If, therefore, the sharp points, edges, and furrows of space are only small enough, there will be nothing to hinder our conviction of its elementary flatness. It has even been remarked by Riemann that we must not shrink from this supposition if it is found useful in explaining physical phenomena." [32]

[31] As Clifford remarks, Euclid's less general equivalent of the postulate seems so childishly self-evident, so tautologous, "that you will wonder how anybody could make all this fuss." His fourth postulate says: "All right angles are equal." It requires the subtlest reasoning and the sharpest scrutiny of the obvious to discern the fact that this "self-evident" postulate entails the not so self-evident principle of elementary flatness.

[32] "Now it seems that the empirical notions on which the metrical determinations of space are founded, the notion of a solid body and of a ray of

The third postulate is that of superposition. "According to this postulate a body can be moved about in space without altering its size or shape." It is at the base of Euclid's propositions relating to congruence. In another form the postulate states that "all parts of space are alike." Considered jointly with the fourth postulate, which Clifford names that of "similarity," the two together are equivalent to the assumption that space is uniformly of zero curvature.

"According to this postulate [the fourth], any figure may be magnified or diminished in any degree without altering its shape. If any figure has been constructed in one part of space, it may be reconstructed to any scale whatever in any other part of space, so that no one of the angles shall be altered, though all the lengths of lines will of course be altered. This seems to be a sufficiently obvious induction from experience; for we have all frequently seen different sizes of the same shape. . . . It is easy to show that this involves the two postulates of Euclid: 'Two straight lines cannot enclose a space,' and 'Lines in one plane which never meet make equal angles with every other line.'"

If the first two postulates are attacked on the side of "the very small," the third and fourth postulates are vulnerable on the side of "the very great." To the extent that a given space deviates from the standard of elementary flatness [33] extraordinarily complicated *ad hoc* geometries may be required. These are closely tied to modern concepts of physics, partly foreshadowed by Clifford, suggesting, roughly speaking, that all phenomena, even matter itself, consist of wrinkles

-----

light, cease to be valid for the infinitely small. We are therefore quite at liberty to suppose that the metric relations of space in the infinitely small do not conform to the hypotheses of geometry; and we ought in fact to suppose it, if we can thereby obtain a simpler explanation of phenomena." (Riemann: *Ueber die Hypothesen, welche der Geometrie zu Grunde liegen.* Clifford's translation.)

[33] It should be remembered that elementary flatness does not preclude curvature. A curved surface which grows less curved the more it is enlarged has this property; "but if every succeeding power of our imaginary microscope disclosed new wrinkles and inequalities without end, then the surface does not possess the property. . . ." (*L & E.*)

or changes of curvature in space.[34] But if the postulate of elementary flatness is retained and the fourth postulate of "similarity," in so far as it relates to parallels, is abandoned, the way is open for the conventional non-Euclidean geometries. Assuming a constant negative curvature of space, the appropriate non-Euclidean geometry is that of Lobachevsky. Now referred to as a geometry of hyperbolic space, Lobachevsky's system replaces the parallel postulate of Euclid, with a hypothesis that through a given point in the plane at least two lines parallel to a third may be drawn. In Lobachevsky's geometry the sum of the angles of every triangle is less than 180° and only triangles equal in area can have the same angles. The non-Euclidean geometry of Riemann, preferred by Clifford, assumes a constant positive curvature of space. Following Felix Klein's terminology, in current use, this geometry is known as elliptic. It adopts the hypothesis that through a given point there can be drawn not a single line parallel to a given line and infers that the sum of the angles of every triangle is greater than 180°.[35] Clifford describes a space of this kind as follows:

[34] In this connection it may be of interest to quote from an abstract of one of Clifford's papers, appearing in the Cambridge Philosophical Society's *Proceedings* (1876). (The subject was introduced at greater length to English mathematicians in Clifford's translation of Riemann's inaugural dissertation: "On the Hypotheses that Lie at the Bases of Geometry.") The paper bearing the title "On the Space-Theory of Matter" concludes with these words:

"... I hold in fact

"(1) That small portions of space *are* in fact of a nature analogous to little hills on a surface which is on the average flat; namely, that the ordinary laws of geometry are not valid in them.

"(2) That this property of being curved or distorted is continually being passed on from one portion of space to another after the manner of a wave.

"(3) That this variation of the curvature of space is what really happens in that phenomenon which we call the *motion of matter*, whether ponderable or etherial.

"(4) That in the physical world nothing else takes place but this variation, subject (possibly) to the law of continuity. . . ."

[35] "This conception [of a constant positive curvature] lies at the bottom of Clifford's theory of biquaternions, to which he devoted much continuous thought, and which was the origin of his researches into the classification of geometric algebras. A space of constant positive curvature is most easily repre-

". . . what is the nature of things on the supposition that the curvature of all space is nearly uniform and positive? In this case the Universe, as known, becomes again a valid conception; for the extent of space is a finite number of cubic miles. And this comes about in a curious way. If you were to start in any direction whatever, and move in that direction in a perfect straight line according to the definition of Leibnitz; after travelling a most prodigious distance, to which the parallactic unit—200,000 times the diameter of the earth's orbit—would be only a few steps, you would arrive at—this place. Only, if you had started upwards, you would appear from below. Now, one of two things would be true. Either, when you had got half-way on your journey, you came to a place that is opposite to this, and which you must have gone through, whatever direction you started in; or else all paths you could have taken diverge entirely from each other till they meet again at this place. In the former case, every two straight lines in a plane meet in two points, in the latter they meet only in one. Upon this supposition of a positive curvature, the whole of geometry is far more complete and interesting; the principle of duality, instead of half breaking down over metric relations, applies to all propositions without exception. In fact, I do not mind confessing that I personally have often found relief from the dreary infinities of homaloidal space in the consoling hope that, after all, this other may be the true state of things."

This discussion of "The Philosophy of the Pure Sciences," extended at some length, has none the less been confined to Clifford's treatment of geometry. His examination of other fundamental concepts in science maintains the same high level. I have been at some pains to quote substantial portions in full so as to preserve the flow of Clifford's style, the richness of his exposition, the aptness of his humour and il-

---

sented to the mathematician (in the absence of any possibility of imaging it to the mind) as the locus of an equation of the form

$$x^2 + y^2 + z^2 + w^2 = \text{constant}$$

in a flat space of four dimensions in which xyzw are rectangular coordinates. It is related to the two-dimensional surface of a sphere, just as in ordinary geometry space of three dimensions is related to a plane surface." (H. J. S. Smith, op. cit.)

lustrative gifts. It seemed appropriate on the further ground that this group of lectures, like all his writings, is out of print, and nowhere except perhaps in his technical memoirs are we afforded a better exhibition of Clifford's powers, a deeper insight into the reach and fecundity of his thought.

IX

In 1874 Clifford was elected a Fellow of the Royal Society, having declined earlier to have his name put forward, though certain of election, on the ground that he "did not want to be respectable yet." [36] The same year he delivered a number of lectures on popular science as well as on social and ethical philosophy. Throughout his life Clifford searched for a general philosophy he could make his own, but developed none that stands out as clearly as his interpretation of the pure sciences. One can make little of his theory of "mind-stuff," obscure, involved, and unconvincing.[37] A harsh critic might condemn it with Clifford's own phrase as "that rhetoric which frequently assumes the name of philosophy." [38] Pollock implies that the concept of "mind-stuff" was a half-hearted idea that could not have satisfied Clifford for long, little more than a scaffolding in his thought: he may have advanced it as a sheer intellectual exercise without even a momentary commitment of belief.[39]

Evolutionist doctrines, to which Clifford gave so deeply of his mind, were the framework of his ethical precepts. To an even greater extent his temperament controlled his social and ethical views. These were imbued with the ideals of

[36] *L & E* (P).

[37] Clifford "was more inclined than most English psychologists to believe in the possibility of constructing a definite metaphysical system, in which he was probably influenced by his admiration for Spinoza. . . . He agreed with Berkeley that mind is the ultimate reality; but held that consciousness as known to us is built up out of simple elements or atoms of 'mind-stuff'— the characteristic phrase which gives the keynote of theories full of suggestions, and showing curious affinities to other philosophies, but not fully worked out." (Article on Clifford by Leslie Stephen, *Dictionary of National Biography*.)

[38] *L & E*.   [39] *L & E* (P).

freedom, with "the duty of independence and spontaneous activity. . . . That alone was right which was done of one's own inner conviction . . . that was lifeless and evil which was done out of obedience to any external authority." [40] "There is one thing in the world," Clifford wrote, "more wicked than the desire to command, and that is the will to obey." [41]

Clifford attempted, in his writings on social, religious, and ethical beliefs, to develop his theories on the same objective basis as underlay his philosophy of science. It was consistent with his precept of denying the name of knowledge to any result not reached by scientific method.[42] His test of theories lay in action and he sought moral and religious values—to quote from a passage remembered, but its author forgotten—"within the flow of experience, not in a realm of pre-existent being outside it." As a protestant against established beliefs, he was no more prepared to accept eternal values in ethics than in geometry. His views are summarized in several passages from the essay on "The Scientific Basis of Morals": [43]

"Every scientific fact is a short hand expression for a vast number of practical directions: if you want so-and-so, do so-and-so. If with this meaning of the word 'Science,' there is such a thing as a scientific basis of Morals, it must be true that,—(1) The maxims of Ethic are hypothetical maxims, (2) derived from experience, (3) on the assumption of uniformity in nature. . . ."

Ethical maxims, Clifford holds, are learned by the tribe and not by the individual.

[40] Ibid.   [41] *L & E* (Clifford's letters).

[42] "Take Professor Clifford's article on the 'Ethics of Belief.' He calls it 'guilt' and 'sin' to believe even the truth without scientific evidence. . . . What we enjoy most in a Huxley or a Clifford is not the professor with his learning, but the human personality ready to go in for what it feels to be right, in spite of all appearances." (William James: "The Sentiment of Rationality," from *The Will to Believe*.) There is a further reference to Clifford, a comparison of his views on psychology with those of Thomas Huxley, in James's *Principles of Psychology*, Vol. I (edition of 1927), pp. 130-2.

[43] *L & E.*

"Those tribes have on the whole survived in which conscience approved such actions as tended to the improvement of men's characters as citizens and therefore to the survival of the tribe. Hence it is that the moral sense of the individual, though founded on the experience of the tribe, is purely intuitive; conscience gives no reasons. Notwithstanding this, the ethical maxims are presented to us as conditional; if you want to live together in this complicated way, your ways must be straight and not crooked, you must seek the truth and love no lie. Suppose we answer, 'I don't want to live together with other men in this complicated way; and so I shall not do as you tell me.' That is not the end of the matter, as it might be with other scientific precepts. For obvious reasons it is *right* in this case to reply, 'Then in the name of my people I do not like you,' and to express this dislike by appropriate methods. And the offender, being descended from a social race, is unable to escape his conscience, the voice of his tribal self which says, 'In the name of the tribe, I hate myself for this treason I have done.'"

But while ethical maxims differ from scientific precepts in their compulsory aspect, they rest upon the same assumption of uniformity in nature. For that uniformity underlies the possibility of even unconscious adaptation to experience, of language, and of general conceptions and statements, and without that adaptation the sense of moral reprobation and responsibility would not come into being.

"It may be asked 'Are you quite sure that these observed uniformities between motive and action, between character and motive, between social influence and change of character, are absolutely exact in the form in which you state them, or indeed that they are exact laws of any form? May there not be very slight divergences from exact laws, which will allow of the action of an "uncaused will," or of the interference of some "extra-mundane force"?' I am sure I do not know. But this I do know: that our sense of right and wrong is derived from such order as we can observe, and not from such caprice of disorder as we may fancifully conjecture; and that to whatever extent a divergence from exactness became sensible, to that extent it would destroy the most widespread and worthy of the acquisitions of mankind.

". . . By these views we are led to conclusions partly negative, partly positive; of which, as might be expected, the negative are the most definite.

"First, then, Ethic is a matter of the tribe or community and therefore there are no 'self regarding virtues.' The qualities of courage, prudence, etc., can only be *rightly* encouraged in so far as they are shown to conduce to the efficiency of a citizen; that is, in so far as they cease to be self-regarding. The duty of private judgement, of searching after truth, the sacredness of belief which ought not to be misused on unproved statements, follow only on showing of the enormous importance to society of a true knowledge of things. And any diversion of conscience from its sole allegiance to the community is condemned *a priori* in the very nature of right and wrong.

"Next, the end of Ethic is not the greatest happiness of the greatest number. Your happiness is of no use to the community, except in so far as it tends to make you a more efficient citizen— that is to say, happiness is not to be desired for its own sake, but for the sake of something else. If any end is pointed to, it is the end of increased efficiency in each man's special work, as well as in the social functions which are common to all. . . .

"Again, Piety is not Altruism. It is not the doing good to others as others, but the service of the community by a member of it, who loses in that service the consciousness that he is anything different from the community. . . ."

On balance, Clifford's more formal system of ethics is stilted by comparison with the warmth and wisdom so manifest in his personal conduct or letters. While he was never given to pontifying, his ethical philosophy appears old-fashioned in an age of Freud and Marx, of general moral and intellectual uncertainties; an age which has veered away from the tidy scientific materialism of the nineteenth century even as it has grown sadly aware of the limitations of science in meeting its social and ethical problems. That we are in need of more scientific method rather than less in all our exertions is a belief that men of reason share with Clifford. It is simply that he would have looked to science for solutions which we are either too wise to expect or too cynical to perceive.

In Clifford's personal life there was never a trace of cant, hypocrisy, or self-righteousness. Writing to Lady Pollock on his "ideal theory" of behaviour, he concludes, characteristically: "All this, by the way, is only theory; my practice is just like other people's." [44] Free from pretentiousness himself, Clifford was sharp in criticizing it in others. Of an acquaintance about to undertake a work in philosophy he remarked:

"He is writing a book on metaphysics, and is really cut out for it; the clearness with which he thinks he understands things and his total inability to express what little he knows will make his fortune as a philosopher." [45]

But he was incapable of malice or personal enmity. Once he wrote:

"A great misfortune has fallen upon me; I shook hands with ——. I believe if all the murderers and all the priests and all the liars in the world were united into one man, and he came suddenly upon me round a corner and said, 'How do you do?' in a smiling way, I could not be rude to him upon the instant." [46]

In a letter Clifford wrote to his wife the year before they were married, there is a noble expression of his faith: [47]

"Still there is room for some earnest person to go and preach around in a simple way the main straightforward rules that society has unconsciously worked out and that are floating in the air; to do as well as possible what one can do best; to work for the improvement of the social organization; to seek earnestly after truth and only to accept provisionally opinions one has not inquired into; to regard men as comrades in work and their freedom as a sacred thing; in fact, to recognize the enormous and fearful difference between truth and falsehood, right and wrong, and how truth and right are to be got at by free enquiry and the love of our comrades for their own sake and nobody else's."

[44] *L & E* (Clifford's letters).   [46] *L & E* (P).
[45] *L & E* (P).   [47] *L & E* (Clifford's letters).

X

On April 7, 1875 Clifford married Lucy Lane. When he took leave of absence from University College on the occasion of his marriage, he informed "his class that he was obliged to be absent on important business which would probably not occur again." [48] His wife outlived him by half a century and became well known as a novelist and dramatist. Their marriage was one of unmixed happiness, and the two little girls that were born to them brought Clifford great joy. He loved all children, and for his own delighted in making up new games, fairy tales, and poems. Some of his fables he contributed to a collection, *The Little People*. He recognized the urgent need to plan the education of children so as to make it alive and interesting, and to extend its opportunities and its benefits.

"I have a scheme [he wrote to Pollock in 1876] which has been communicated in part to MacMillan, and which grows like a snowball. It is founded on *Pleasant Pages* the book I was taught out of; which is a series of ten minutes' lessons on the Pestalozzian plan of making the kids find out things for themselves: history of naughty boys on Monday, animals on Tuesday, bricks on Wednesday, Black Prince on Thursday, and so on. . . . Well, I first want that brought up to today, both in choice of subject and in accuracy . . . then I want it taught on the Russian system, in different languages on successive days . . . more particularly we must get published excellent little manuals at twopence or threepence for the use of Board and other primary schools. I do not even know that penny schoolbooks would not be a successful move . . . printed by the million. . . . Of such a size could be made a very good elementary schoolbook of arithmetic, geometry, animals, plants, physics. . . ." [49]

In a letter to Lady Pollock after the birth of his first child Clifford wrote: [50]

[48] *L & E* (P).   [49] *L & E* (Clifford's letters).   [50] Ibid.

"I wrote to Fred about the education of our infants. I am very glad we have both begun with girls, because it will be so good for the other children to have an elder sister. . . . I have thought of a way to make them read and write shorthand by means of little sticks (not to whop them with but to put together on a table and make the shorthand signs). Ask G whether she thinks they had better learn to sing on the sol-fa system; it is very amusing and seems to me more adapted for children than the other. Of course I can teach them to stand on their heads."

As for the ethical training of children, in his last essay, and one of his best, "Virchow on the Teaching of Science," appearing in *Nineteenth Century*, April 1878, Clifford makes a strong plea against the teaching of "unproved doctrine about body and mind; the conclusion that a man's consciousness survives the decay of his body." We have no right "to teach little children as a known fact" what is "a hope, a conjecture, an aspiration," however strongly we may desire that it should be true, "that better evidence will shortly be forthcoming." If you must teach it at all, teach it as something that may possibly be true but is certainly not the established fact. The reasons for this caution "are deeper and stronger than the merely intellectual ones, because of the vast hold of this doctrine upon the hearts, and its serious influence upon the actions of men." For one thing, by teaching it too early, you "make it familiar as an ill-understood conception, weaken the power it might have for good and help the perversion of it to superstitious uses. The second point to be considered is the frightful loss and disappointment you prepare for your child if, as is most probable in these days, he becomes convinced that the doctrine is founded on insufficient evidence. It is not merely that you have brought him up as a prince, to find himself a pauper at eighteen. He may have allowed this doctrine to get inextricably intertwined with his feelings of right and wrong. Then the overthrow of one will, at least for a time, endanger the other. . . ."

The happiness Clifford shared with children, his unaf-

fected gaiety in their company, his deep concern with their
problems of learning and adjustment, stand in poignant con-
trast to the brief period he lived to spend with his own.

In 1876 the first alarming signs of tuberculosis appeared. All
his life he had burdened his physical powers. The abundant
but self-consuming nervous energy, the warfare against false
beliefs, the self-goading search for new riddles and new chal-
lenges, the full submission to the demands of his intellect, were
altogether out of proportion to what the physical machine
could endure. His mother's early death should have served
as forewarning and precept; there were other signs, before
the more serious ones, that he was using his substance faster
than it could be replaced. Rational in other matters, to this
he would give no heed. Indeed in his charming and perverse
naïveté he imagined that to overtax himself, to talk or write
through the entire night, was good "training in versatility
and disregard of circumstances." [51] But, as Pollock remarks,
"he fancied himself to be making investments when he was
in fact living on his capital." [52]

Reluctantly he agreed to take six months' leave of absence,
which he spent travelling with his wife in Algeria and Spain.
The rest and change were beneficial and he returned to England somewhat improved. In the next year and a half, despite his illness and the distress occasioned by the death of
his father, Clifford accelerated his work, issuing two of his
most celebrated papers, "On the Canonical Form and Dissection of a Riemann's Surface," "On the Classification of
Loci," [53] along with other mathematical memoirs, an excel-

[51] *L & E* (P).   [52] Ibid.

[53] Unfortunately an unfinished memoir.

"The application of Abelian functions to this new aspect of geometry
awakened all Clifford's enthusiasm. He spoke to me of this part of his theory
as opening a boundless field for new researches—as 'altogether too big a thing'
for one man to manage. . . . How much may have perished unrecorded we
cannot tell, but, however this may be, no geometer will look for a more splen-
did monument of Clifford's genius, or for a more touching memorial of his
early death, than is to be found in the unfinished pages 'On the Classification
of Loci' which embody the last and perhaps the greatest effort of his inventive
powers." (H. J. Stephen Smith, op. cit.)

lent volume on dynamics, a number of essays, lectures, and reviews. He made no concession in his manner to the terrible disease that was destroying him; he charged his strength as carelessly as before. There came, inevitably—surprising only that he was given so much grace—a collapse, in February 1878. So dangerous was his condition that as soon as he had recovered sufficiently to travel, he left England, accompanied by his wife, for the Mediterranean. At Monte Generoso, in Italy, he appeared to improve. On strict orders his work had been left behind, but he wrote a few letters, which even in their casual phrase carried his talent and his spirit. In August 1878 he came home "looking very ill and feeble to ordinary observation, but much better to those who had seen him before he started." [54] Before he had a chance to leave in the autumn, he suffered another relapse. His condition was so hopeless that it was difficult for his friends to understand "how he maintained his cheerfulness, patience and unselfishness." [55]

At the beginning of 1879 Clifford was fast losing strength. Travel was dangerous, but the English climate was worse. It was certain he would be more comfortable in the south, and so, although his friends feared he would not live through the journey, he sailed for Madeira.[56] For some weeks after his arrival there was a slight improvement—not enough to warrant hope, but enough to give him a few hours of peace in the fine sunshine. Knowing the end was coming, he gave

---

[54] *L & E* (P).   [55] Ibid.

[56] After Clifford had left for Madeira, a number of his friends got together to offer him a testimonial of their affection and admiration. The meeting is described in *Nature* (February 13, 1879, Vol. XIX, p. 349): "The friends of Professor Clifford, who has been compelled by ill health to relinquish active work and reside in Madeira, are anxious to present him with a substantial testimonial in public recognition of his great scientific and literary attainments. At a meeting held at the Royal Institution . . . it was resolved that a fund should be raised for the above-mentioned purpose, and that the sums received should be placed in the hands of trustees for the benefit of Professor Clifford and his family." Among the signatories were Dr. William Spottiswood, president of the Royal Society, T. H. Huxley, Sir Frederick Pollock, H. J. S. Smith, John Tyndall, Sir John Lubbock, Hon. Mr. Justice Stephen.

careful directions for the disposal of his works. To the last
he retained interest in his friends and world affairs. On March
3, 1879, aged thirty-five, he died.

"And this," writes Pollock, "is the witness of his ending,
that as never man loved life more, so never man feared death
less. He fulfilled well and truly that great saying of Spinoza,
often in his mind and on his lips: '*Homo liber de nulla re
minus quam de morte cogitat.*' " [57]

XI

Clifford's own writings, a few letters, Pollock's biographical introduction to the *Lectures and Essays*, the article by
Leslie Stephen, another friend, in the *Dictionary of National
Biography*, the obituary notices,[58] and a handful of scattered
articles and reviews of Clifford's books in the pages of
Nature, the *Fortnightly Review*, and other English magazines
—out of these meagre sources, all that were available, this
wholly inadequate appreciation has been drawn. In the
histories and literature of mathematics there are tributes
abundant to Clifford's powers as a mathematician,[59] powers

[57] "There is nothing over which a free man ponders less than death."
(Spinoza's *Ethics*, P. IV, Prop. 67.) *L & E* (P).
[58] Perhaps the best-known of the obituaries is the one in the *Athenæum* of
March 8, 1879. It states in part: "Clifford was admitted on all hands to be
the most remarkable mathematician of his generation, and promised to be a
second Cayley. His general acquirements, too, were singularly great." It is
conceded that even if some of his philosophical articles "failed to convince,"
they always "commanded attention." "The continued strain of mathematical
study and metaphysical polemic proved too severe for his physical powers. . . .
Of his gentle, affectionate disposition, his unaffected simplicity, and his
charm of manner, this is not the place to speak. To his friends his loss is almost
irreparable." The obituary in *Nature* of March 13 refers to Clifford as "One
of the deepest thinkers and most brilliant writers this century has seen."
"He was,—some of his friends may think unfortunately,—most generally
known for his philosophical and polemical writings. [But his] fame will rest
on no such narrow basis."
[59] Writing of the growth of non-Euclidean geometry in his *Vorlesungen über
die Entwicklung der Mathematik im 19 Jahrhundert*, the famous geometer Felix
Klein comments on Clifford: "I remember him with particular pleasure as one
who immediately fully understood me and, also, soon went beyond me."

embodied in his many papers, some of clarity and depth, artistically finished; others fragmentary, but rich with ideas. No detailed critique of his mathematical contributions has been attempted, an appropriate task, rather, for a full biography, long overdue. Certainly in this study there is nothing of novelty or originality. So far as Pollock's biographical essay is concerned, I admit to a shameless plagiarism: there was no alternative on consideration of the unique importance of the source. I might have reprinted Pollock's piece entire, but not all was suited to the present purpose and it seemed preferable to devote more space than did he to Clifford's philosophy of science. The debt must be acknowledged with the hope that as a result of my incurring it the reader will have come closer to Clifford as he really was.

How *The Common Sense of the Exact Sciences* came to be written is described by Karl Pearson in his Preface (retained in this volume) to the original edition. Clifford had ambitious plans for writing a fresh series of texts re-evaluating basic concepts in mathematics and physics, but he lived to finish no more than the *Elements of Dynamics* and several chapters of the present work. Sharing his views on the foundations of science, Pearson, a noted mathematician and geneticist, later the author of the well-known *Grammar of Science*, decided as a tribute to Clifford to revise his manuscript and complete it by adding a large amount of new material. It may thus be supposed that the work presents Clifford's judgments, more fully worked out, as he himself would have wished. Despite the measure of his contribution Pearson permitted the use of his name only in the form of initials under the introduction.

The task of collecting Clifford's scattered notes and assembling the crude manuscript was originally undertaken by Professor R. C. Rowe, but at his death Pearson continued the job.

To laud *The Common Sense of the Exact Sciences* would be superfluous. It is known to every student of the physical sciences; leading scientific works contain references and quo-

tations; it is most often mentioned in writings on popular
science and the philosophy of science.[60] Like other great
books it is praised more often than read, a neglect partly
attributable to the fact that the volume has been so long
out of print.

Much of the book exhibits Clifford's (and Pearson's) ex-
traordinary virtuosity in the art of making hard things
seem easy. Throughout, one feels the impulsion, the intellectual range and vigour of Clifford's spirit. But it is not an
easy book. It treats of ideas inherently subtle and difficult,
rendered more so by dogmatic preconceptions as to their
obvious and unanalysable character. In dissecting such
concepts as space, number, motion, Clifford adopts the geometric, intuitive method. Some concepts, however, are im-
permeable to this approach, while others lend themselves
not merely to a clearer understanding but to an unhampered
development only by the use of analytic instruments. The
enormous fruitfulness of the union of algebra and geometry
must not be permitted to obscure the fact that algebra,[61] as
well as geometry, retains autonomous functions; there are
paths that one can travel and the other cannot. Pure reason sometimes lights the way where the lamp of intuition
will not avail. That abstract transactions in symbols can
be translated into the pictures of geometry and vice versa is
æsthetically and intellectually satisfying. It demonstrates
the generality, the interrelatedness, and the symmetry of

[60] The *Athenæum* of July 11, 1885 in reviewing *The Common Sense of the
Exact Sciences* comments: "There is a marvellous charm about Clifford's
writing. He had a singular faculty of presenting difficult truths in words of a
startling clearness and brevity . . . [throughout] he eschews the ponderous
phrases of learned pedantry. . . ." P. G. Tait, in *Nature* (June 11, 1885), concludes that it is "in many respects a very good book," but his review fails to
conceal a note of asperity as well as condescension. Tait, an eminent physicist,
had on at least one occasion fared poorly at Clifford's hands: in Clifford's
smashing review of *The Unseen Universe; or Physical Speculations on a Future
State*, a somewhat confused philosophical work of which Tait was co-author.
The review, appearing in the *Fortnightly Review*, was one of Clifford's best-
known polemics and, with its biting sarcasm and agnosticism, was not destined to win friends.

[61] The term here is used broadly to include analysis.

mathematics; it gives to mathematics a concreteness emphasizing its connection with the physical world. While these are values not to be contemned, they must not be regarded as the touchstone of mathematical activity. The final stamp of the Q.E.D. depends upon logic, not pictures.

Although Clifford's exposition of the number concept is an instance of his singular skill, the real number system as developed since his time affords a more convincing and logical structure. The greater portion of the chapters on "Space," "Position," and "Motion" are brilliant examples of the didactic art and have not been outmoded by newer methods. Wherever possible Clifford and Pearson eschew the algebraic symbol and equation; inordinately complex ideas, such as the bending of space, are untangled and their elements laid bare with the aid of a prose style, clean and of measured pace, embodying the first principles of successful teaching. Yet Pearson admits that to arrive at complete understanding in certain parts of mathematics, or at least an understanding sufficient to permit of further advances, we cannot depend on geometric conception alone:

"It may be held by some that the postulate of the sameness of our space is based upon the fact that no one had hitherto been able to form any geometrical conception of space-curvature. Apart from the fact that mankind habitually assumes many things of which it can form no geometrical conception (mathematicians the circular points at infinity, theologians transubstantiation), I may remark that we cannot expect any being to form a geometrical conception of the curvature of his space till he views it from space of a higher dimension, that is, practically, never."

The minor qualifications may frankly be admitted, for the whole of the book forms a distinguished legacy of an outstanding intellect. Modern advances in mathematics and physics, advances either superseding Clifford's ideas or, more often, following along paths he had charted to regions he had prefigured, have been so extensive since *The Common Sense of the Exact Sciences* appeared that one cannot but admire

how fresh it remains in outlook, how little left behind by
another century.

I have assumed few editorial prerogatives. Except for
modernization of some of the symbols, correction of obvious
misprints and errors, the addition of a number of diagrams,
and the redrawing of all, the text of the present edition of
The Common Sense of the Exact Sciences is taken unaltered
from the third edition of 1899. Alterations in the text itself
were never considered. Such notes as appear are intended to
clarify occasional obscurities.

James R. Newman

PREFACE

In MARCH 1879 Clifford died at Madeira, six years afterwards a posthumous work is for the first time placed before the public. Some explanation of this delay must be attempted in the present preface.

The original work as planned by Clifford was to have been entitled *The First Principles of the Mathematical Sciences Explained to the Non-Mathematical*, and to have contained six chapters, on *Number, Space, Quantity, Position, Motion*, and *Mass* respectively. Of the projected work Clifford in the year 1875 *dictated* the chapters on Number and Space completely, the first portion of the chapter on Quantity, and somewhat later nearly the entire chapter on Motion. The first two chapters were afterwards seen by him in proof, but never finally revised. Shortly before his death he expressed a wish that the book should only be published after very careful revision, and that its title should be changed to *The Common Sense of the Exact Sciences*.

Upon Clifford's death the labour of revision and completion was entrusted to Mr. R. C. Rowe, then Professor of Pure Mathematics at University College, London. That Professor Rowe fully appreciated the difficulty and at the same time the importance of the task he had undertaken is very amply evidenced by the time and care he devoted to the matter. Had he lived to complete the labour of editing, the work as a whole would have undoubtedly been better and more worthy of Clifford than it at present stands. On the sad death of Professor Rowe, in October 1884, I was requested by Messrs. Kegan Paul, Trench, & Co. to take up the task of editing, thus left incomplete. It was with no light heart, but with a grave sense of responsibility that I undertook to see through the press the labour of two men for whom I held the highest scientific admiration and per-

sonal respect. The reader will perhaps appreciate my difficulties better when I mention the exact state of the work
when it came into my hands. Chapters I and II, *Space* and
Number; half of Chapter III, *Quantity* (then erroneously
termed Chapter IV); and Chapter V, *Motion*, were in proof.
With these proofs I had only some half-dozen pages of the
corresponding manuscript, all the rest having unfortunately been considered of no further use, and accordingly
destroyed. How far the contents of the later proofs may
have represented what Clifford dictated I have had no means
of judging except from the few pages of manuscript in my
possession. In revising the proofs of the first two chapters,
which Clifford himself had seen, I have made as little alteration as possible, only adding an occasional foot-note where
it seemed necessary.

After examining the work as it was placed in my hands,
and consulting Mrs. Clifford, I came to the conclusion that
the chapter on Quantity had been misplaced, and that the
real gaps in the work were from the middle of Chapter III
to Chapter V, and again at the end of Chapter V. As to the
manner in which these gaps were to be filled I had no definite information whatever; only after my work had been
completed was an early plan of Clifford's for the book discovered. It came too late to be of use, but it at least con-
firmed our rearrangement of the chapters.

For the latter half of Chapter III and for the whole of
Chapter IV (pp. 134–204) I am alone responsible. Yet whatever there is in them of value I owe to Clifford; whatever
is feeble or obscure is my own.

With Chapter V my task has been by no means light. It
was written at a time when Clifford was much occupied
with his theory of "Graphs," and found it impossible to con-
centrate his mind on anything else: parts of it are clear and
succinct, parts were such as the author would never have
allowed to go to press. I felt it impossible to rewrite the
whole without depriving the work of its right to be called
Clifford's, and yet at the same time it was absolutely neces-

sary to make considerable changes. Hence it is that my revision of this chapter has been much more extensive than
in the case of the first two. With the result I fear many will
be dissatisfied; they will, however, hardly be more conscious of its deficiencies than I am. I can but plead the conditions under which I have had to work. One word more as
to this chapter. Without any notice of mass or force it seemed
impossible to close a discussion on motion; something I felt
must be added. I have accordingly introduced a few pages
on the laws of motion. I have since found that Clifford intended to write a concluding chapter on mass. How to express the laws of motion in a form of which Clifford would
have approved was indeed an insoluble riddle to me, because
I was unaware of his having written anything on the subject. I have accordingly expressed, although with great
hesitation, my own views on the subject; these may be con-
cisely described as a strong desire to see the terms matter
and force, together with the ideas associated with them,
entirely removed from scientific terminology—to reduce, in
fact, all dynamic to kinematic. I should hardly have ven-
tured to put forward these views had I not recently discovered that they have (allowing for certain minor differences) the weighty authority of Professor Mach, of Prag.[1]
But since writing these pages I have also been referred to a
discourse delivered by Clifford at the Royal Institution in
1873, some account of which appeared in *Nature*, June 10,
1880. Therein it is stated that "no mathematician can give
any meaning to the language about matter, force, inertia
used in current text-books of mechanics."[2] This fragmentary
account of the discourse undoubtedly proves that Clifford
held on the categories of matter and force as clear and
original ideas as on all subjects of which he has treated; only,
alas! they have not been preserved.

[1] See his recent book, *Die Mechanik in ihrer Entwickelung*. Leipzig, 1883.

[2] Mr. R. Tucker, who has kindly searched Clifford's note-books for anything on the subject, sends me a slip of paper with the following words in
Clifford's handwriting: "Force is not a fact at all, but an idea embodying what
is approximately the fact."

In conclusion I must thank those friends who have been ever ready with assistance and advice. Without their aid I could not have accomplished the little that has been done. My sole desire has been to give to the public as soon as possible another work of one whose memory will be revered by all who have felt the invigorating influence of his thought. Had this work been published as a fragment, even as many of us wished, it would never have reached those for whom Clifford had intended it. Completed by another hand, we can only hope that it will perform some, if but a small part, of the service which it would undoubtedly have fulfilled had the master lived to put it forth.

K. P.

University College, London:
February 26, 1885

The third edition of this book is a reprint of the first, with a few corrections, which I owe principally to the kindness of readers.

K. P.

October 10, 1886

THE

COMMON SENSE

OF THE

EXACT SCIENCES

CHAPTER I

Number

§1. *Number is Independent of the order of Counting* [1]

THE word which stands at the head of this chapter contains six letters. In order to find out that there are six, we count them; *n* one, *u* two, *m* three, *b* four, *e* five, *r* six. In this process we have taken the letters one by one, and have put beside them six words which are the first six out of a series of words that we always carry about with us, the names of numbers. After putting these six words one to each of the letters of the word *number*, we found that the last of the words was *six*; and accordingly we called that set of letters by the name six.

If we counted the letters in the word "chapter" in the same way, we should find that the last of the numeral words thus used would be *seven*; and accordingly we say that there are seven letters.

But now a question arises. Let us suppose that the letters of the word *number* are printed upon separate small pieces of wood belonging to a box of letters; that we put these into a bag and shake them up and bring them out, putting them down in any other order, and then count them again; we shall still find that there are six of them. For example, if they come out in the alphabetical order *b e m n r u*, and we put to each of these one of the names of numbers that we have before used, we shall still find that the last name will be six. In the assertion that any group of things consists of six things, it is implied that the word six will be the last of the ordinal words used, in whatever order we take up this

---

[1] Clifford confines his discussion to *cardinal* numbers. *Ordinal* numbers require a separate mathematical treatment.—J.R.N.

group of things to count them. That is to say, *the number of any set of things is the same in whatever order we count them.*

Upon this fact, which we have observed with regard to the particular number six, and which is true of all numbers whatever, the whole of the science of number is based. We shall now go on to examine some theorems about numbers which may be deduced from it.

§2. *A Sum is Independent of the order of Adding*

Suppose that we have two groups of things; say the letters in the word "number," and the letters in the word "chapter." We may count these groups separately, and find that they come respectively to the numbers six and seven. We may then put them all together, and we find in this case that the aggregate group which is so formed consists of thirteen letters.

Now this operation of putting the things all together may be conceived as taking place in two different ways. We may first of all take the six things and put them in a heap, and then we may add the seven things to them one by one. The process of counting, if it is performed in this order, amounts to counting seven more ordinal words after the word six. We may however take the seven things first and put them into a heap, and then add the six things one by one to them. In this case the process of counting amounts to counting six more ordinal words after the word seven.

But from what we observed before, that if we count any set of things we come to the same number in whatever order we count them, it follows that the number we arrive at, as belonging to the whole group of things, must be the same whichever of these two processes we use. This number is called the *sum* of the two numbers 6 and 7; and, as we have seen, we may arrive at it either by the first process of adding 7 to 6, or by the second process of adding 6 to 7.

The process of adding 7 to 6 is denoted by a shorthand symbol, which was first used by Leonardo da Vinci. A little

Maltese cross (+) stands for the Latin *plus*, or the English *increased by*. Thus the words *six increased by seven* are written in shorthand $6 + 7$. Now we have arrived at the result that *six increased by seven is the same number as seven increased by six*. To write this wholly in shorthand, we require a symbol for the words, *is the same number as*. The symbol for these is =; it was first used by an Englishman, Robert Recorde. Our result then may be finally written in this way:—

$$6 + 7 = 7 + 6.$$

The proposition which we have written in this symbolic form states that the sum of two numbers 6 and 7 is independent of the order in which they are added together. But this remark which we have made about two particular numbers is equally true of any two numbers whatever, in consequence of our fundamental assumption that the number of things in any group is independent of the order in which we count them. For by the sum of any two numbers we mean a number which is arrived at by taking a group of things containing the first number of individuals, and adding to them one by one another group of things containing the second number of individuals; or, if we like, by taking a group of things containing the second number of individuals, and adding to them one by one the group of things containing the first number of individuals. Now, in virtue of our fundamental assumption, the results of these two operations must be the same. Thus we have a right to say, not only that $6 + 7 = 7 + 6$, but also that $5 + 13 = 13 + 5$, and so on, whatever two numbers we like to take.

This we may represent by a method which is due to Vieta, viz., by denoting each number by a letter of the alphabet. If we write a in place of the first number in either of these two cases, or in any other case, and b in place of the second number, then our formula will stand thus:—

$$a + b = b + a.$$

By means of this representation we have made a statement which is not about two numbers in particular, but about all numbers whatever. The letters a and b so used are something like the names which we give to things, for example, the name *horse*. When we say a horse has four legs, the statement will do for any particular horse whatever. It says of that particular horse that it has four legs. If we said "a horse has as many legs as an ass," we should not be speaking of any particular horse or of any particular ass, but of any horse whatever and of any ass whatever. Just in the same way, when we assert that $a + b = b + a$, we are not speaking of any two particular numbers, but of all numbers whatever.

We may extend this rule to more numbers than two. Suppose we add to the sum $a + b$ a third number, c, then we shall have an aggregate group of things which is formed by putting together three groups, and the number of the aggregate group is got by adding together the numbers of the three separate groups. This number, in virtue of our fundamental assumption, is the same in whatever order we add the three groups together, because it is always the same set of things that is counted. Whether we take the group of a things first, and then add the group of b things to it one by one, and then to this compound group of $a + b$ things add the group of c things one by one; or whether we take the group of c things, and add to it the group of b things, and then to the compound group of $c + b$ things add the group of a things, the sum must in both cases be the same. We may write this result in the symbolic form $a + b + c = c + b + a$, or we may state in words that *the sum of three numbers is independent of the order in which they are added together*.

This rule may be extended to the case of any number of numbers.[1] However many groups of things we have, if we put them all together, the number of things in the resulting aggregate group may be counted in various ways. We may start with counting any one of the original groups, then we may follow it with any one of the others, following these by

---

[1] To the case of any *finite* number of numbers. For an infinite number of numbers (e.g., infinite series) the rule as stated would not be correct.—J.R.N.

any one of those left, and so on. In whatever order we have taken these groups, the ultimate process is that of counting the whole aggregate group of things; and consequently the numbers that we arrive at in these different ways must all be the same.

§3. *A Product is Independent of the order of Multiplying*

Now let us suppose that we take six groups of things which all contain the same number, say 5, and that we want to count the aggregate group which is made by putting all these together. We may count the six groups of five things one after another, which amounts to the same thing as adding 5 five times over to 5. Or if we like we may simply mix up the whole of the six groups, and count them without reference to their previous grouping. But it is convenient in this case to consider the six groups of five things as arranged in a particular way.

Let us suppose that all these things are dots which are made upon paper, that every group of five things is five dots arranged in a horizontal line, and that the six groups are placed vertically under one another as in Figure 1.

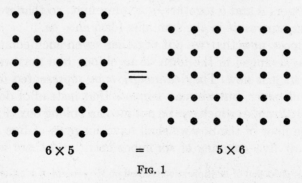

6 × 5   =   5 × 6

Fig. 1

We then have the whole of the dots of these six groups arranged in the form of an oblong which contains six rows of five dots each. Under each of the five dots belonging to the top group there are five other dots belonging to the remaining groups; that is to say, we have not only six *rows* containing five dots each, but five *columns* containing six dots each. Thus the whole set of dots can be arranged in five groups of six each, just as well as in six groups of five each. The whole number of things contained in six groups of five each, is called six times five. We learn in this way therefore that six times five is the same number as five times six.[1]

As before, the remark that we have here made about two particular numbers may be extended to the case of any two numbers whatever. If we take any number of groups of dots, containing all of them the same number of dots, and arrange these as horizontal lines one under the other, then the dots will be arranged not only in lines but in columns; and the number of dots in every column will obviously be the same as the number of groups, while the number of columns will be equal to the number of dots in each group. Consequently the number of things in a groups of b things each is equal to the number of things in b groups of a things each, no matter what the numbers a and b are.

The number of things in a groups of b things each is called a times b; and we learn in this way that a times b is equal to b times a. The number a times b is denoted by writing the two letters a and b together, a coming first; so that we may express our result in the symbolic form $ab = ba$.

Suppose now that we put together seven such compound groups arranged in the form of an oblong like that we constructed just now. They cannot now be represented on one sheet of paper, but we may suppose that instead of dots we have little cubes which can be put into an oblong box (Fig. 2). On the floor of the box we shall have six rows of five cubes each, or five columns of six cubes each; and there will be

[1] This definition of multiplication is based on the concept of addition alone. The modern definition uses two concepts: combination and addition. The number 5, say, is represented by a set consisting of five elements; the number 6 by a set consisting of six elements. The product 5 times 6 is represented by a new set, each element of which is a combination of two elements, one from each of the original sets. The elements of the new set are then counted in the usual way.—J.R.N.

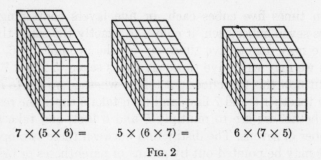

$$7 \times (5 \times 6) = \qquad 5 \times (6 \times 7) = \qquad 6 \times (7 \times 5)$$

Fig. 2

seven such layers, one on the top of another. Upon every cube therefore which is in the bottom of the box there will be a pile of six cubes, and we shall have altogether five times six such piles. That is to say, we have five times six groups of seven cubes each, as well as seven groups of five times six cubes each. The whole number of cubes is independent of the order in which they are counted, and consequently we may say that seven times five times six is the same thing as five times six times seven.

But it is here very important to notice that when we say seven times five times six, what we mean is that seven layers have been formed, each of which contains five times six things; but when we say five times six times seven, we mean that five times six columns have been formed, each of which contains seven things. Here it is clear that in the one case we have first multiplied the last two numbers, and then multiplied the result by the first mentioned (seven times five times six = seven times thirty), while in the other case it is the first two numbers mentioned that are multiplied together, and then the third multiplied by the result (five times six times seven = thirty times seven). Now it is quite evident that when the box is full of these cubes it may be set upon any side or upon any end; and in all cases there will be a number of layers of cubes, either 5 or 6 or 7. And whatever is the number of layers of cubes, that will also be the number of cubes in each pile. Whether therefore we take seven layers containing five times six cubes each, or six layers containing seven times five cubes each, or five layers containing six times seven cubes each, it comes to exactly the same thing.

We may denote five times six by the symbol 5 × 6, and then we may write five times six times seven, 5 × 6 × 7.

But now this form does not tell us whether we are to multiply together 6 and 7 first, and then take 5 times the result, or whether we are to multiply 5 and 6 first, and take that number of sevens. The distinction between these two operations may be pointed out by means of parentheses or brackets; thus, 5 × (6 × 7) means that the 6 and 7 must be first multiplied together and 5 times the result taken, while (5 × 6) × 7 means that we are to multiply 5 and 6 and then take the resulting number of sevens.

We may now state two facts that we have learned about multiplication.

First, that the brackets make no difference in the result, although they do make a difference in the process by which the result is attained; that is to say, 5 × (6 × 7) = (5 × 6) × 7.

Secondly, that the product of these three numbers is independent of the order in which they are multiplied together.

The first of these statements is called the *associative* law of multiplication, and the second the *commutative* law.

Now these remarks that we have made about the result of multiplying together the particular three numbers, 5, 6, and 7, are equally applicable to any three numbers whatever.

We may always suppose a box to be made whose height, length, and breadth will hold any three numbers of cubes. In that case the whole number of cubes will clearly be independent of the position of the box; but however the box is set down it will contain a certain number of layers, each layer containing a certain number of rows, and each row containing a certain number of cubes. The whole number of cubes in the box will then be the product of these three numbers; and it will be got at by taking any two of the three numbers, multiplying them together, and then multiplying the result by the third number.

This property of any three numbers whatever may now be stated symbolically.

In the first place it is true that $a(bc) = (ab)c$; that is, it comes to the same thing whether we multiply the product of the second and third numbers by the first, or the third number by the product of the first and second.

In the next place it is true that $abc = acb = bca$, &c., and we may say that the product of any three numbers is independent of the order and of the mode of grouping in which the multiplications are performed.

We have thus made some similar statements about two numbers and three numbers respectively. This naturally suggests to us that we should inquire if corresponding statements can be made about four or five numbers, and so on.

We have arrived at these two statements by considering the whole group of things to be counted as arranged in a layer and in a box respectively. Can we go any further, and so arrange a number of boxes as to exhibit in this way the product of four numbers? It is pretty clear that we cannot.

Let us therefore now see if we can find any other sort of reason for believing that what we have seen to be true in the case of three numbers—viz., that the result of multiplying them together is independent of the order of multiplying—is also true of four or more numbers.

In the first place we will show that it is possible to interchange the order of a pair of these numbers which are next to one another in the process of multiplying, without altering the product.

Consider, for example, the product of four numbers, $abcd$. We will endeavour to show that this is the same thing as the product $acbd$. The symbol $abcd$ means that we are to take c groups of d things and then b groups like the aggregate so formed, and then finally a groups of bcd things.

Now, by what we have already proved, b groups of cd things come to the same number as c groups of bd things. Consequently, a groups of bcd things are the same as a groups of cbd things; that is to say, $abcd = acbd$.

It will be quite clear that this reasoning will hold no matter how many letters come after *d*. Suppose, for example, that we have a product of six numbers *abcdef*. This means that we are to multiply *f* by *e*, the result by *d*, then *def* by *c*, and so on.

Now in this case the product *def* simply takes the place which the number *d* had before. And *b* groups of *c* times *def* things come to the same number as *c* groups of *b* times *def* things, for this is only the product of three numbers, *b*, *c*, and *def*. Since then this result is the same in whatever order *b* and *c* are written, there can be no alteration made by multiplications coming after, that is to say if we have to multiply by ever so many more numbers after multiplying by *a*. It follows therefore that no matter how many numbers are multiplied together, we may change the places of any two of them which are close together without altering the product.

In the next place let us prove that we may change the places of any two which are not close together. For example, that *abcdef* is the same thing as *aecdbf*, where *b* and *e* have been interchanged. We may do this by first making the *e* march backwards, changing places successively with *d* and *c* and *b*, when the product is changed into *aebcdf*; and then making *b* march forwards so as to change places successively with *c* and *d*, whereby we have now got *e* into the place of *b*.

Lastly, I say that by such interchanges as these we can produce any alteration in the order that we like. Suppose for example that I want to change *abcdef* into *dcfbea*. Here I will first get *d* to the beginning; I therefore interchange it with *a*, producing *dbcaef*. Next, I must get *c* second; I do this by interchanging it with *b*, this gives *dcbaef*. I must now put *f* third by interchanging it with *b*, giving *dcfaeb*, next put *b* fourth by interchanging it with *a*, producing *dcfbea*. This is the form required. By five such interchanges at most, I can alter the order of six letters in any way I please. It has now been proved that this alteration in the order may be produced by successive interchanges of two letters which are close together. But these interchanges, as we have before shown, do not alter the product; consequently the product of six numbers in any order is equal to the product of the same six numbers in any other order; and it is easy to see how the same process will apply to any number of numbers.

But is not all this a great deal of trouble for the sake of proving what we might have guessed beforehand? It is true we might have guessed beforehand that a product was independent of the order and grouping of its factors; and we might have done good work by developing the consequences of this guess before we were quite sure that it was true. Many beautiful theorems have been guessed and widely used before they were conclusively proved; there are some even now in that state. But at some time or other the inquiry has to be undertaken, and it always clears up our ideas about the nature of the theorem, besides giving us the right to say that it is true. And this is not all; for in most cases the same mode of proof or of investigation can be applied to other subjects in such a way as to increase our knowledge. This happens with the proof we have just gone through; but at present, as we have only numbers to deal with, we can only go backwards and not forwards in its application. We have been reasoning about multiplication; let us see if the same reasoning can be applied to addition.

What we have proved amounts to this. A certain result has been got out of certain things by taking them in a definite order; and it has been shown that *if we can interchange any two consecutive things without altering the result, then we may make any change whatever in the order without altering the result.* Let us apply this to counting. The process of counting consists in taking certain things in a definite order, and applying them to our fingers one by one; the result depends on the last finger, and its name is called the number of the things so counted. We learn then that this result will be independent of the order of counting, provided only that it remains unaltered when we interchange any two consecutive things; that is, provided that two adjacent fingers can be crossed, so that each rests on the object previously under

the other, without employing any new fingers or setting free
any that are already employed. With this assumption we
can *prove* that the number of any set of things is independent
of the order of counting; a statement which, as we have seen,
is the foundation of the science of number.

§4. *The Distributive Law*

There is another law of multiplication which is, if possible,
still more important than the two we have already considered. Here is a particular case of it: the number 5 is the
sum of 2 and 3, and 4 times 5 is the sum of 4 times 2 and 4
times 3. We can make this visible by an arrangement of dots
as follows (Fig. 3):—

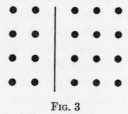

FIG. 3

Here we have four rows of five dots each, and each row is
divided into two parts, containing respectively two dots and
three dots. It is clear that the whole number of dots may be
counted in either of two ways; as four rows of five dots, or
as four rows of two dots together with four rows of three
dots. By our general principle the result is independent of
the order of counting, and therefore

$$4 \times 5 = (4 \times 2) + (4 \times 3);$$

or, if we put in evidence that $5 = 2 + 3$,

$$4(2 + 3) = (4 \times 2) + (4 \times 3).$$

The process is clearly applicable to any three numbers
whatever, and not only to the particular numbers 4, 2, 3.
We may construct an oblong containing a rows of $b + c$ dots;
and this may be divided by a vertical line into a rows of b

dots and a rows of c dots. Counted in one way, the whole number of dots is $a(b + c)$; counted in another way, it is $ab + ac$. Hence we must always have

$$a(b + c) = ab + ac.$$

This is the *first form* of the distributive law.

Now the result of multiplication is independent of the order of the factors, and therefore

$$a(b + c) = (b + c)a,$$
$$ab = ba,$$
$$ac = ca;$$

so that our equation may be written in the form

$$(b + c)a = ba + ca.$$

This is called the *second form* of the distributive law. Using the numbers of our previous example, we say that since 5 is the sum of 2 and 3, 5 times 4 is the sum of 2 times 4 and 3 times 4. This form may be arrived at independently and very simply as follows. We know that 2 things and 3 things make 5 things, whatever the things are; let each of these things be a group of 4 things; then 2 fours and 3 fours make 5 fours, or

$$(2 \times 4) + (3 \times 4) = 5 \times 4.$$

The rule may now be extended. It is clear that our oblong may be divided by vertical lines into more parts than two, and that the same reasoning will apply. This figure (Fig. 4),

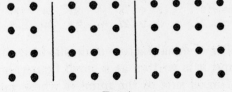

Fig. 4

for example, makes visible the fact that just as 2 and 3 and 4 make 9, so 4 times 2, and 4 times 3, and 4 times 4 make 4 times 9. Or generally—

$$a(b + c + d) = ab + ac + ad,$$
$$(b + c + d)a = ba + ca + da;$$

and the same reasoning applies to the addition of any number of numbers and their subsequent multiplication.

§5. *On Powers*

When a number is multiplied by itself it is said to be squared. The reason of this is that if we arrange a number of lines of equally distant dots in an oblong, the number of lines being equal to the number of dots in each line, the oblong will become a square.

If the square of a number is multiplied by the number itself, the number is said to be *cubed*; because if we can so fill a box with cubes as to have the same number of them in its height, length, and breadth, the shape of the box itself must be a cube.

If we multiply together four numbers which are all equal, we get what is called the fourth power of any one of them; thus if we multiply 4 3's we get 81, if we multiply 4 2's we get 16.

If we multiply together any number of equal numbers, we get in the same way a power of one of them which is called its fifth, or sixth, or seventh power, and so on, according to the number of numbers multiplied together.

Here is a table of the powers of 2 and 3:—

Index	1	2	3	4	5	6	7	8
Powers of 2 . . .	2	4	8	16	32	64	128	256
" 3 . . .	3	9	27	81	243	729	2187	6561

The number of equal factors multiplied together is called the *index*, and it is written as a small figure above the line on the right-hand side of the number whose power is thus expressed. To write in shorthand the statement that if you multiply seven threes together you get 2187, it is only needful to put down:—

$$3^7 = 2187.$$

It is to be observed that every number is its own *first power*; thus $2^1 = 2$, $3^1 = 3$, and in general $a^1 = a$.

§6. *Square of a + 1*

We may illustrate the properties of square numbers by means of a common arithmetical puzzle, in which one person tells the number another has thought of by means of the result of a round of calculations performed with it.

Think of a number . . . . say 3
Square it 9
Add 1 to the original number 4
Square that 16
Take the difference of the two squares . . 7

This last is always an odd number, and the number thought of is what we may call the *less half* of it; viz., it is the half of the even number next below it. Thus, the result being given as 7, we know that the number thought of was the half of 6, or 3.

We will now proceed to prove this rule. Suppose that the square of 5 is given us, in the form of twenty-five dots arranged in a square, how are we to form the square of 6 from it? We may add five dots on the right, and then five dots along the bottom, and then one dot extra in the corner. That is, to get the square of 6 from the square of 5, we must add one more than twice 5 to it. Accordingly—

$$36 = 25 + 10 + 1.$$

And, conversely, the number 5 is the less half of the difference between its square and the square of 6.

The form of this reasoning shows that it holds good for any number whatever. Having given a square of dots, we can make it into a square having one more dot in each side by adding a column of dots on the right, a row of dots at the bottom, and one more dot in the corner (Fig. 5). That is, we must add one more than twice the number of dots in a side of the original square. If, therefore, this number is given to

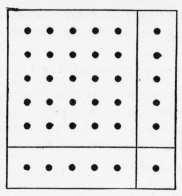

FIG. 5

us, we have only to take one from it and divide by 2, to have the number of dots in the side of the original square.

We will now write down this result in shorthand. Let a be the original number; then $a + 1$ is the number next above it; and what we want to say is that the square of $a + 1$, that is $(a + 1)^2$, is got from the square of a, which is a^2, by adding to it one more than twice a, that is $2a + 1$. Thus the shorthand expression is

$$(a + 1)^2 = a^2 + 2a + 1.$$

This theorem is a particular case of a more general one, which enables us to find the square of the sum of any two numbers in terms of the squares of the two numbers and their product. We will first illustrate this by means of the square of 5, which is the sum of 2 and 3 (Fig. 6).

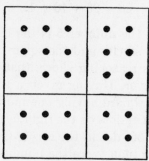

FIG. 6

The square of twenty-five dots is here divided into two squares and two oblongs. The squares are respectively the squares of 3 and 2, and each oblong is the product of 3 and 2. In order to make the square of 3 into the square of $3 + 2$, we must add two columns on the right, two rows at the bottom, and then the square of 2 in the corner. And in fact, $25 = 9 + 2 \times 6 + 4$.

§7. *On Powers of $a + b$*

To generalize this, suppose that we have a square with a dots in each side, and we want to increase it to a square with $a + b$ dots in each side. We must add b columns on the right, b rows at the bottom, and then the square of b in the corner. But each column and each row contains a dots. Hence what we have to add is twice ab together with b^2, or in shorthand:—

$$(a + b)^2 = a^2 + 2ab + b^2.$$

The theorem we previously arrived at may be got from this by making $b = 1$.

Now this is quite completely and satisfactorily proved; nevertheless we are going to prove it again in another way. The reason is that we want to extend the proposition still further; we want to find an expression not only for the square of $(a + b)$, but for any other power of it, in terms of the powers and products of powers of a and b. And for this purpose the mode of proof we have hitherto adopted is unsuitable. We might, it is true, find the cube of $a + b$ by adding the proper pieces to the cube of a; but this would be somewhat cumbrous, while for higher powers no such representation can be used. The proof to which we now proceed depends on the distributive law of multiplication.

According to this law, in fact, we have

$$\begin{aligned}(a + b)^2 = (a + b)(a + b) &= a(a + b) + b(a + b) \\ &= aa + ab + ba + bb \\ &= a^2 + 2ab + b^2.\end{aligned}$$

It will be instructive to write out this shorthand at length. The square of the sum of two numbers means that sum multiplied by itself. But this product is the first number multiplied by the sum together with the second number multiplied by the sum. Now the first number multiplied by the sum is the same as the first number multiplied by itself together with the first number multiplied by the second number. And the second number multiplied by the sum is the same as the second number multiplied by the first number together with the second number multiplied by itself. Putting all these together, we find that the square of the sum is equal to the sum of the squares of the two numbers together with twice their product.

Two things may be observed on this comparison. First, how very much the shorthand expression gains in clearness from its brevity. Secondly, that it is only shorthand for something which is just straightforward common sense and nothing else. We may always depend upon it that algebra, which cannot be translated into good English and sound common sense, is bad algebra.

But now let us put this process into a graphical shape which will enable us to extend it. We start with two numbers, a and b, and we are to multiply each of them by a and also by b, and to add all the results.

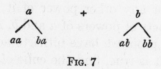

FIG. 7

Let us put in each case the result of multiplying by a to the left, and the result of multiplying by b to the right, under the number multiplied. The process is then shown in the figure.

If we now want to multiply this by $a + b$ again, so as to make $(a + b)^3$, we must multiply each part of the lower line by a, and also by b, and add all the results, thus:—

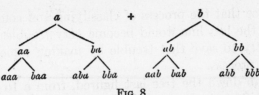

FIG. 8

Here we have eight terms in the result. The first and last are a^3 and b^3 respectively. Of the remaining six, three are *baa*, *aba*, *aab*, containing two *a*'s and one *b*, and therefore each equal to a^2b; and three are *bba*, *bab*, *abb*, containing one *a* and two *b*'s, and therefore each equal to ab^2. Thus we have:—

$$(a + b)^3 = a^3 + 3a^2b + 3ab^2 + b^3.$$

For example, $11^3 = 1331$. Here $a = 10$, $b = 1$, and

$$(10 + 1)^3 = 10^3 + 3 \times 10^2 + 3 \times 10 + 1,$$

for it is clear that any power of 1 is 1.

We shall carry this process one step further, before making remarks which will enable us to dispense with it.

In this case there are sixteen terms, the first and last being a^4 and b^4 respectively. Of the rest, some have three *a*'s and

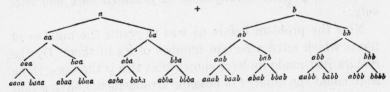

FIG. 9

one *b*, some two *a*'s and two *b*'s, and some one *a* and three *b*'s. There are four of the first kind, since the *b* may come first, second, third, or fourth; so also there are four of the third kind, for the *a* occurs in each of the same four places; the remaining six are of the second kind. Thus we find that,

$$(a + b)^4 = a^4 + 4a^3b + 6a^2b^2 + 4ab^3 + b^4.$$

We might go on with this process as long as we liked, and we should get continually larger and larger trees. But it is easy to see that the process of classifying and counting the terms in the last line would become very troublesome. Let us then try to save that trouble by making some remarks upon the process.

If we go down the tree last figured, from *a* to *abaa*, we shall find that the term *abaa* is built up from right to left as we descend. The *a* that we begin with is the last letter of *abaa*; then in descending we move to the right, and put another *a* before it; then we move to the left and put *b* before that; lastly we move to the right and put in the first *a*. From this there are two conclusions to be drawn.

First, *the terms at the end are all different*; for any divergence in the path by which we descend the tree makes a difference in some letter of the result.

Secondly, *every possible arrangement of four letters which are either* a's *or* b's *is produced*. For if any such arrangement be written down, say *abab*, we have only to read it backwards, making *a* mean "turn to the left" and *b* "turn to the right," and it will indicate the path by which we must descend the tree to find that arrangement at the end.

We may put these two remarks into one by saying that *every such possible arrangement is produced once and once only*.

Now the problem before us was to count the number of terms which have a certain number of *b*'s in them. By the remark just made we have shown that this is the same thing as to count the number of possible arrangements having that number of *b*'s.

Consider for example the terms containing one *b*. When there are three letters to each term, the number of possible arrangements is 3, for the *b* may be first, second, or third, *baa, aba, aab*. So when there are four letters the number is 4, for the *b* may be first, second, third, or fourth; *baaa, abaa, aaba, aaab*. And generally it is clear that whatever be the number of letters in each term, that is also the number of places in which the *b* can stand. Or, to state the same thing in shorthand, if *n* be the number of letters, there are *n* terms containing one b. And then, of course, there are n terms containing one a and all the rest b's.

And these are the terms which come at the beginning and end of the nth power of $a + b$; viz. we must have $(a + b)^n$ $= a^n + na^{n-1}b + $ other terms $+ nab^{n-1} + b^n$.

The meaning of this shorthand is that we have n $(a + b)$'s multiplied together, and that the result of that multiplying is the sum of several numbers, four of which we have written down. The first is the product of n a's multiplied together, or a^n; the next is n times the product of b by $(n - 1)$ a's, namely, $na^{n-1}b$. The last but one is n times the product of a by $(n - 1)$ b's, namely, nab^{n-1}; and the last is the product of n b's multiplied together, which is written b^n.

The problem that remains is to fill up this statement by finding what the "other terms" are, containing each more than one a and more than one b.

§8. *On the Number of Arrangements of a Group of Letters*

This problem belongs to a very useful branch of applied arithmetic called the theory of "permutations and combinations," or of arrangement and selection. The theory tells us how many arrangements may be made with a given set of things, and how many selections can be made from them. One of these questions is made to depend on the other, so that there is an advantage in counting the number of arrangements first.

With two letters there are clearly two arrangements, ab and ba. With three letters there are these six:—

$$abc, \ acb, \ bca, \ bac, \ cab, \ cba,$$

namely, two with a at the beginning, two with b at the beginning, and two with c at the beginning; three times two. It would not be much trouble to write down all the arrangements that can be made with four letters $abcd$. But we may count the number of them without taking that trouble; for if we write d before each of the six arrangements of abc, we shall have six arrangements of the four letters beginning with d, and these are clearly all the arrangements which can begin with d. Similarly, there must be six beginning with a, six beginning with b, and six beginning with c; in all, four times six, or *twenty-four*.

Let us put these results together:

With two letters, number of arrangements is two =   2
"   three   "   three times two . . . . =   6
"   four   "   four times three times two = 24

Here we have at once a rule suggested. *To find the number of arrangements which can be made with a given group of letters, multiply together the numbers two, three, four, &c., up to the number of letters in the group.* We have found this rule to be right for two, three, and four letters; is it right for any number whatever of letters?

We will consider the next case of five letters, and deal with it by a method which is applicable to all cases. Any one of the five letters may be placed first; there are then five ways of disposing of the first place. For each of these ways there are four ways of disposing of the second place; namely, any one of the remaining four letters may be put second. This makes five times four ways of disposing of the first two places. For each of these there are three ways of disposing of the third place, for any one of the remaining three letters may be put third. This makes five times four times three ways of disposing of the first three places. For each of these there are two ways of disposing of the last two places; in all, five times four times three times two, or 120 ways of arranging the five letters.

Now this method of counting the arrangements will clearly do for any number whatever of letters; so that our rule must be right for all numbers.

We may state it in shorthand thus: the number of arrangements of n letters is $1 \times 2 \times 3 \times \ldots \times n$; or putting dots instead of the sign of multiplication, it is $1 \cdot 2 \cdot 3 \ldots n$.

The 1 which begins is of course not wanted for the multiplication, but it is put in to include the extreme case of there being only one letter, in which case, of course, there is only one arrangement.

The product $1 \cdot 2 \cdot 3 \ldots n$, or, as we may say, the product of the first n natural numbers, occurs very often in the exact sciences. It has therefore been found convenient to have a special short sign for it, just as a parliamentary reporter has a special sign for "the remarks which the Honourable Member has thought fit to make." Different mathematicians, however, have used different symbols for it. The symbol $\underline{|n}$ is very much used in England, but it is difficult to print. Some continental writers have used a note of admiration, thus, $n!$[1] We may now state that—

$$1! = 1,\ 2! = 2,\ 3! = 6,\ 4! = 24,\ 5! = 120,\ 6! = 720,$$

and generally that

$$(n+1)! = (n+1)(n)!$$

for the product of the first $n+1$ numbers is equal to the product of the first n numbers multiplied by $n+1$.

§9. *On a Theorem concerning any Power of a + b*

We will now apply this rule to the problem of counting the terms in $(a+b)^n$; and for clearness' sake, as usual, we will begin with a particular case, namely the case in which $n = 5$. We know that here there is one term whose factors are all a's, and one whose factors are all b's; five terms which are the product of four a's by one b, and five which are the product of one a and four b's. It remains only to count the number of terms made by multiplying three a's by two b's, which is naturally equal to the number made by multiplying

[1] In the original text Clifford used the symbol Π, which he justified as follows: "I myself prefer a symbol which has the weighty authority of Gauss, namely a Greek Π (Pi), which may be taken as short for *product* if we like, thus, Π."

In this edition the symbol ! (factorial) has been used, following modern usage.—J.R.N.

two a's by three b's. The question is, therefore, *how many different arrangements can be made with three* a's *and two* b's?

Here the three a's are all alike, and the two b's are alike.
To solve the problem we shall have to think of them as different; let us therefore replace them for the present by capital letters and small ones. How many different arrangements
can be made with three capital letters A B C and two small
ones *de*?

In this question the capital letters are to be considered
as equivalent to each other, and the small letters as equivalent to each other; so that the arrangement A B C d e counts
for the *same* arrangement as C A B e d. Every arrangement
of capitals and smalls is one of a group of $6 \times 2 = 12$ equivalent arrangements; for the 3 capitals may be arranged among
one another in $3! = 6$ ways, and the 2 smalls may be arranged
in $2! = 2$ ways. Now it is clear that by taking all the arrangements in respect of capital and small letters, and then permuting the capitals among themselves and the small letters
among themselves, we shall get the whole number of arrangements of the five letters A B C d e; namely $5!$ or 120.
But since each arrangement in respect of capitals and smalls
is here repeated twelve times, and since 12 goes into 120 *ten*
times exactly, it appears that the number we require is ten.
Or the number of arrangements of three a's and two b's is
$5!$ divided by $3!$ and $2!$.

The arrangements are in fact—

bbaaa, babaa, baaba, baaab

abbaa, ababa, abaab

aabba, aabab

aaabb

The first line has a b at the beginning, and there are *four*
positions for the second b; the next line has a b in the second
place, and there are *three* new positions for the other b, and
so on. We might of course have arrived at the number of arrangements in this particular case by the far simpler process
of direct counting, which we have used as a verification; but

the advantage of our longer process is that it will give us a general formula applicable to all cases whatever.

Let us stop to put on record the result just obtained; viz. we have found that

$$(a + b)^5 = a^5 + 5a^4b + 10a^3b^2 + 10a^2b^3 + 5ab^4 + b^5.$$

Observe that $1 + 5 + 10 + 10 + 5 + 1 = 32$, that is, we have accounted for the whole of the 32 terms which would be in the last line of the tree appropriate to this case.

We may now go on to the solution of our general problem. Suppose that p is the number of a's and q is the number of b's which are multiplied together in a certain term; we want to find the number of possible arrangements of these p a's and q b's. Let us replace them for the moment by p capital letters and q small ones, making $p + q$ letters altogether. Then any arrangement of these in respect of capital letters and small ones is one of a group of equivalent arrangements got by permuting the capitals among themselves and the small letters among themselves. Now by permuting the capital letters we can make $p!$ arrangements, and by permuting the small letters $q!$ arrangements. Hence every arrangement in respect of capitals and smalls is one of a group of $p! \times q!$ equivalent arrangements. Now the whole number of arrangements of the $p + q$ letters is $(p + q)!$; and, as we have seen, every arrangement in respect of capitals and smalls is here repeated $p! \times q!$ times. Consequently the number we are in search of is got by dividing $(p + q)!$ by $p! \times q!$. This is written in the form of a fraction, thus:—

$$\frac{(p + q)!}{p! \cdot q!},$$

although it is not a fraction, for the denominator always divides the numerator exactly. In fact, it would be absurd to talk about half a quarter of a way of arranging letters.

We have arrived then at this result, that *the number of ways of arranging p a's and q b's is*

$$\frac{(p + q)!}{p! \cdot q!}.$$

This is also (otherwise expressed) the number of ways of dividing $p + q$ places into p of one sort and q of another; or again, it is the number of ways of selecting p things out of $p + q$ things.

Applying this now to the expression of $(a + b)^n$, we find that each term, other than the first and last, is of the form

$$\frac{n\,!}{p\,!\cdot q\,!}\,a^p b^q,$$

where $p + q = n$; and that we shall get them all by giving to q successively the values 1, 2, 3, &c., and to p the values got by subtracting these from n. For example, we shall find that

$$(a + b)^6 = a^6 + 6a^5b + \frac{6\,!}{4\,!\cdot 2\,!}\,a^4b^2 + \frac{6\,!}{3\,!\cdot 3\,!}\,a^3b^3$$
$$+ \frac{6\,!}{2\,!\cdot 4\,!}\,a^2b^4 + 6ab^5 + b^6.$$

The calculation of the numbers may be considerably shortened. Thus we have to divide $1 \cdot 2 \cdot 3 \cdot 4 \cdot 5 \cdot 6$ by $1 \cdot 2 \cdot 3 \cdot 4$; the result is of course $5 \cdot 6$. This has to be further divided by 2, so that we finally get $5 \cdot 3$ or 15. Similarly, to calculate

$$\frac{6\,!}{3\,!\cdot 3\,!},$$

we have only to divide $4 \cdot 5 \cdot 6$ by $1 \cdot 2 \cdot 3$ or 6, and we get simply $4 \cdot 5$ or 20.

To write down our expression for $(a + b)^n$ we require another piece of shorthand. We have seen that it consists of a number of terms which are all of the form

$$\frac{n\,!}{p\,!\cdot q\,!}\,a^p b^q,$$

but which differ from one another in having for p and q different pairs of numbers whose sum is n. Just as we used ! for a product, so we use the Greek letter Σ (Sigma) for a sum. Namely, the sum of all such terms will be written down thus:—

$$\Sigma \frac{n\,!}{p\,!\cdot q\,!}\,a^p b^q, \qquad\qquad [p + q = n].$$

Now we may very reasonably include the two extreme terms a^n and b^n in the general shape of these terms. For suppose we made $p = n$ and $q = 0$, the corresponding term would be:—

$$\frac{n!}{n! \cdot 0!} a^n b^0,$$

and this will be simply a^n if $0! = 1$ and $b^0 = 1$. Of course there is no sense in "the product of the first no numbers"; but if we consider the rule

$$(n + 1)! = (n + 1)(n)!,$$

which holds good when n is any number, to be also true when n stands for nothing, and consequently $n + 1 = 1$, it then becomes

$$1! = 0!,$$

and we have already seen reason to make $1!$ mean 1. Next if we say that b^q means the result of multiplying 1 by b q times, then b^0 must mean the result of multiplying 1 by b no times, that is, of not multiplying it at all; and this result is 1.

Making then these conventional interpretations, we may say that

$$(a + b)^n = \Sigma \frac{n!}{p! \cdot q!} a^p b^q, \qquad [p + q = n],$$

it being understood that p is to take all values from n down to 0, and q all values from 0 up to n.

This result is called the *Binomial Theorem*, and was originally given by Sir Isaac Newton. An expression containing *two* terms, like $a + b$, is sometimes called *binomial*; and the name *Binomial Theorem* is an abbreviation for *theorem concerning any power of a binomial expression*.

§10. *On Operations which appear to be without Meaning*

We have so far considered the operations by which, when two numbers are given, two others can be determined from them.[1]

First, we can add the two numbers together and get their sum.

Secondly, we can multiply the two numbers together and get their product.

To the questions what is the sum of these two numbers, and what is the product of these two numbers, there is always an answer. But we shall now consider questions to which there is not always an answer.

Suppose that I ask what number added to 3 will produce 7. I know, of course, that the answer to this is 4, and the operation of getting 4 is called subtracting 3 from 7, and we denote it by a sign and write it

$$7 - 3 = 4.$$

But if I ask, what number added to 7 will make 3, although this question seems good English when expressed in words, yet there is no answer to it; and if I write down in symbols the expression $3 - 7$, I am asking a question to which there is no answer.

There is then an essential difference between adding and subtracting, for two numbers always have a sum.

If I write down the expression $3 + 4$, I can use it as meaning something, because I know that there is a number which is denoted by that expression. But if I write down the expression $3 - 7$, and then speak of it as meaning something, I shall be talking nonsense, because I shall have put together symbols the realities corresponding to which will not go together. To the question, what is the result when one number is taken from another, there is only an answer in

---

[1] The phrase is awkward. What is meant is that the operation of addition performed on two numbers yields one new number; the operation of multiplication, another new number.—J.R.N.

the case where the second number is greater than the first.

In the same way, when I multiply together two numbers I know that there is always a product, and I am therefore free to use such a symbol as 4×5, because I know that there is some number that is denoted by it. But I may now ask a question; I may say, What number is it which, being multiplied by 4, produces 20? The answer I know in this case is 5, and the operation by which I get it is called dividing 20 by 4. This is denoted again by a symbol, $20 \div 4 = 5$.

But suppose I say divide 21 by 4. To this there is no answer. There is no number in the sense in which we are at present using the word—that is to say, there is no whole number—which being multiplied by 4 will produce 21: and if I take the expression $21 \div 4$, and speak of it as meaning something, I shall be talking nonsense, because I shall have put together symbols whose realities will not go together.

The things that we have observed here will occur again and again in mathematics: for every operation that we can invent amounts to asking a question, and this question may or may not have an answer according to circumstances.

If we write down the symbols for the answer to the question in any of those cases where there is no answer and then speak of them as if they meant something, we shall talk nonsense. But this nonsense is not to be thrown away as useless rubbish. We have learned by very long and varied experience that nothing is more valuable than the nonsense which we get in this way; only it is to be recognized as nonsense, and by means of that recognition made into sense.

We turn the nonsense into sense by giving a new meaning to the words or symbols which shall enable the question to have an answer that previously had no answer.

Let us now consider in particular what meaning we can give to our symbols so as to make sense out of the at present nonsensical expression, $3 - 7$.

§11. *Steps* [1]

The operation of adding 3 to 5 is written $5 + 3$, and the result is 8. We may here regard the $+3$ as a way of stepping from 5 to 8, and the symbol $+3$ may be read in words, *step forward three*.

In the same way, if we subtract 3 from 5 and get 2, we write the process symbolically $5 - 3 = 2$, and the symbol -3 may be regarded as a step from 5 to 2. If the former step was forward this is backward, and we may accordingly read -3 in words, *step backwards three*.

A step is always supposed to be taken from a number which is large enough to make sense of the result. This restriction does not affect *steps forward*, because from any number we can step forward as far as we like; but backward a step can only be taken from numbers which are larger than the step itself.

The next thing we have to observe about steps is that when two steps are taken in succession from any number, it does not matter which of them comes first. If the two steps are taken in the same direction this is clear enough. $+3+4$, meaning step forward 3 and then step forward 4, directs us to step forward by the number which is the sum of the numbers in the two steps; and in the same way $-3-4$ directs us to step backward the sum of 3 and 4, that is 7.

If the steps are in opposite directions, as, for example, $+3-7$, we have to step forward 3 and then backward 7, and the result is that we must step backwards 4. But the same result would have been attained if we first stepped backward 7 and then forward 3. The result, in fact, is always a step which is in the direction of the greater of the two steps, and is in magnitude equal to their difference.

---

[1] Here the transition from cardinal numbers to numbers bearing signs: $+$, $-$, is abrupt in the sense that the connection between them is not shown. In modern mathematics signed numbers are defined in terms of cardinal numbers. It thus becomes unnecessary to conceive of signed numbers as analogous to physical steps—forward or backward, albeit the analogy is not without didactic value.—J.R.N.

We thus see that when two steps are taken in succession they are equivalent to one step, which is independent of the order in which they are taken.

We have now supplied a new meaning for our symbols, which makes sense and not nonsense out of the symbol $3 - 7$. The 3 must be taken to mean $+ 3$, that is, step forward 3; the $- 7$ must be taken to mean step backward 7, and the whole expression no longer means take 7 from 3, but add 3 to and then subtract 7 from any number which is large enough to make sense of the result. And accordingly we find that the result of this operation is $- 4$, or, as we may write it, $+ 3 - 7 = - 4$.

From this it follows by a mode of proof precisely analogous to that which we used in the case of multiplication, that any number of steps taken in succession have a resultant which is independent of the order in which they are taken, and we may regard this rule as an extension of the rule already proved for the addition of numbers.

A step may be multiplied or taken a given number of times, for example, $2(- 3) = - 6$; that is to say, if two backward steps of 3 be possible, they are equivalent to a step backwards of 6.

In this operation of multiplying a step it is clear that what we do is to multiply the number which is stepped, and to retain the character of the step. On multiplying a step forwards we still have a step forwards, and on multiplying a step backwards we still have a step backwards.

This multiplying may be regarded as an operation by which we change one step into another. Thus in the example we have just considered the multiplier 2 changes the step backwards 3 into the step backwards 6. But this operation, as we have observed, will only change a step into another of the same kind, and the question naturally presents itself, Is it possible to find an operation which shall change a step into one of a different kind? Such an operation we should naturally call reversal. We should say that a step forwards is reversed, when it is made into a step backwards; and a

step backwards is reversed when it is made into a step forwards.

If we denote the operation of reversal by the letter r, we
can, by combining this with a multiplication, change -3
into $+6$, a step backwards 3 into a step forwards 6; viz. we
should have the expression $r2(-3) = +6$. Now the operation, which is performed on one step to change it into another, may be of two kinds: either it keeps a step in the
direction which it originally had, or it reverses it. If to make
things symmetrical we insert the letter k when a step is
kept in its original direction, we may write the equation
$k2(-3) = -6$ to express the operation of simply multiplying.

Of course it is possible to perform on any given step a
succession of these operations. If I take the step $+4$, treble
it, and reverse it, I get -12. If I double this and keep it, I
get -24, and this may be written, $k2(r3)(+4) = -24$. But
this is equal to $r6(+4)$, which tells us that the two successive
operations which we have performed on this step, trebling
and reversing it, doubling and keeping it, are equivalent to
the single operation of multiplying by 6 and reversing it.
It is clear also that whatever step we had taken the two
first operations performed successively are always equivalent
to the third, and we may thus write the equation $k2(r3) = r6$.

Suppose however we take another step and treble it and
reverse it, and then double it and reverse it again; we should
have the result of multiplying it by six and keeping its
direction unchanged.

This may be written $r2(r3) = k \cdot 6$.

If we compare the last two formulæ with those which we
previously obtained, viz. $k2(-3) = -6$ and $r2(-3) = +6$,
we shall see that the two sets are alike, except that in the
one last obtained k and r are written instead of $+$ and $-$
respectively.

The two sets however express entirely different things.
Thus, taking the second formulæ of either set on the one
hand, the statement is, Double and reverse the step backward 3, and you have a step forward 6; on the other hand,

Treble and reverse and then double and reverse any step whatever, and you have the effect of *sextupling* and keeping the step. We shall find that this analogy holds good in general, that is, if we write down the effect of any number of successive operations performed upon a step, there will always be a corresponding statement in which this stepping is replaced by an operation; or we may say, any operation which converts one step into another will also convert one operation into another where the converted operation is a multiplying by the number expressing the step and a keeping or reversing according as the step is forward or backward.

§12. *Extension of the Meaning of Symbols*

We now proceed to do something which must apparently introduce the greatest confusion, but which, on the other hand, increases enormously our powers.

Having two things which we have so far quite rightly denoted by different symbols, and finding that we arrive at results which are uniform and precisely similar to one another except that in one of them one set of symbols is used, in the other another set, we alter the meaning of our symbols so as to see only one set instead of two. We make the symbols $+$ and $-$ mean for the future what we have here meant by k and r, viz. keep and reverse. We give them these meanings in addition to their former meanings, and leave it to the context to show which is the right meaning in any particular case. Thus, in the equation $(-2)(-3) = +6$ there are two possible meanings; the -3 and $+6$, may both mean steps, in this case the statement is: Double and reverse the step backwards of 3 and you get the step forward 6. But the -3 and the $+6$ may also mean not steps but operations, and in this case the meaning is triple and reverse and then double and reverse any step whatever, and you get the same result as if you had sextupled and kept the step.

Let us now see what the reason is for saying that these

two meanings can always exist together. Let us first of all take the second meaning, and frame a rule for finding the result of any number of successive operations.

First, the number which is the multiplier in the result must clearly be the product of all the numbers in the successive operations.

Next, every pair of reversals cancel one another, so that, if there is an even number of them, the result must be an operation of *retaining*.

This then is the rule: Multiply together the numbers in the several operations, prefixing to them + if there is an even number of *minus* or reversing operations, prefixing − if there is an odd number.

In the next place, suppose that many successive operations are performed upon a step. The number in the resulting step will clearly be the product of all the numbers in the operations and in the original step.

If there is an even number of reversing operations, the resulting step will be of the same kind as the original one; if an odd number, of the opposite kind. Now let us suppose that the original step were a step backwards; then if there is an even number of reversing operations, the resulting step will also be a step backwards. But in this case the number of (−) signs, reckoned independently of their meaning, will be odd; and so the rule coincides with the previous one.

If an odd number of reversing operations is performed on a negative step, the result is a positive step. But here the whole number of (−) signs, irrespective of their meaning, is an even number; and the result again agrees with the previous one.

In all cases therefore by using the same symbols to mean either a "forward" and a "backward" step respectively, or "keep" and "reverse" respectively, we shall be able to give to every expression two interpretations, and neither of these will ever be untrue.

In the process of examining this statement we have shown by the way that the result of any number of successive operations on a step is independent of the order of them. For it is always a step whose magnitude is the product of the numbers in the original step and in the operations, and whose character is determined by the number of reversals.

§13. *Addition and Multiplication of Operations*

We may now go on to find a rule which connects together the multiplication and the addition of steps.

If I multiply separately the steps + 3 and − 7 by 4, and then take the resultant of the two steps which I so obtain, I shall get the same thing as if I had first formed the resultant of + 3 and − 7, and then multiplied it by 4. In fact, + 12 − 28 = − 16, which is 4(− 4). This is true in general, and it obviously amounts to the original rule that a set of things comes to the same number in whatever order we count them. Only that now some of the counting has to be done backwards and some again forwards.

But now, besides adding together steps, we may also in a certain sense add together operations. It seems natural to assume at once that by adding together + 3 and − 7 regarded as operations, we must needs get the operation − 4. It is very important not to assume anything without proof, and still more important not to use words without attaching a definite meaning to them.

The meaning is this. If I take any step whatever, treble it without altering its character, and combine the result with the result of multiplying the original step by 7 and reversing it, then I shall get the same result as if I had multiplied the original step by 4 and reversed it. This is perfectly true, and we may see it to be true by, as it were, performing our operations in the form of steps. Suppose I take the step + 5, and want to treble it and keep its character unchanged. I can do this by taking three steps of five numbers each in the same direction (viz. the forward direction) as the original step was to be taken. Similarly, if I want to multiply it by − 7, this means that I must take 7 steps of five numbers each in the opposite or backward direction. Then finally, what I have to do is to take three steps forwards and seven steps backwards, each of these steps consisting of five numbers; and it appears at once that the result is the same as that of taking 4 steps backwards of five numbers each.

We have thus a definition of the sum of two operations; and it appears from the way in which we have arrived at it that this sum is independent of the order of the operations.

We may therefore now write the formulæ:—

$$a + b = b + a$$
$$a(b + c) = ab + ac$$
$$(a + b)c = ac + bc$$
$$ab = ba,$$

and consider the letters to signify operations performed upon steps. In virtue of the truth of these laws the whole of that reasoning which we applied to finding a power of the sum of two numbers is applicable to the finding of a power of the sum of two operations. If it did not take too much time and space, we might go through it again, giving to all the symbols their new meanings.

It is worth while, perhaps, by way of example, to explain clearly what is meant by the square of the sum of two operations.

We will take for example, $+ 5$ and $- 3$.

The formula tells us that $(+ 5 - 3)^2$ is equal to $(+ 5)^2 + (- 3)^2 + 2(+ 5)(- 3)$. This means that if we apply to any step twice over the sum of the operations $+ 5$ and $- 3$, that is to say, if we multiply it by 5 and keep its direction, and combine with this step the result of multiplying the original step by 3 and reversing it, and then apply the same process to the result so obtained, we shall get a step which might also have been arrived at by combining together the following three steps:—

First, the original step twice multiplied by 5.

Secondly, the original step twice multiplied by 3 and twice reversed; that is to say, unaltered in direction.

Thirdly, twice the result of tripling the original step and reversing it, and then multiplying by 5 and retaining the direction.

§14. *Division of Operations*

We have now seen what is meant by the multiplication of operations; let us go on to consider what sort of question is asked by *division*.

Let us take for example the symbolic statement − 3(+ 5) = − 15; and let us give it in the first place the meaning that to triple and reverse the step forward 5 gives the step backward 15. We may ask two questions upon this statement. First, What operation is it which, being performed on the step forwards 5, will give the step backwards 15? The answer, of course, is triple and reverse. Or we may ask this question. What step is that, which, being tripled and reversed, will give the step backwards 15? The answer is, Step forwards 5. But we have only one word to describe the process by which we get the answer in these two cases. In the first case we say that we *divide* the step − 15 by the step + 5; in the second case we say we divide the step − 15 by the operation − 3.

The word *divide* thus gets two distinct meanings. But it is very important to notice that symbolically the answer is the same in the two cases, although the interpretation to be given to it is different.

The step − 15 may be got in two ways; by tripling and reversing the forward step + 5, or by quintupling the backward step − 3. In symbols,

$$(- 3)(+ 5) = (+ 5)(- 3) = - 15.$$

Hence the problem, *Divide* − 15 by − 3 may mean either of these two questions: What step is that which, being tripled and reversed, gives the step − 15? Or, What operation is that which, performed on the step − 3, gives the step − 15? The answer to the first question is, the step + 5; the answer to the second is the operation of quintupling and retaining

direction, that is, the operation + 5. So that although the word
divide, as we have said, gets two distinct meanings, yet the two
different results of division are expressed by the same symbol.

In general we may say that the problem, Divide the step
a by the step *b*, means, Find the operation (if any) which
will convert *b* into *a*. But the problem, Divide the step *a* by
the operation *b*, means, Find the step (if any) which *b* will
convert into *a*. In both cases, however, the process and the
symbolic result are the same. We must divide the number
of *a* by the number of *b*, and prefix to it + if the signs of
a and *b* are alike, − if they are different.

We may also give to our original equation

$$(-3) \times (+5) = -15$$

its other meaning, in which both − 3 and + 5 are operations,
and − 15 is the operation which is equivalent to performing
one of them after the other. In this case the problem, Divide
the operation − 15 by the operation − 3 means, Find the
operation which, being succeeded by the operation − 3, will
be equivalent to the operation − 15. Or generally, Divide
the operation *a* by the operation *b*, means, Find the operation which, being succeeded by *b*, will be equivalent to *a*.

Now it is worth noticing that the division of step by step
and the division of operation by operation, have a certain
likeness between them, and a common difference from the
division of step by operation. Namely, the result of dividing
a by *b*, or, as we may write it, $\frac{a}{b}$, when *a* and *b* are both
steps or both operations, is an operation which converts *b*
into *a*. This we may write in shorthand,

$$\frac{a}{b} \cdot b = a.$$

But when *a* is a step and *b* an operation, the result of division
is a step on which the operation *b* must be performed to convert it into *a*; or, in shorthand,

$$b \cdot \frac{a}{b} = a.$$

The fact that the symbolic result is the same in the two cases may be stated thus:—

$$\frac{a}{b} \cdot b = b \cdot \frac{a}{b},$$

and in this form we see that it is a case of the commutative law. So long, then, as the commutative law is true, there is no occasion for distinguishing symbolically between the two meanings. But, as we shall see by-and-by, there is occasion to deal with other kinds of steps and operations in which the commutative law does not hold; and for these a convenient notation has been suggested by Professor Cayley. Namely, $\frac{a|}{|b}$ means the operation which makes b into a; but $\frac{|a}{b|}$ represents that which the operation b will convert into a. So that—

$$\frac{a|}{|b} \cdot b = a, \text{ but } b \cdot \frac{|a}{b|} = a.$$

It is however convenient to settle beforehand that whenever the symbol $\frac{a}{b}$ is used without warning it is to have the first meaning—namely, the operation which makes b into a.

§15. *General Results of our Extension of Terms*

It will be noticed that we have hereby passed from the consideration of mere numbers, with which we began, to the consideration first of steps of addition or subtraction of number from number, and then of operations of multiplying and keeping or multiplying and reversing, performed on these steps; and that we have greatly widened the meaning of all the words that we have employed.

To *addition*, which originally meant the addition of two numbers, has been given the meaning of a combination of steps to form a resultant step equivalent in effect to taking them in succession.

To *multiplication*, which was originally applied to two

numbers only, has been given the meaning of a combination of operations upon steps to form a resultant operation equivalent to their successive performance.

We have found that the same properties which characterize the addition and multiplication of numbers belong also to the addition and multiplication of steps and of operations. And it was this very fact of the similarity of properties which led us to use our old words in a new sense. We shall find that this same process is carried on in the consideration of those other subjects which lie before us; but that the precise similarity which we have here observed in the properties of more simple and more complex operations will not in every case hold good; so that while this gradual extension of the meaning of terms is perhaps the most powerful instrument of research which has yet been used, it is always to be employed with a caution proportionate to its importance.

CHAPTER II

Space

§1. *Boundaries take up no Room*

GEOMETRY is a physical science. It deals with the sizes and shapes and distances of things. Just as we have studied the *number* of things by making a simple and obvious observation, and then using this over and over again to see where it would bring us; so we shall study the science of the shapes and distances of things by making one or two very simple and obvious observations, and then using these over and over again, to see what we can get out of them.

The observations that we make are:—

First, that a thing may be moved about from one place to another without altering its size or shape.

Secondly, that it is possible to have things of the same shape but of different sizes.

Before we can use these observations to draw any exact conclusions from them, it is necessary to consider rather more precisely what they mean.

Things take up room. A table, for example, takes up a certain part of the room where it is, and there is another part of the room where it is not. The thing makes a difference between these two portions of space.

Between these two there is what we call the *surface* of the table.

We may suppose that the space all round the table is filled with air. The surface of the table is then something just between the air and the wood, which separates them from one another, and which is neither the one nor the other.

It is a mistake to suppose that the surface of the table is a very thin piece of wood on the outside of it. We can see that this is a mistake, because any reason which led us to say so, would lead us also to say that the surface was a very thin layer of air close to the table. The surface in fact is common to the wood and to the air, and takes up itself no room whatever.[1]

Part of the surface of the table may be of one colour and part may be of another.

On the surface of this sheet of paper there is drawn a round black spot (Fig. 10). We call the black part a circle. It divides

FIG. 10

the surface into two parts, one where it is and one where it is not.

This circle takes up room on the surface, although the surface itself takes up no room in space. We are thus led to consider two different kinds of *room*; space-room, in which solid bodies are, and in which they move about; and surface-room, which may be regarded from two different points of view. From one point of view it is the boundary between two adjacent portions of space, and takes up no space-room whatever. From the other point of view it is itself also a kind of room which may be taken up by parts of it.

These parts in turn have their boundaries.

Between the black surface of the circle and the white surface of the paper round it there is a line, the circum-

---

[1] It is certain that however smooth a *natural* surface may *appear* to be, it could be magnified to roughness. Hence, in the case of the surface of the table and the air, it would seem probable that there is a layer in which particles of wood and air are mingled. The boundary in this case of air and table would not be what we "see and feel" (cf. p. 46), nor would it correspond to the surface of the geometer. We are, I think, compelled to consider the surface of the geometer as an "idea or imaginary conception," drawn from the *apparent* (not real) boundaries of physical objects, such as the writer is describing. Strongly as I feel the ideal nature of geometrical conceptions in the exact sciences, I have thought it unadvisable to alter the text. The distinction is made by Clifford himself (*Essays*, I. pp. 306–321).—K.P.

ference of the circle. This line is neither part of the black
nor part of the white, but is between the two. It divides one
from the other, and takes up no surface-room at all. The line
is not a very thin strip of surface, any more than the surface
is a very thin layer of solid.

Anything which led us to say that this line, the boundary
of the black spot, was a thin strip of black, would also lead
us to say that it was a thin strip of white.

We may also divide a line into two parts. If the paper

Fig. 11

with this black circle upon it were dipped into water so that
part of the black circle were submerged, then the line surrounding it would be partly in the water and partly out
(Fig. 11).

The submerged part of the line takes up room on it. It
goes a certain part of the way round the circumference.
Thus we have to consider line-room as well as space-room
and surface-room. The line takes up absolutely no room on
the surface; it is merely the boundary between two adjacent
portions of it. Still less does it take up any room in space.
And yet it has a certain room of its own, which may be
divided into parts, and taken up or filled by those parts.

These parts again have boundaries. Between the submerged portion of the circumference and the other part
there are two *points*, one at each end. These points are
neither in the water nor out of it. They are in the surface
of the water, just as they are in the surface of the paper, and
on the boundary of the black spot. Upon this line they take
up absolutely no room at all.

A point is not a very small length of the line, any more
than the line is a very thin strip of surface. It is a division
between two parts of the line which are next one another,
and it takes up no room on the line at all.

The important thing to notice is that we are not here

talking of ideas or imaginary conceptions, but only making
common-sense observations about matters of every-day experience.

The surface of a thing is something that we constantly
observe. We can see it and feel it, and it is a mere common-
sense observation to say that this surface is common to the
thing itself and to the space surrounding it.

A line on a surface which separates one part of the surface
from another is also a matter of every-day experience. It is
not an idea got at by supposing a string to become indefinitely thin, but it is a thing given directly by observation as
belonging to both portions of the surface which it divides,
and as being therefore of absolutely no thickness at all. The
same may be said of a point. The point which divides the
part of our circumference which is in water from the part
which is out of water is an observed thing. It is not an idea
got at by supposing a small particle to become smaller and
smaller without any limit, but it is the boundary between
two adjacent parts of a line, which is the boundary between
two adjacent portions of a surface, which is the boundary
between two adjacent portions of space. A point is a thing
which we can see and know, not an abstraction which we
build up in our thoughts.

When we talk of drawing lines or points on a sheet of
paper, we use the language of the draughtsman and not of
the geometer. Here is a picture of a cube represented by
lines, in the draughtsman's sense (Fig. 12). Each of these so-
called "lines" is a black streak of printer's ink, of varying
breadth, taking up a certain amount of room on the paper.

Fig. 12

By drawing such "lines" sufficiently close together, we might
entirely cover up as large a patch of paper as we liked. Each
of these streaks has a line on each side of it, separating the

black surface from the white surface; these are true geometrical lines, taking up no surface-room whatever. Millions of millions of them might be marked out between the two boundaries of one of our streaks, and between every two of these there would be room for millions more.

Still, it is very convenient, in drawing geometrical figures, to represent lines by black streaks. To avoid all possible misunderstanding in this matter, we shall make a convention once for all about the sense in which a black streak is to represent a line. When the streak is vertical, or comes straight down the page, like this |, the *line* represented by it is its *right-hand boundary*. In all other cases the line shall be the *upper boundary* of the streak.

So also in the case of a point. When we try to represent a point by a dot on a sheet of paper, we make a black patch of irregular shape. The boundary of this black patch is a line. When one point of this boundary is higher than all the other points, that highest point shall be the one represented by the dot. When however several points of the boundary are at the same height, but none higher than these, so that the boundary has a flat piece at the top of it, then the right-hand extremity of this flat piece shall be the point represented by the dot.

This determination of the meaning of our figures is of no practical use. We lay it down only that the reader may not fall into the error of taking patches and streaks for geometrical points and lines.

§2. *Lengths can be Moved without Change*

Let us now consider what is meant by the first of our observations about space, viz., that a thing can be moved about from one place to another without altering its size or shape.

First as to the matter of size. We measure the size of a thing by measuring the distances of various points on it. For example, we should measure the size of a table by meas-

uring the distance from end to end, or the distance across
it, or the distance from the top to the bottom. The measurement of distance is only possible when we have something,
say a yard measure or a piece of tape, which we can carry
about and which does not alter its length while it is carried
about. The measurement is then effected by holding this
thing in the place of the distance to be measured, and observing what part of it coincides with this distance.

Two lengths or distances are said to be *equal* when the
same part of the measure will fit both of them. Thus we
should say that two tables are equally broad, if we marked
the breadth of one of them on a piece of tape, and then carried the tape over to the other table and found that its
breadth came up to just the same mark. Now the piece of
tape, although convenient, is not absolutely necessary to the
finding out of this fact. We might have turned one table up
and put it on top of the other, and so found out that the
two breadths were equal. Or we may say generally that two
lengths or distances of any kind are equal, when, one of
them being brought up close to the other, they can be made
to fit without alteration. But the tape is a thing far more
easily carried about than the table, and so in practice we
should test the equality of the two breadths by measuring
both against the same piece of tape. We find that each of
them is equal to the same length of tape; and we assume
that *two lengths which are equal to the same length are equal to
each other*. This is equivalent to saying that if our piece of
tape be carried round any closed curve and brought back to
its original position, it will not have altered in length.

How so? Let us assume that, when not used, our piece
of tape is kept stretched out on a board, with one end against
a fixed mark on the board. Then we know what is meant by
two lengths being equal which are both measured along the
tape from that end. Now take three tables, A, B, C, and suppose we have measured and found that the breadth of A is
equal to that of B, and the breadth of B is equal to that of
C, then we say that the breadth of A is equal to that of C.

This means that we have marked off the breadth of A on the tape, and then carried this length of tape to B, and found it fit. Then we have carried the same length from B to C, and found it fit. In saying that the breadth of C is equal to that of A, we assert that on taking the tape from C to A, whether we go near B or not, it will be found to fit the breadth of A. That is, if we take our tape from A to B, then from B to C, and then back to A, it will still fit A if it did so at first.

These considerations lead us to a very singular conclusion. The reader will probably have observed that we have defined length or distance by means of a measure which can be carried about *without changing its length*. But how then is this property of the measure to be tested? We may carry about a yard measure in the form of a stick, to test our tape with; but all we can prove in that way is that the two things are always of the same length when they are in the same place; not that this length is unaltered.

The fact is that everything would go on quite as well if we supposed that things did change in length by mere travelling from place to place, provided that (1) different things changed equally, and (2) anything which was carried about and brought back to its original position filled the same space.[1] All that is wanted is that two things which fit in one place should also fit in another place, although brought there by different paths; unless, of course, there are other reasons to the contrary. A piece of tape and a stick which fit one another in London will also fit one another in New York, although the stick may go there across the Atlantic, and the tape via India and the Pacific. Of course the stick may expand from damp and the tape may shrink from dryness; such non-geometrical circumstances would have to be allowed for. But so far as the geometrical conditions alone are concerned—the mere carrying about and change of place—two things which fit in one place will fit in another.

[1] These remarks refer to the geometrical, and not necessarily to all the physical properties of bodies.—K.P.

Upon this fact are founded, as we have seen, the notion of length as measured, and the axiom that lengths which are equal to the same length are equal to one another.

Is it possible, however, that lengths do really change by mere moving about, without our knowing it?

Whoever likes to meditate seriously upon this question will find that it is wholly devoid of meaning. But the time employed in arriving at that conclusion will not have been altogether thrown away.

§3. The Characteristics of Shape

We have now seen what is meant by saying that a thing can be moved about without altering its size; namely, that any length which fits a certain measure in one position will also fit that measure when both have been moved by any paths to some other position. Let us now inquire what we mean by saying that a thing can be moved about without altering its shape.

First let us observe that the shape of a thing depends only on its bounding surface, and not at all upon the inside of it. So that we may always speak of the shape of the surface, and we shall mean the same thing as if we spoke of the shape of the thing.

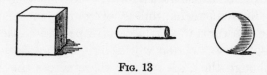

Fig. 13

Let us observe then some characteristics of the surface of things. Here are a cube, a cylinder, and a sphere (Fig. 13). The surface of the cube has six flat sides, with edges and corners. The cylinder has two flat ends and a round surface between them; the flat ends being divided from the round part by two circular edges. The sphere has a round smooth surface all over.

We observe at once a great distinction in shape between *smooth* parts of the surface, and *edges*, and *corners*. An edge being a line on the surface is not any *part* of it, in the sense of taking up surface room; still less is a corner, which is a mere point. But still we may divide the points of the surface into those where it is smooth (like all the points of the sphere, the round and flat parts of the cylinder, and the flat sides of the cube), into points on an edge, and into corners. For convenience, let us speak of these points respectively as *smooth-points*, *edge-points*, and *corner-points*. We may also put the edges and corners together, and call them *rough-points*.

Now let us take the sphere, and put it upon a flat face of the cube (Fig. 14). The two bodies will be in contact at one

Fig. 14

point; that is to say, a certain point on the surface of the sphere and a certain point on the surface of the cube are made to coincide with one another and to be the same point. And these are both smooth-points. Now *we cannot move the sphere ever so little without separating these points*. If we roll it a very little way on the face of the cube, we shall find that a different point of the sphere is in contact with a different

Fig. 15

point of the cube. And the same thing is true if we place the sphere in contact with a smooth-point on the cylinder (Fig. 15).

Next let us put the round part of the cylinder on the flat face of the cube (Fig. 16). In this case there will be contact all along a line. At any point of this line, a certain point on the surface of the cylinder and a certain point on the surface of the cube have been made to coincide with one another and to be the same point. And these are both smooth-points. It is just as true as before, that we cannot move one of these bodies ever so little relatively to the other without separating the

FIG. 16

points of their surfaces which are in contact. If we roll the cylinder a very little way on the face of the cube, we shall find that a different line of the cylinder is in contact with a different line of the cube. All the points of contact are changed.

Now put the flat end of the cylinder on the face of the cube (Fig. 17). These two surfaces fit throughout and make but one surface; we have contact, not (as before) at a point or along a line, but over a surface. Let us fix our attention upon

FIG. 17

a particular point on the flat surface of the cylinder and the point on the face of the cube with which it now coincides; these two being smooth-points. We observe again, that *it is*

*impossible to move one of these bodies ever so little relatively to
the other without separating these two points.*[1]

Here, however, something has happened which will give
us further instruction. We have all along supposed the flat

FIG. 18

face of the cylinder to be smaller than the flat face of the
cube. When these two are in contact, let the cylinder stand
on the middle of the cube, as in Fig. 17, the circle being wholly
enclosed by the square. Then when we tilt the cylinder over
we shall get it into the position of Fig. 18. We have already
observed that in this case no smooth-points which were
previously in contact remain in contact. But there are two
points which remain in contact; for in the tilted position a
point on the circular edge of the cylinder rests on a point on
the face of the cube; and these two points were in contact
before. We may tilt the cylinder as much or as little as we
like—provided we tilt always in the same direction, not roll-
ing the cylinder on its edge—and these two points will remain in contact. We learn therefore that *when an edge-point
is in contact with a smooth-point, it may be possible to move one
of the two bodies relatively to the other without separating those
two points.*

The same thing may be observed if we put the round or flat

[1] In all these cases (Figs. 14–17) the relative motion spoken of must be either
motion of *translation* or of *tilting*; one body might have a *spin* about a vertical
axis without any separation of these two points. The true distinction between
the contact of smooth-points and of smooth- and rough-points seems to be this:
in the former case without separating two points there is only *one* degree of
freedom—namely, spin about an axis normal to the smooth surfaces at the
points in question; in the latter case there are at least two (edge-point or
smooth-point) and may be an infinite number of degrees of freedom—namely,
spins about two or more axes passing through the rough-point. The reader
will understand these terms better after the chapter on Motion.—K.P.

surface of the cylinder against an edge of the cube (Fig. 19, *a*, *b*), or if we put the sphere against an edge of either of the

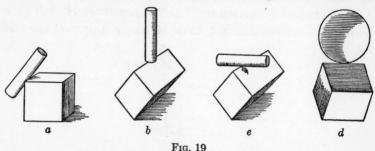

FIG. 19

other bodies. Holding either of them fast, we may move the other so as to keep the same two points in contact; but in order to do this, we must always tilt in the same direction.

If, however, we put a *corner* of the cube in contact with a smooth point of the cylinder, as in Fig. 20, we shall find that

FIG. 20

we can keep these two points in contact without any restriction on the direction of tilting. We may tilt the cube any way we like, and still keep its corner in contact with the smooth-point of the cylinder.

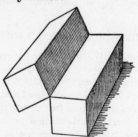

Edge in contact with edge *lengthwise* = 1 degree of freedom

FIG. 21

When we put two edge-points together, it makes a difference whether the edges are in the same direction at the point of contact (Fig. 21) or whether they cross one another (Fig. 22). In the former case we may be able to keep the same two points in contact by tilting in a particular direction; in the latter case we may tilt in any direction. So if a corner is in contact with an edge-point there is no restriction on

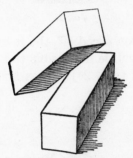

Edge in contact with edge *crosswise* = 2 degrees of freedom

FIG. 22

the direction of tilting, and much more if a corner is in contact with a corner.

The upshot of all this is, that *in a certain sense all surfaces are of the same shape at all smooth-points*; for when we put two smooth-points in contact, the surfaces so fit one another at those points that we cannot move one of them relatively to the other without separating the points.[1]

It is possible for two edges to fit so that we cannot move either of the bodies without separating the points in contact.[2] For this it is necessary that one of them should be re-entrant (that is, should be a depression in the surface, not a projection), as in Fig. 23; and here we can see the propriety of saying that the two surfaces are of the same shape at a point where they fit in this way. The body placed in

[1] See, however, the footnote, p. 53.—K.P.
[2] In this case the system which formerly had 2 degrees of rotational freedom has been cut down by "constraint" to zero degrees of rotational freedom.—J.R.N.

contact with the cube is formed by joining together two
spheres from which pieces have been sliced off. If only very

FIG. 23

small pieces have been sliced off, the re-entrant edge will be
very sharp, and it will be impossible to bring the cube-edge
into contact with it (Fig. 24); if nearly half of each sphere

FIG. 24   FIG. 25   FIG. 26

Note that in Fig. 24 the angle between the spheres is less than 90°; in Fig. 25,
greater than 90°; in Fig. 26, exactly equal to 90°.

Only in the last case, where the angle between the spheres is the same as
the dehedral angle of the two faces of the cube in contact with the spheres,
is it not possible to "move either of the bodies without separating the points
in contact."—J.R.N.

has been cut off the re-entrant edge will be wide open, and
the cube will rock in it (Fig. 25). There is clearly one intermediate form in which the two edges will just fit (Fig. 26);
contact at the edge will be possible, but no rocking. Now in
this case, although one edge sticks out and the other is a
dint, we may still say that the two surfaces are of the same
shape at the edge. For if we suppose our twin-sphere body
to be made of wood, its surface is not only surface of the
wood, but also surface of the surrounding air. And that
which is a dint or depression in the wood is at the same time
a projection in the air. In just the same way, each of the
projecting edges and corners of the cube is at the same time

a dint or depression in the air. But the *surface* belongs to one as much as the other; it knows nothing of the difference between inside and outside; elevation and depression are arbitrary terms to it. So in a thin piece of embossed metal, elevation on one side means depression on the other, and vice versa; but it is purely arbitrary which side we consider the *right* one. (Observe that the thin piece of metal is in no sense a representation of a *surface*; it is merely a thin solid whose two surfaces are very nearly of the same shape.)

Thus we see that the edge of wood in our cube is of the same shape as the edge of air in the twin-sphere solid; or, which is the same thing, that the two surfaces are of the same shape at the edge.

Now this twin-sphere solid is a very convenient one, because we can so modify it as to make an edge of any shape we like. Hitherto we have supposed the slices cut off to be less than half of the spheres; let us now fasten together these pieces, and so form a solid with a projecting edge, as in Fig. 27 at right. The two solids so formed, one with a re-entrant edge from the larger pieces, the other with a projecting edge from the smaller pieces, will be found always to have their edges of the same shape, or to fit one another at the edge in the sense just explained.

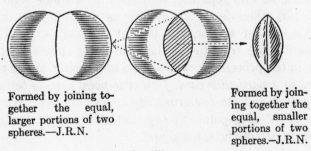

Formed by joining together the equal, larger portions of two spheres.—J.R.N.

Formed by joining together the equal, smaller portions of two spheres.—J.R.N.

Fig. 27

Now suppose that we cut our spheres very nearly in half. (Of course they must always be cut both alike, or the flat faces would not fit together.) Then when we join together the larger pieces and the smaller pieces, we shall form solids with

very wide open edges. The projecting edge will be a very
slight ridge, and the re-entrant one a very slight depression.

If we now go a step further, and cut our spheres actually
in half, of course each of the new solids will be again a sphere;
and there will be neither ridge nor depression; the surfaces
will be smooth all over. But we have arrived at this result
by considering a projecting edge as gradually widening out

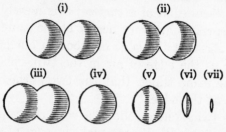

Fig. 28

until the ridge disappears, or by considering a re-entrant
edge as gradually widening out until the dint disappears. Or
we may suppose the projecting edge to go on widening out
till it becomes smooth, and then to turn into a re-entrant
edge. We might represent this process to the eye by putting
into a wheel of life a succession of pictures like that in Fig. 28,
and then rapidly turning the wheel. We should see the two
spheres, at first separate, coalesce into a single solid in (ii)
and (iii), then form one sphere as at (iv), then contract
into a smaller and smaller lens at (v), (vi), (vii). The important thing to notice is that the single sphere at (iv) is a
step in the process; or, what is the same thing, that *a smooth-
point is a particular case of an edge-point coming between the
projecting and the re-entrant edges.* As being this particular
case of the edge-point, we say that at all smooth-points the
surfaces are of the same shape.

§4. *The Characteristics of Surface Boundaries*

Remarks like these that we have made about solid bodies
or portions of space may be made also about portions of surface. Only we cannot now say that the shape of a piece of

surface depends wholly on that of the curve which bounds it. Still the only thing that remains for us to consider is the shape of the boundary, because we have already discussed (so far as we profitably can at present) the shape of the included surface.

We shall find it useful to restrict ourselves still further, and only consider those boundaries which have no rough points of the surface in them. Thus on the surface of the cube we will only consider portions which are entirely included in one of the plane faces; on the surface of the cylinder, only portions which are entirely included in one of the flat faces, or in the curved part, or which include one of the flat faces and part of the curved portion.

This being so, the characteristics which we have to remark in the boundaries of pieces of surface may be sufficiently studied by means of figures drawn on paper. We may bend the paper to assure ourselves that the same general properties belong to figures on a cylinder, and to make our ideas quite distinct it is worth while to draw some on a sphere or other such surface.

In Fig. 29 are some patches of surface; a square, a three-cornered piece, and two overlapping circles. For distinct-

Fig. 29

ness, the part where the circles overlap is left white, the rest being made black.

Attending now specially to the boundary of these patches, we observe that it consists of smooth parts and of corners or angles. Some of these corners project and some are reentrant. The pieces of surface are not solid moveable things like the portions of space we considered before, but we can in a measure imitate our previous experiments by cutting out the figures with a penknife, so as to leave their previous positions marked by the holes. We shall then find, on applying the cut-out pieces to one another, or to the holes, that at all smooth-points the boundaries fit one another in a certain sense. Namely, if we place two smooth-points in contact we cannot roll one figure on the other without separating these points; whereas if we place a sharp-point (or angle) on a smooth-point we can roll one figure on the other without separating the points. If we attempt to put two angles together without letting the figures overlap, the same things may happen that we found true in the case of the edges of solid bodies. Suppose, for example, that we try to put an angle of the square into one of the re-entrant angles of the figure made by the two overlapping circles. If the re-entrant angle is too sharp, we shall not be able to get it in at all; this is the case of Fig. 21. If it is wide enough, the square will be able to rock in it; this is the case of Fig. 22. Between these two there is an intermediate case in which one angle just fits the other; actual contact takes place, and no rocking is possible. In this case we say that the two angles are of the same shape, or that they are *equal* to one another.

From all this we are led to conclude that *shape is a matter of angles*, and that identity of shape depends on equality of angle. We dealt with the size of a body by considering a simple case of it, viz. length or distance, and by measuring a sufficient number of lengths in different directions could find out all that is to be known about the size of a body. It is, indeed, also true that a knowledge of all the lengths which can be measured in a body would carry with it a knowledge of its shape; but still length is not in itself an element of shape. That which does the same for us in regard to shape that length does with regard to size, is angle. In other words, just as we say that two bodies are of the same size if to any line that can be drawn in the one there corresponds an exactly equal line in the other, so we say that two bodies are of the same shape, if to every angle that can be drawn on one of them there corresponds an exactly equal angle on the other.

Just as we measured lengths by a stick or a piece of tape so we measure angles with a pair of compasses; and two angles are said to be equal when they fit the same opening of the compasses. And as before, the statement that a thing can be moved about without altering its shape may be shown to amount only to this, that two angles which fit in one place will fit also in another, no matter how they have been brought from the one place to the other.

§5. *The Plane and the Straight Line*

We have now to describe a particular kind of surface and a particular kind of line with which geometry is very much concerned. These are the *plane* surface and the *straight* line.

The plane surface may be defined as one which is of the same shape all over and on both sides. This property of it is illustrated by the method which is practically used to make such a surface. The method is to take three surfaces and grind them down until any two will fit one another all over. Suppose the three surfaces to be A, B, C; then, since A will fit B, it follows that the space outside A is of the same shape as the space inside B; and because B will fit C, that the space inside B is of the same shape as the space outside C. It follows therefore that the space outside A is of the same shape as the space outside C. But since A will fit C when we put them together, the space inside A is of the same shape as the space outside C. But the space outside C was shown to be of the same shape as the space outside A; consequently the space outside A is of the same shape as the space inside; and so, if three surfaces are ground together so that each pair of them will fit, each of them becomes a surface which is of the same shape on both sides: that is to say, if we take a body which is partly bounded by a plane surface, we can slide it all over this surface and it will fit everywhere, and we may also turn it round and apply it to the other side of the surface and it will fit there too. This property is sometimes more technically expressed by saying that a plane is a surface which divides space into two *congruent regions*.

A straight line may be defined in a similar way. It is a

division between two parts of a plane, which two parts are, so far as the dividing line is concerned, of the same shape; or we may say what comes to the same effect, that a straight line is a line of the same shape all along and on both sides.

A body may have two plane surfaces; one part of it, that is, may be bounded by one plane and another part by another. If these two plane surfaces have a common edge, this edge, which is called their *intersection*, is a straight line. We may then, if we like, take as our definition of a straight line that it is the intersection of two planes.

It must be understood that when a part of the surface of a body is plane, this plane may be conceived as extending beyond the body in all directions. For instance, the upper surface of a table is plane and horizontal. Now it is quite an intelligible question to ask about a point which is anywhere in the room whether it is higher or lower than the surface of the table. The points which are higher will be divided from those which are lower by an imaginary surface which is a continuation of the plane surface of the table. So then we are at liberty to speak of the line of intersection of two plane surfaces of a body whether these are adjacent portions of surface or not, and we may in every case suppose them to meet one another and to be prolonged across the edge in which they meet.

Leibniz, who was the first to give these definitions of a plane and of a straight line, gave also another definition of a straight line. If we fix two points of a body, it will not be entirely fixed, but it will be able to turn round. All points of it will then change their position excepting those which are in the straight line joining the two fixed points; and Leibniz accordingly defined a straight line as being the aggregate of those points of a body which are unmoved when it is turned about with two points fixed. If we suppose the body to have a plane face passing through the two fixed points, this definition will fall back on the former one which defines a straight line as the intersection of two planes.

It hardly needs any words to prove that the first two definitions of a plane are equivalent; that is, that two surfaces, each of which is of the same shape all over and on both sides, will have for their intersection a line which is of the same shape all along and on both sides. For if we slide each plane upon itself it will, being of the same shape all over, occupy as a whole the same unchanging position (*i.e.* wherever there was part of the planes before there will be part, though a different part, of the planes now), so that their line of intersection occupies the same position throughout (though the part of the line occupying any particular position is different). The line is therefore of the same shape all along. And in a similar way we can, without changing the position of the planes as a whole, move them so that the right-hand part of each shall become the left-hand part, and the upper part the lower; and this will amount to changing the line of intersection end for end. But this line is in the same place after the change as before; and it is therefore of the same shape on both sides.

From the first definition we see that two straight lines cannot coincide for a certain distance and then diverge from one another. For since the plane surface is of the same shape on the two sides of a straight line, we may take up the surface on one side and turn it over and it will fit the surface on the other side. If this is true of one of our supposed straight lines, it is quite clear that it cannot at the same time be true of the other; for we must either be bringing over more to fit less, or less to fit more.

§6. *Properties of Triangles*

We can now reduce to a more precise form our first observation about space, that a body may be moved about in it without altering its size or shape. Let us suppose that our body has for one of its faces a *triangle*, that is to say, the portion of a plane bounded by three straight lines. We find that this triangle can be moved into any new position that we like, while the lengths of its sides and its angles remain

the same; or we may put the statement into the form that
when any triangle is once drawn, another triangle of the
same size and shape can be drawn in any part of space.

From this it will follow that if there are two triangles
which have a side of the one equal to a side of the other, and
the angles at the ends of that side in the one equal to the
angles at the ends of the equal side in the other, then the
two triangles are merely the same triangle in different positions; that is, they are of the same size and shape. For if we
take the first triangle and so far put it into the position of
the second that the two equal sides coincide, then because
the angles at the ends of the one are respectively equal to
those at the ends of the other, the remaining two sides of the
first triangle will begin to coincide with the remaining two
sides of the second.[1] But we have seen that straight lines
cannot begin to coincide and then diverge; and consequently these sides will coincide throughout and the triangles
will entirely coincide.

Our second observation, that we may have things which
are of the same shape but not of the same size, may also be
made more precise by application to the case of triangles.
It tells us that any triangle may be magnified or diminished
to any degree without altering its angles, or that if a triangle
be drawn, another triangle having the same angles may be
drawn of any size in any part of space.

From this statement we are able to deduce two very important consequences. One is, that two straight lines cannot intersect in more points than one; and the other that,
if two straight lines can be drawn in the same plane so as
not to intersect at all, the angles they make with any third
line in their plane which meets them, will be equal.

To prove the first of these, let A B and A C (Fig. 30) be two
straight lines which meet at A. Draw a third line B C, meet-

---

[1] This proposition, like many others of Euclidean geometry involving
superposition, cannot be proved except in three dimensions. The manipula-
tion of certain types of congruent triangles reveals the fact that to super-
impose one upon the other, it is necessary to lift one of the triangles out of the
plane and *turn it over* before superposition is possible.—J.R.N.

ing both of them, and the three lines then form a triangle. If we now make a point P travel along the line A B it must, in virtue of our second observation, be always possible to draw through this point a line which shall meet A C in Q so as to make a triangle A P Q of the same shape as A B C. But

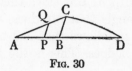

FIG. 30

if the line A C were to meet A B in some other point D besides A, then through this point D it would clearly not be possible to draw a line so as to make a triangle at all. It follows then that such a point as D does not exist, and in fact that two straight lines which have once met must go on diverging from each other and can never meet again.[1]

To prove the second, suppose that the lines A C and B D (Fig. 31) are in the same plane, and are such as never to meet

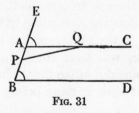

FIG. 31

at all (in which case they are called *parallel*), while the line A B meets them both. If we make a point P travel along B A towards A, and, as it moves, draw through it always a line making the same angle with B A that B D makes with B A, then this moving line can never meet A C until it wholly coincides with it. For if it can, let P Q be such a position of the moving line; then it is possible to draw through B a line which, with A B and A C, shall form a triangle of the same shape as the triangle A P Q. But for this to be the case the line

---

[1] This property might also be deduced from the first definition of a straight line, by the method already used to show that two straight lines cannot coincide for part of their length and then diverge.

drawn through B must make the same angle with A B that
P Q makes with it, that is, it must be the line B D. And the
three lines B D, B A, A C cannot form a triangle, for B D and
A C never meet. Consequently there can be no such triangle
as A P Q, or the moveable line can never meet A C until it
entirely coincides with it. But since this line always makes
with B A the same angle that B D does, and in one position
coincides with A C, it follows that A C makes with B A the
same angle that B D does. This is the famous proposition
about parallel lines.[1]

The first of these deductions will now show us that if two
triangles have an angle of the one equal to an angle of the
other and the sides containing these angles respectively
equal, they must be equal in all particulars. For if we take
up one of the triangles and put it down on the other so that
these angles coincide and equal sides are on the same side
of them, then the containing sides will begin to coincide,
and cannot therefore afterwards diverge. But as they are of
the same length in the one triangle as they are in the other,
the ends of them belonging to the one triangle will rest upon
the ends belonging to the other, so that the remaining sides
of the two triangles will have their ends in common and
must therefore coincide altogether, since otherwise two
straight lines would meet in more points than one. The one

---

[1] Two straight lines which cut one another form at the point where they
cross four angles which are equal in pairs. It is often necessary to distinguish
between the two different angles which the lines make with one another. This
is done by the understanding that A B shall mean the line drawn from A to B,

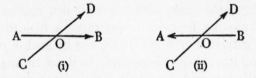
(i)   (ii)

and B A the line drawn from B to A, so that the angle between A B and C D (i)
is the angle B O D, but the angle between B A and C D (ii) is the angle D O A.

So the angle spoken of above as made by A C with B A is not the angle C A B
(which is clearly, in general, unequal to the angle D B A), but the angle C A E,
where E is a point in B A produced through A.

triangle will then exactly cover the other; that is to say, they are equal in all respects.

In the same way we may see that if two triangles have two angles in the one equal to two angles in the other, they are of the same shape. For one of them can be magnified or diminished until the side joining these two angles in it becomes of the same length as the side joining the two corresponding angles in the other; and as no alteration is thereby made in the shape of the triangle, it will be enough for us to prove that the new triangle is of the same shape as the other given triangle. But if we now compare these two, we see that they have a pair of corresponding sides which have been made equal, and the angles at the ends of these sides equal also (for they were equal in the original triangles, and have not been altered by the change of size), so that we fall back on a case already considered, in which it was shown that the third angles are equal, and the triangles consequently of the same shape.

If we apply these propositions not merely to two different triangles but to the same triangle, we find that if a triangle has two of its sides equal it will have the two angles opposite to them also equal; and that, conversely, if it has two angles equal it will have the two sides opposite to them also equal; for in each of these cases the triangle may be turned over and made to fit itself. Such a triangle is called *isosceles*.

The theorem about parallel lines which we deduced from our second assumption about space leads very easily to a theorem of especial importance, viz. that the three angles of a triangle are together equal to two right angles.

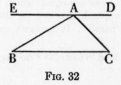

Fig. 32

If we draw through A, a corner of the triangle A B C (Fig. 32), a line D A E, making with the side A C the same angle as

B C makes with it, this line will, as we have proved, never meet B C, that is, it will be parallel to it.[1] It will consequently make with A B the same angle as B C makes with it,[2] so that the three angles A B C, B A C, and B C A are respectively equal to the angles E A B, B A C, and C A D, and these three make up two right angles.

Another statement of this theorem is sometimes of use.

If the sides of a triangle be produced, what are called the *exterior angles* of the triangle are formed. If, for example, the side B C of the triangle A B C (Fig. 33) is produced beyond C to D, A C D is an exterior angle of the triangle, while of the interior angles of the triangle A C B is said to be *adjacent*, and C A B and A B C to be *opposite* to this exterior angle. It is clear that as each side of the triangle may be produced in two directions, any triangle has six exterior angles.

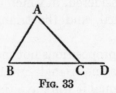

FIG. 33

The other form into which our proposition may be thrown is that either of the exterior angles of a triangle is equal to the sum of the two interior angles opposite to it. For, in the figure, the exterior angle A C D, together with A C B, makes two right angles, and it must therefore be equal to the sum of the two angles which also make up two right angles with A C B.

---

[1] This is *not* what Clifford proved before. He proved that if two lines are parallel the corresponding angles are equal; which is *not the equivalent* of the proposition that if the corresponding angles (or alternate interior angles) are equal, the two lines are parallel. It happens that both propositions are true.—J.R.N.

[2] The convention mentioned in footnote 1 on page 66 must be remembered.

§7. *Properties of Circles; Related Circles and Triangles*

We may now apply this proposition to prove an important property of the circle, viz. that if we take two fixed points on the circumference of a circle and join them to a third point on the circle, the angle between the joining lines will depend only upon the first two points and not at all upon the third. If, for example, we join the points A, B (Fig. 34) to c we shall show that, wherever on the circumference c may be, the angle A c B is always one-half of A o B; o being the centre of the circle.

Let c o produced meet the circumference in D. Then since the triangle o A c is isosceles, the angles o A c and o c A are equal, and so for a similar reason are the angles o B c and o c B.

But we have just shown that the exterior angle A o D is equal to the sum of the angles o A c and o c A; and since these are equal to one another it must be double of either of them, say of o c A. Similarly the angle B o D is double of o c B, and consequently A o B is double of A c B.

In the case of the first figure (i) we have taken the sum of two angles each of which is double of another, and asserted that the sum of the first pair is twice the sum of the second pair; in the case of the second figure (ii) we have taken the

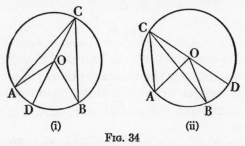

FIG. 34

difference of two angles each of which is double of another, and asserted that the difference of the first pair is twice the difference of the second pair.

Since therefore A c B is always half of A o B, wherever c

may be placed in the upper of the two segments into which
the circle is divided by the straight line A B, we see that the
magnitude of this angle depends only on the positions of A
and B, and not on the position of C. But now let us consider
what will happen if C is in the lower segment of the circle.
As before, the triangles O A C and O B C (Fig. 35) are isosceles,
and the angles D O A and D O B are respectively double of
O C A and O C B. Consequently, the whole angle A O B formed
by making O A turn round O into the position O B, so as to
pass through the position O D (in the way, that is, in which
the hands of a clock turn), this whole angle is double of A C B.

By our previous reasoning the angle A D B, formed by
joining A and B to D, is one-half of the angle A O B, which is
made by turning O B towards O A as the hands of a clock
move. The sum of these two angles, each of which we have
denoted by A O B, is a complete revolution about the point
O; in other words, is four right angles. Hence the sum of the

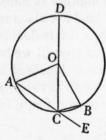

FIG. 35

angles A D B, A C B, which are the halves of these, is two right
angles. Or we may put the theorem otherwise, and say that
the opposite angles of a four-sided figure whose angles
lie on the circumference of a circle are together equal to two
right angles.

We appear therefore to have arrived at two different statements according as the point C is in the one or the other of
the segments into which the circle is divided by the straight
line A B. But these statements are really the same, and it is
easy to include them in one proposition. If we produce A C

in the last figure to E, the angles A C B and B C E are together equal to two right angles; and consequently B C E is equal to A D B. This angle B C E is the angle through which C B must be turned in the way the hands of a clock move, so that its direction may coincide with that of A C. But we may describe in precisely the same words the angle A C B in Fig. 34, where C was in the upper segment of the circle; so that we may always put the theorem in these words:—If A and B are fixed points on the circumference of a circle, and C any other point on it, the angle through which C B must be turned clockwise in order to coincide with C A or A C, whichever happens first, is equal to half the angle through which O B must be turned clockwise in order to coincide with O A.

We shall now make use of this to prove another interesting proposition. If three points D, E, F (Fig. 36) be taken on the

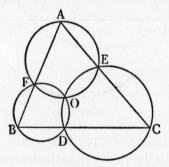

Fig. 36

sides of a triangle A B C, D being on B C, E on C A, F on A B, then three circles can be drawn passing respectively through A F E, B D F, C E D. These three circles can be shown to meet in the same point O. For let O in the first place stand for the intersection of the two circles A F E and B F D, then the angles F A E and F O E make up two right angles, and so do the angles D O F and D B F. But the three angles at O make four right angles, and the three angles of the triangle A B C make two right angles; and of these six angles two pairs have been shown to make up two right angles each. Therefore the remaining pair, viz. the angles D O E and D C E, make up two right angles. It follows that the circle which goes through the points c e d will pass through o, that is, the three circles all meet in this point.[1]

There is no restriction imposed on the positions of the points D, E, F,[2] they may be taken either on the sides of the

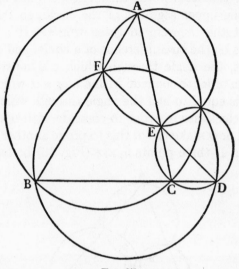

Fig. 37

triangle or on those sides produced, and in particular we may take them to lie on any fourth straight line D E F; and the theorem may be stated thus:—If any four straight lines be taken (Fig. 37), one of which meets the triangle A B C formed by the other three in the points D, E, F, then the circles through the points A F E, B D F, C E D meet in a point. But there is no reason why we should not take A F E as the

[1] Clifford again avails himself of the converse of a theorem when all he has proved, in fact, is the theorem itself. If a quadrilateral is inscribed in a circle, then the sum of the opposite angles is equal to two right angles. This is what Clifford proved earlier. The converse, on which the present theorem rests (i.e., if the sum of the opposite angles of a quadrilateral equals two right angles, the quadrilateral can be inscribed in a circle), was not proved.—J.R.N.

[2] If either of the points D, E, F, is taken on a side produced, the proof given above will not apply literally; but the necessary changes are slight and obvious.

triangle formed by three lines, and the fourth line D C B as the line which cuts the sides of this triangle. The proposition is equally true in this case, and it follows that the circles through A B C, E C D, F B D will meet in one point. This must be the same point as before,[1] since two of the circles of this set are the same as two of the previous set; consequently all four circles meet in a point, and we can now state our proposition as follows:

Given four straight lines, there can be formed from them four triangles by leaving out each in turn; the circles which circumscribe these four triangles meet in a point.

This proposition is the third of a series.

If we take any two straight lines they determine a point, viz. their point of intersection.

If we take three straight lines we get three such points of intersection; and these three determine a circle, viz. the circle circumscribing the triangle formed by the three lines.

Four straight lines determine four sets of three lines by leaving out each in turn; and the four circles belonging to these sets of three meet in a point.

In the same way five lines determine five sets of four, and each of these sets of four gives rise, by the proposition just proved, to a point. It has been shown by Miquel, that these five points lie on the same circle.

And this series of theorems has been shown[2] to be endless. Six straight lines determine six sets of five by leaving them out one by one. Each set of five has, by Miquel's theorem, a circle belonging to it. These six circles meet in the same point, and so on for ever. Any even number $(2n)$ of straight lines determines a point as the intersection of the same number of circles. If we take one line more, this odd number $(2n + 1)$ determines as many sets of $2n$ lines, and to each of these sets belongs a point; these $2n + 1$ points lie on a circle.

[1] The inference is not quite correct. Since two circles may intersect in two points, not merely in one, there is an ambiguity in the text, which, however, in no way vitiates the result.—J.R.N.

[2] By Prof. Clifford himself in the *Oxford, Cambridge, and Dublin Messenger of Mathematics*, vol. v. p. 124. See his *Mathematical Papers*, pp. 51–54.

§8. *The Conic Sections*

The shadow of a circle cast on a flat surface by a luminous point may have three different shapes. These are three curves of great historic interest, and of the utmost importance in geometry and its applications. The lines we have so far treated, viz. the straight line and circle, are special cases of these curves; and we may naturally at this point investigate a few of the properties of the more general forms.

If a circular disc be held in any position so that it is altogether below the flame of a candle, and its shadow be allowed to fall on the table, this shadow will be of an oval form, except in two extreme cases, in one of which it also is a circle, and in the other is a straight line. The former of these cases happens when the disc is held parallel to the table, and the latter when the disc is held edgewise to the candle; or, in other words, is so placed that the plane in which it lies passes through the luminous point. The oval form which, with these two exceptions, the shadow presents is called an *ellipse* (Fig. 38, i). The paths pursued by the planets round the sun are of this form.

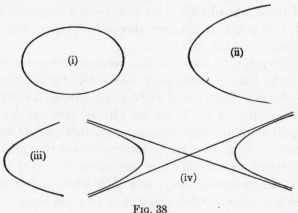

FIG. 38

If the circular disc be now held so that its highest point is just on a level with the flame of the candle, the shadow will as before be oval at the end near the candle; but instead of

closing up into another oval end as we move away from the
candle, the two sides of it will continue to open out without
any limit, tending however to become more and more parallel. This form of the shadow is called a *parabola* (ii). It is
very nearly the orbit of many comets, and is also nearly
represented by the path of a stone thrown up obliquely. If
there were no atmosphere to retard the motion of the stone
it would exactly describe a parabola.

If we now hold the circular disc higher up still, so that a
horizontal plane at the level of the candle flame divides it
into two parts, only one of these parts will cast any shadow
at all, and that will be a curve such as is shown in the figure,
the two sides of which diverge in quite different directions,
and do not, as in the case of the parabola, tend to become
parallel (iii).

But although for physical purposes this curve is the whole
of the shadow, yet for geometrical purposes it is not the
whole. We may suppose that instead of being a shadow our
curve was formed by joining the luminous point by straight
lines to points round the edge of the disc, and producing
these straight lines until they meet the table.

This geometrical mode of construction will equally apply
to the part of the circle which is above the candle flame,
although that does not cast any shadow. If we join these
points of the circle to the candle flame, and prolong the
joining lines beyond it, they will meet the table on the other
side of the candle, and will trace out a curve there which is
exactly similar and equal to the physical shadow (iv). We
may call this the *anti-shadow* or *geometrical shadow* of the
circle. It is found that for geometrical purposes these two
branches must be considered as forming only one curve,
which is called an *hyperbola*. There are two straight lines to
which the curve gets nearer and nearer the further away it
goes from their point of intersection, but which it never
actually meets. For this reason they are called *asymptotes*,
from a Greek word meaning "not falling together." These
lines are parallel to the two straight lines which join the

candle flame to the two points of the circle which are level
with it.

We saw some time ago that a surface was formed by the
motion of a line. Now if a right line in its motion always
passes through one fixed point, the surface which it traces out
is called a *cone*, and the fixed point is called its *vertex*. And
thus the three curves which we have just described are called
conic sections, for they may be made by cutting a cone by a
plane. In fact, it is in this way that the shadow of the circle
is formed; for if we consider the straight lines which join
the candle flame to all parts of the edge of the circle we see
that they form a cone whose vertex is the candle flame and
whose base is the circle.

We must suppose these lines not to end at the flame but
to be prolonged through it, and we shall so get what would
commonly be called two cones with their points together,
but what in geometry is called one *conical surface* having
two *sheets*. The section of this conical surface by the horizontal plane of the table is the shadow of the circle; the sheet
in which the circle lies gives us the ordinary physical shadow,
the other sheet (if the plane of section meets it) gives what
we have called the geometrical shadow.

The consideration of the shadows of curves is a method
much used for finding out their properties, for there are certain geometrical properties which are always common to a
figure and its shadow. For example, if we draw on a sheet
of glass two curves which cut one another, then the shadows
of the two curves cast through the sheet of glass on the table
will also cut one another. The shadow of a straight line is
always a straight line, for all the rays of light from the
flame through various points of a straight line lie in a plane,
and this plane meets the plane surface of the table in a
straight line which is the shadow. Consequently if any curve
is cut by a straight line in a certain number of points, the
shadow of the curve will be cut by the shadow of the straight
line in the same number of points. Since a circle is cut by a
straight line in two points or in none at all, it follows that

any shadow of a circle must be cut by a straight line in two points or in none at all.

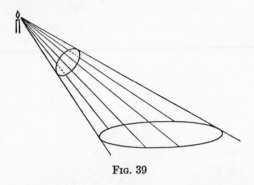

Fig. 39

When a straight line touches a circle the two points of intersection coalesce into one point. We see then that this must also be the case with any shadow of the circle. Again, from a point outside the circle it is possible to draw two lines which touch the circle; so from a point outside either of the three curves which we have just described, it is possible to draw two lines to touch the curve. From a point inside the circle no tangent can be drawn to it, and accordingly no tangent can be drawn to any conic section from a point inside it.

This method of deriving the properties of one curve from those of another of which it is the shadow, is called the method of *projection*.

The particular case of it which is of the greatest use is that in which we suppose the luminous point by which the shadow is cast to be ever so far away. Suppose, for example, that the shadow of a circle held obliquely is cast on the table by a star situated directly overhead, and at an indefinitely great distance. The lines joining the star to all the points of the circle will then be vertical lines, and they will no longer form a cone but a cylinder. One of the chief advantages of this kind of projection is that the shadows of two parallel lines will remain parallel, which is not generally the case in the other kind of projection. The shadow of the

circle which we obtain now is always an ellipse; and we are
able to find out in this way some very important properties
of the curve, the corresponding properties of the circle being
for the most part evident at a glance on account of the symmetry of the figure.

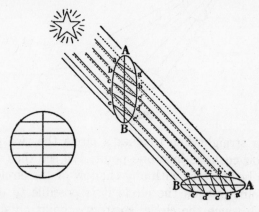

FIG. 40

For instance, let us suppose that the circle whose shadow
we are examining is vertical, and let us take a vertical diameter of it, so that the tangents at its ends are horizontal.
It will be clear from the symmetry of the figure that all
horizontal lines in it are divided into two equal parts by
the vertical diameter, or we may say that the diameter of
the circle bisects all chords parallel to the tangents at its
extremities. When the shadow of this figure is cast by an
infinitely distant star (which we must not now suppose to
be directly overhead, for then the shadow would be merely
a straight line), the point of bisection of the shadow of any
straight line is the shadow of the middle point of that line,
and thus we learn that it is true of the ellipse that any line
which joins the points of contact of parallel tangents bisects
all chords parallel to those tangents. Such a line is, as in the
case of the circle, termed a *diameter*. Since the shadow of a
diameter of the circle is a diameter of the ellipse, it follows
that all diameters of the ellipse pass through one and the

same point, namely, the shadow of the centre of the circle; this common intersection of diameters is termed the *centre* also of the ellipse.

Again, a horizontal diameter in the circle just considered will bisect all vertical chords, and thus we see that if one diameter bisects all chords parallel to a second, the second will bisect all chords parallel to the first.

The method of projection tells us that this is also true of the ellipse. Such diameters are called *conjugate diameters*, but they are no longer at right angles in the ellipse as they were in the case of the circle.

Since the shadow of a circle which is cast in this way by an infinitely distant point is always an ellipse, we cannot use the same method in order to obtain the properties of the hyperbola. But it is found by other methods that these same statements are true of the hyperbola which we have just seen to be true of the ellipse. There is however this great difference between the two curves. The centre of the ellipse is inside it, but the centre of the hyperbola is outside it. Also all lines drawn through the centre of the ellipse meet the curve in two points, but it is only certain lines through the centre of the hyperbola which meet the curve at all. Of two conjugate diameters of the hyperbola one meets the curve and the other does not. But it still remains true that each of them bisects all chords parallel to the other.

§9. *On Surfaces of the Second Order*

We began with the consideration of the simplest kind of line and the simplest kind of surface, the straight line and the plane; and we have since found out some of the properties of four different curved lines—the circle, the ellipse, the parabola, and the hyperbola. Let us now consider some curved surfaces; and first, the surface analogous to the circle. This surface is the *sphere*. It is defined, as a circle is, by the property that all its points are at the same distance from the centre.

Perhaps the most important question to be asked about a surface is, What are the shapes of the curved lines in which it is met by other surfaces, especially in the case when these other surfaces are planes? Now a plane which cuts a sphere cuts it, as can easily be shown, in a circle (Fig. 41). This circle,

FIG. 41

as we move the plane further and further away from the centre of the sphere, will get smaller and smaller, and will finally contract into a point. In this case the plane is said to *touch* the sphere; and we notice a very obvious but important fact, that the sphere then lies entirely on one side of the plane. If the plane be moved still further away from the centre it will not meet the sphere at all.

Again, if we take a point outside the sphere we can draw a number of planes to pass through it and touch the sphere, and all the points in which they touch it lie on a circle. Also a cone can be drawn whose vertex is the point, and which touches the sphere all round the circle in which these planes touch it (Fig. 42). This is called the *tangent-cone* of the point.

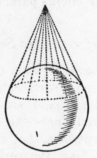

FIG. 42

It is clear that from a point inside the sphere no tangent-cone can be drawn.

Similar properties belong also to certain other surfaces which resemble the sphere in the fact that they are met by a straight line in *two* points at most; such surfaces are on this account called of the *second order*.

Just as we may suppose an ellipse to be got from a circle by pulling it out in one direction, so we may get a *spheroid* from a sphere either by pulling it out so as to make a thing like an egg, or by squeezing it so as to make a thing like an orange. Each of these forms is symmetrical about one diameter, but not about all. A figure like an orange, for example, or like the earth, has a diameter through its poles less than any diameter in the plane of its equator, but all diameters in its equator are equal. Again, a spheroid like an egg has all the diameters through its equator equal to one another, but the diameter through its poles is longer than any other diameter.

If we now take an orange or an egg and make its equator into an ellipse instead of a circle, say by pulling out the equator of the orange or squeezing the equator of the egg, so that the surface has now three diameters at right angles all unequal to one another, we obtain what is called an *ellipsoid* (Fig. 43). This surface plays the same part in the geometry

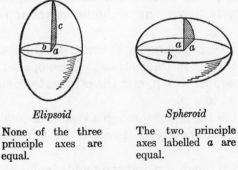

Elipsoid

None of the three principle axes are equal.

Spheroid

The two principle axes labelled *a* are equal.

Fig. 43

of surfaces that the ellipse does in the geometry of curves. Just as every plane which cuts a sphere cuts it in a circle, so every plane which cuts an ellipsoid cuts it in an ellipse.

It is indeed possible to cut an ellipsoid by a plane so that
the section shall be a circle, but this must be regarded as a
particular kind of ellipse, viz. an ellipse with two equal axes.
Again, just as was the case with the sphere, we can draw a
set of planes through an external point all of which touch
the ellipsoid. Their points of contact lie on a certain ellipse,
and a cone can be drawn which has the external point for its
vertex and touches the ellipsoid all round this ellipse. The
ellipsoid resembles a sphere in this respect also, that when
it is touched by a plane it lies wholly on one side of that
plane.

There are also surfaces which bear to the hyperbola and
the parabola relations somewhat similar to those borne to
the circle by the sphere, and to the ellipse by the ellipsoid.
We will now consider one of them, a surface with many
singular properties.

Let A B C D be a figure of card-board having four equal
sides, and let it be half cut through all along B D, so that the
triangles A B D, C B D can turn about the line B D. Then let
holes be made along the four sides of it at equal distances,
and let these holes be joined by threads of silk parallel to
the sides. If now the figure be bent about the line B D and
the silks are pulled tight it will present an appearance like
that in Fig. 44, resembling a saddle, or the top of a mountain pass.

This surface is composed entirely of straight lines, and
there are two sets of these straight lines; one set which was
originally parallel to A B, and the other set which was originally parallel to A D.

A section of the figure through A C and the middle point of
B D will be a parabola with its concave side turned upwards
(Fig. 45).

A section through B D and the middle point of A C will be
another parabola with its concave side turned downwards,
the common vertex of these parabolas being the summit of
the pass.

The tangent plane at this point will cut the surface in two

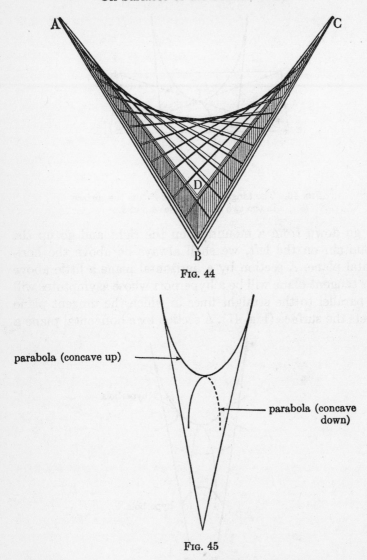

FIG. 44

FIG. 45

parabola (concave up)

parabola (concave down)

straight lines, while part of the surface will be above the tangent plane and part below it (Fig. 46). We may regard this tangent plane as a horizontal plane at the top of a mountain pass. If we travel over the pass, we come up on one side to the level of the plane and then go down on the other. But if

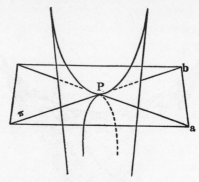

FIG. 46.   The tangent plane π at P cuts the surface
in the two straight lines a and b.

we go down from a mountain on the right and go up the
mountain on the left, we shall always be above the horizontal plane. A section by a horizontal plane a little above
this tangent plane will be a hyperbola whose asymptotes will
be parallel to the straight lines in which the tangent plane
meets the surface (Fig. 47). A section by a horizontal plane a

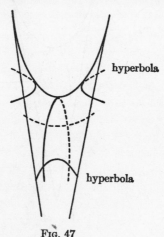

FIG. 47

little below will also be a hyperbola with its asymptotes parallel to these lines, but it will be situated in the other pair
of angles formed by these asymptotes. If we suppose the cutting plane to move downwards from a position above the

tangent plane (remaining always horizontal), then we shall see the two branches of the first hyperbola approach one another and get sharper and sharper until they meet and become simply two crossing straight lines. These lines will then have their corners rounded off and will be divided in the other direction and open out into the second hyperbola.

This leads us to suppose that a pair of intersecting straight lines is only a particular case of a hyperbola, and that we may consider the hyperbola as derived from the two crossing straight lines by dividing them at their point of intersection and rounding off the corners.

§10. *How to form Curves of the Third and Higher Orders*

The method of the preceding paragraph may be extended so as to discover the forms of new curves by putting known curves together. By a mode of expression which sounds paradoxical, yet is found convenient, a straight line is called a curve of the first order, because it can be met by another straight line in only one point; but two straight lines taken together are called a curve of the second order, because they can be met by a straight line in two points. The circle, and its shadows, the ellipse, parabola, and hyperbola, are also called curves of the second order, because they can be met by a straight line in two points, but not in more than two points; and we see that by this process of rounding off the corners and the method of projection we can derive all these curves of the second order from a pair of straight lines.

A similar process enables us to draw curves of the third order. An ellipse and a straight line taken together form a curve of the third order. If now we round off the corners at both the points where they meet we obtain (Fig. 48) a curve consisting of an oval and a sinuous portion called a "snake." Now just as when we move a plane which cuts a sphere away from the centre, the curve of intersection shrinks up into a point and then disappears, so we can vary our curve of the third order so as to make the oval which belongs to

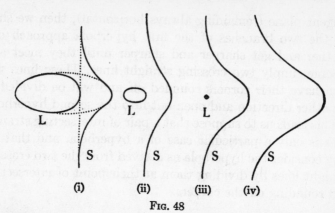

Fig. 48

(i) Full loop and snake.　　(iii) The loop has shrunk to a point.
(ii) Shrunk loop and snake.　　(iv) Snake only.

it shrink up into a point, and then disappear altogether, leaving only the sinuous part, but no variation will get rid of the "snake."

We may, if we like, only round off the corners at one of the intersections of the straight line and the ellipse, and we then have a curve of the third order crossing itself, having a

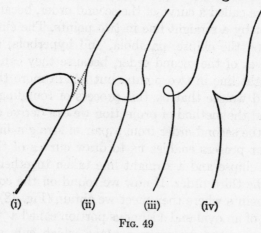

Fig. 49

knot or *double point* (Fig. 49); and we can further suppose this loop to shrink up, and the curve will then be found to have a sharp point or *cusp*.

It was shown by Newton that all curves of the third order might be derived as shadows from the five forms which we have just mentioned, viz. the oval and snake, the point and snake, the snake alone, the form with a knot, and the form with a cusp.

In the same way curves of the fourth order may be got by combining together two ellipses. If we suppose them to

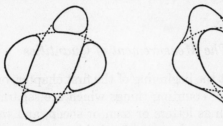

FIG. 50

cross each other in four points we may round off all the corners at once and so obtain two different forms, either four ovals all outside one another or an oval with four dints in it, and another oval inside it (Fig. 50).

But the number of forms of curves of the fourth order is so great that it has never yet been completely catalogued; and curves of higher orders are of still more varied shapes.

CHAPTER III

Quantity

§1. *The Measurement of Quantities*

WE considered at the beginning of the first chapter, on Number, the process of counting things which are separate from one another, such as letters or men or sheep, and we found it to be a fundamental property of this counting that the result was not affected by the order in which the things to be counted were taken; that one of the things, that is, was as good as another at any stage of the process.

We may also count things which are not separate but all in one piece. For example, we may say that a room is sixteen feet broad. And in order to count the number of feet in the breadth of this room we should probably take a foot rule and measure off first a foot close to the wall, then another beginning where that ended, and so on until we reached the opposite wall. Now when these feet are thus marked off they may, just like any other separate things, be counted in whatever order we please, and the number of them will always be sixteen.

But this is not all the variety in the process of counting which is possible. For suppose that we take a stick whose length is equal to the breadth of the room. Then we may cut out a foot of it wherever we please, and join the ends together. And if we then cut out another foot from any part of the remainder and join the ends, and repeat the process fifteen times, we shall find that there will always be a foot length left when the last two ends are joined together. So, when we are counting things that are all in one piece, like

88

the length of the stick or the breadth of the room, not only is the order in which we count the feet immaterial, but also the position of the actual feet which we count.

Again, if we say that a packet contains a pound, or sixteen ounces, of tea, we mean that if we take any ounce of it out, then any other ounce out of what is left, and so on until we have taken away fifteen ounces, there will always be an ounce left.

If I say that I have been writing for fifteen minutes it will of course have been impossible actually to count these minutes except in the order in which they really followed one another, but it will still be true that, if any separate fourteen minutes had been marked off during that interval of time, the remainder of it, made up of the interstices between these minutes, would amount on the whole to one minute.

In all these cases we have been counting things that hang together in one piece; and we find that we may choose at will not only the order of counting but even the things that we count without altering the result. This process is called the *measurement of quantities*.

But now suppose that when we measure the breadth of a room we find it to be not sixteen feet exactly, but sixteen feet and something over. It may be sixteen feet and five inches. And if so, in order to measure the something over, we merely repeat the same process as before; only that instead of counting feet we count inches, which are smaller than feet. If the breadth is found not to be an exact number of inches, but that something is left beside the five inches, we might measure that in eighths of an inch. There might, for example, be three eighths of an inch over. But there is no security that the process will end here; for the breadth of the room may not contain an exact number of eighths of an inch. Still it may be said that nobody wants to know the breadth of a room more exactly than to within an eighth of an inch.

Again, when we measure a quantity of tea it may be nearly, but not exactly, sixteen ounces; there may be something over. This remainder we shall then measure in grains. And here, as before, we are repeating the same process by which we count things which are all in one piece; only we count grains, which are smaller things than ounces. There may still not be an exact number of grains in the packet of tea, but then nobody wants to know the weight of a packet of tea so nearly as to a grain.

And it is the same with time. A geological period may, if we are very accurate, be specified in hundreds of centuries; the length of a war in years; the time of departure of a train to within a minute; the moment of an eclipse to a second; our care being, in each case, merely to secure that the measurement is accurate enough for the purpose we have in hand.

To sum up. There is in common use a rough or approximate way of describing quantities, which consists in saying how many times the quantity to be described contains a certain standard quantity, and in neglecting whatever may remain. The smaller the standard quantity is the more accurate is the process, but it is in general no better than an approximation.

If then we want to describe a quantity accurately and not by a mere approximation, what are we to do? There is no way of doing this in words; the only possible method is to carry about either the quantity itself or some other quantity which shall serve to represent it. For instance, to represent the exact length and breadth of a room we may draw it upon a scale of, say, one inch to a foot and carry this drawing about.

Here we are representing a length by means of another length; but it is not necessary to represent weights by means of weights, or times by means of times; they are both in practice represented by lengths. When a chemist, wishing to weigh with great delicacy, has gone as near as he can with the drachms which he puts into his scales, he hangs a little rider upon the beam of the scale, and the distance of this rider from the middle indicates how much weight there is over. And, if we suppose the balance to be perfectly true, and that no friction or other source of error has to be taken into account, it indicates this weight with real accuracy.

Here then is a case in which a weight is indicated by a length, namely, the distance from the centre of the scale to the rider. Again, we habitually represent time by means of a clock, and in this case the minute hand moves by a succession of small jerks, possibly twice a second. Such a clock will only reckon time in half seconds, and can tell us nothing about smaller intervals than this. But we may easily conceive of a clock in which the motion of the minute hand is steady, and not made by jerks. In this case the interval of time since the end of the last hour will be accurately represented by the length round the outer circle of the clock measured from the top of it to the point of the minute hand. And we notice that here also the quantity which is measured in this way by a length is probably not the whole quantity which was to be estimated, but only that which remains over after the greater part has been counted by reference to some standard quantity.

We may thus describe weight and time, and indeed quantities of any kind whatever, by means of the lengths of lines; and in what follows, therefore, we shall only speak of quantities of length as completely representing measurable things of any sort.

§2. *The Addition and Subtraction of Quantities*

For the addition of two lengths it is plainly sufficient to place them end to end in the same line. And we must notice that, as was the case with counting, so now, the possible variety in the mode of adding is far greater in the case of two

quantities than in the case of two numbers. For either of
the lengths, the aggregate of which we wish to measure, may
be cut up into any number of parts, and these may be in-
serted at any points we please of the other length, without
any change in the result of our addition.

Or the same may be seen, perhaps more clearly, by reference to the idea of "steps." Suppose we have a straight line
with a mark upon it agreed on as a starting-point, and a
series of marks ranged at equal distances along the line and
numbered 1, 2, 3, 4. . . . Then any particular number is
shown by making an index point to the right place on the
line. And to add or subtract any other number from this, we
have only to make the index move forwards or backwards
over the corresponding number of divisions. But in the case
of lengths we are not restricted to the places which are
marked on the scale. Any length is shown by carrying the
index to a place whose distance from the starting-point is
the length in question (of which places there may be as many
as we please between any two points which correspond to
consecutive numbers), and another length is added or sub-
tracted by making the index take a "step" forwards or
backwards of the necessary amount.

It is seen at once that, for quantities in general as well as
for numbers, a succession of given steps may be made in
any order we please and the result will always be the
same.

§3. *The Multiplication and Division of Quantities*

We have already considered cases in which a quantity is
multiplied; that is to say, in which a certain number of equal
quantities are added together, a process called the *multiplication* of one of them by that number. Thus the length
sixteen feet is the result of multiplying one foot by
sixteen.

We may now ask the inverse question: Given two lengths,

what number must be used to multiply one of them in order to produce the other? And it has been implied in what we have said about the measurement of quantities that it is only in special cases that we can find a number which will be the answer to this question. If we ask, for example, by what number a foot must be multiplied in order to produce fifteen inches, the word "number" requires to have its meaning altered and extended before we can give an answer. We know that an inch must be multiplied by fifteen in order to become fifteen inches. We may therefore first ask by what a foot must be multiplied in order to produce an inch. And the question seems at first absurd; because an inch must be multiplied by twelve in order to give a foot, and a foot has to be, not multiplied at all, but divided by twelve, in order to become an inch.

In order then to turn a foot into fifteen inches, we must go through the following process; we must divide it into twelve equal parts and take fifteen of them; or, shortly, divide by twelve and multiply by fifteen. Or we may produce the same result by performing the steps of our process in the other order: we may first multiply by fifteen, so that we get fifteen feet, and then divide this length into twelve equal parts, each of which will be fifteen inches.

Now if instead of inventing a new name for this compound operation we choose to call it by the old name of multiplication, we shall be able to speak of multiplying a foot so as to get fifteen inches. The operation of multiplying by fifteen and dividing by twelve is written thus: $\frac{15}{12}$; and so, to change a foot into fifteen inches, we multiply by the *fraction* $\frac{15}{12}$. Of this fraction the upper number (15) is termed the *numerator*, the lower (12) the *denominator*.

Now it was explained in the first chapter, that the formulæ of arithmetic and algebra are capable of a double interpretation. For instance, such a symbol as 3 meant, in the first place, a number of letters or men, or any other things; but afterwards was regarded as meaning an operation, namely, that of trebling anything. And so now the symbol $\frac{15}{12}$ may be taken either as meaning "so much" of a foot, or as meaning the operation by which a foot is changed into fifteen inches.

The degree in which one quantity is greater or less than another; or, to put it more precisely, that amount of stretching or squeezing which must be applied to the latter in order to produce the former, is called the *ratio* of the two quantities. If a and b are any two lengths, the ratio of a to b is the operation of stretching or squeezing which will make b into a; and this operation can be always approximately, and sometimes exactly, represented by means of numbers.[1]

§4. *The Arithmetical Expression of Ratios*

For the approximate expression of ratios there are two methods in use. In each, as in measuring quantities in general, we proceed by using standards which are taken smaller and smaller as we go on. In the first, these standards are chosen according to a fixed law; in the second, our choice is suggested by the particular ratio which we are engaged in measuring.

The first method consists in using a series of standards each of which is a tenth part of the preceding. Thus to express the ratio of fifteen inches to a foot, we proceed thus. The fifteen inches contain a foot once, and there is a piece of length three inches, or a quarter of a foot, left over. This quarter of a foot is then measured in tenths of a foot, and we find that it is 2-tenths, with a piece—which proves to be half a tenth—over. So, if we chose to neglect this half-tenth we should call the ratio 12-tenths, or as we write it 1.2. But if we do not neglect the half-tenth, it has to be measured in hundredths of a foot; of which it makes 5 exactly. So that the result is 125 hundredths, or 1.25, accurately.

[1] Integers or fractions.—J.R.N.

Again we will try to express in this way the length of the diagonal of a square in terms of a side. We find at once that the diagonal contains the side once, with a piece over: so that the ratio in question is 1 together with some fraction. If we now measure this remaining piece in tenth parts of a side we shall find that it contains 4 of them, with something left. Thus the ratio of the diagonal to the side may be approximately expressed by 14-tenths, or 1.4. If we now measure the piece left over in hundredth parts of the side we shall find that it contains one and a bit. Thus 141-hundredths, or 1.41 is a more accurate description of the ratio. And this bit can be shown to contain 4-thousandths of the side, and a bit over; so that we arrive at a still more accurate value, 1414-thousandths, or 1.414. And this process might be carried on to any degree of accuracy that was required; but in the present case, unlike that considered before, it would never end; for the ratio of the diagonal of a square to its side is one which cannot be accurately expressed by means of numbers.

The other method of approximation differs from the one just explained in this respect—that the successively smaller and smaller standard quantities in terms of which we measure the successive remainders are not fixed quantities, an inch, a tenth of an inch, a hundredth of an inch, and so on; but are suggested to us in the course of the approximation itself.

We begin, as we did before, by finding how many times the lesser quantity is contained in the greater, say, the side of a square in its diagonal. The answer in this case is, once and a piece over. Let the piece left over be called a. We then go on to try how many times this remainder, a, is contained in the side of the square. It is contained twice, and there is a remainder, say b. We then find how many times b is contained in a. Again twice, with a piece over, say c. And this process is repeated as often as we please, or until no remainder is left. It will, in the present case, be found that each remainder is contained twice, with something over, in the previous remainder.[1]

Let us now inquire how this process enables us to find successive approximations to the ratio of the diagonal to the side of the square.

Suppose, first, that the piece a had been exactly half the length of the side; that is, that we may neglect the remainder b. Then the diagonal would be equal to the side together with half the side, that is, to three-halves of the side.[2]

Next let us include b in our approximation, but neglect

[1] For the more algebraically minded reader the process described above may be explained as follows:

$$\frac{\beta}{\alpha} = ?$$

$$\frac{\beta}{\alpha} = 1 + \frac{a}{\alpha} = 1 + \frac{1}{\alpha}$$

$$= 1 + \cfrac{1}{2 + \cfrac{b}{a}}$$

$$= 1 + \cfrac{1}{2 + \cfrac{1}{\cfrac{a}{b}}}$$

$$= 1 + \cfrac{1}{2 + \cfrac{1}{2 + \cfrac{c}{b}}}$$

$$= 1 + \cfrac{1}{2 + \cfrac{1}{2 + \cfrac{1}{\cfrac{b}{c}}}}$$

$$= 1 + \cfrac{1}{2 + \cfrac{1}{2 + \cfrac{1}{2 + \cfrac{1}{2}}}} \cdots \text{—J.R.N.}$$

[2] Again, algebraically: Assuming $b = 0$

$$\frac{\beta}{\alpha} = 1 + \cfrac{1}{2 + \cfrac{b}{a}} = 1 + \cfrac{1}{2 + \cfrac{0}{a}} = \frac{3}{2} \left(> \frac{\beta}{\alpha} \right) \text{—J.R.N.}$$

c; that is, let us suppose that b is exactly one half of a. Then the side contains a twice, and half of a; that is to say, contains five-halves of a; or a is two-fifths of the side. But the diagonal contains the side together with a, that is, contains the side and two-fifths of the side, or seven-fifths of the side. The piece neglected is here less than b, and b is one-fifth of the side of the square.[1]

Again, let us include c in our approximation, and suppose it to be exactly one half of b. Then a, which contains b twice with c over, will be five-halves of b; that is, b will be two-fifths of a. Hence the side will contain twice a and two-fifths of a, that is, twelve-fifths of a; so that a is five-twelfths of the side. And the diagonal is equal to the side together with a; that is, to seventeen-twelfths of the side.[2] Also this approximation is closer than the preceding, for the piece neglected is now less than c, which is one-half of b, which is two-fifths of a, which is five-twelfths of the side; so that it is less than one-twelfth of the side.

By continuing this process we may find an approximation of any required degree of accuracy.

The first method of approximation is called the method of *decimals*; the second, that of *continued fractions*.

---

[1] Assuming $c = 0$

$$\frac{\beta}{\alpha} = 1 + \cfrac{1}{2 + \cfrac{1}{2 + \cfrac{c}{b}}} = 1 + \cfrac{1}{2 + \cfrac{1}{2 + \cfrac{0}{b}}} = \cfrac{1}{2 + \cfrac{1}{2}} = \frac{7}{5}\left(< \frac{\beta}{\alpha}\right) \text{—J.R.N.}$$

[2] Assuming $d = 0$

$$\frac{\beta}{\alpha} = 1 + \cfrac{1}{2 + \cfrac{1}{2 + \cfrac{1}{2 + \cfrac{d}{c}}}} = 1 + \cfrac{1}{2 + \cfrac{1}{2 + \cfrac{1}{2 + \cfrac{0}{c}}}} = 1 + \cfrac{1}{2 + \cfrac{1}{2 + \cfrac{1}{2}}}$$

$$= 1 + \cfrac{1}{2 + \cfrac{1}{2\frac{1}{2}}} = \frac{17}{12}\left(> \frac{\beta}{\alpha}\right) \text{—J.R.N.}$$

§5. *The Fourth Proportional*

One of the chief differences between quantities and numbers is that, while the division of one number by another is only possible when the first number happens to be a multiple of the other, in the case of quantities it appears, and we are indeed accustomed to assume, that any quantity may be divided by any number we like; that is to say, any length—quantities of all kinds being represented by lengths—may be divided into any given number of equal parts. And, if division is always possible, that compound operation made up of multiplication and division which we have called "multiplying by a fraction" must also be always possible; for example, we can find five-twelfths not only of a foot but of any other length that we like.

The question now naturally arises whether that general operation of stretching or squeezing which we have called a *ratio* can be applied to all quantities alike. If we have three lengths, *a*, *b*, *c*, there is a certain operation of stretching or squeezing which will convert *a* into *b*. Can the same operation be performed upon *c* with the result of producing a fourth quantity *d*, such that the ratio of *c* to *d* shall be the same as the ratio of *a* to *b*? We assume that this quantity—the *fourth proportional*, as it is called—does always exist; and this assumption, as it really lies at the base of all subsequent mathematics, is of so great importance as to deserve further study.

We shall find that it is really included in the second of the two assumptions that we made in the chapter about space; namely, that figures of the same shape may be constructed of different sizes. We found, in considering this point, that it was sufficient to take the case of triangles of different sizes of which the angles were equal; and showed that one triangle might be made into another of the same shape by the equal magnifying of all its three sides; that is to say, when two triangles have the same angles, the three ratios of either side of one to the corresponding side of the other are

equal. If this is true, it is clear that the problem of finding
the fourth proportional is reduced to that of drawing two
triangles of the same shape. Thus, for example, let A B and
A C represent the first two given quantities, and A D the third
(Fig. 51); and let it be required to find that quantity which
is got from A D by the same operation of stretching as is re-

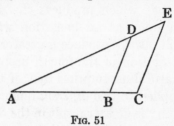

Fɪɢ. 51

quired to turn A B into A C. Suppose that we join B D, and
draw the line C E making the angle A C E equal to the angle
A B D. The two triangles A B D and A C E are now of the same
shape, and consequently A C E can be got from A B D by the
equal stretching of all its sides; that is to say, the stretching
which makes A B into A C is the same as the stretching which
makes A D into A E. A E is therefore the fourth proportional
required.

To render these matters clearer, it is well that we should
get a more exact notion of what we mean by the fourth proportional. We have so far only described it as something
which is got from A D by the same process which makes A B
into A C. In what way are we to tell whether the process is
the same? We might, if we liked, give a geometrical definition of it, founded upon the construction just explained; and
say that the ratio of A D to A E shall be called "equal" to the
ratio of A B to A C, when triangles of the same shape can have
for their respective sides the lengths A B, A D, A C, and A E.
But it is better, if we can do it, to keep the science of quantity
distinct from the science of space, and to find some definition
of the fourth proportional which depends upon quantity
alone. Such a definition has been found, and it is very important to notice the nature of it. For we shall find that

similar definitions have to be given of other quantities whose existence is assumed by what is called *the principle of continuity*.[1] This principle is simply the assumption, which we have stated already, that all quantities can be divided into any given number of equal parts.

If we apply two different operations of stretching to the same quantity, that which produces the greater result is naturally looked upon as an operation which under like circumstances will always produce a greater effect. Now we will make our definition of the fourth proportional depend upon the very natural assumption that, if two processes of stretching are applied to two *different* quantities, that process which produces the greater result in the one case will also produce the greater result in the other.

Suppose now that we have tried to approximate to the ratio which A C bears to A B, and that we have found that A C is between seventeen-twelfths and eighteen-twelfths of A B, then we have two processes of stretching which can be applied to A B, the process denoted by $\frac{17}{12}$ (that is, multiplying by 17 and dividing by 12), and the process which makes A C of it. The result of the former process is, by hypothesis, less than the result of the latter, because A C is more than seventeen-twelfths of A B. Let us now apply these two processes to A D. The former will produce seventeen-twelfths of A D, the latter will produce the fourth proportional required. Consequently this fourth proportional must be greater than seventeen-twelfths of A D.

But we know further that A C is less than eighteen-twelfths of A B. Then the operation which makes A B into A C gives a less result than the operation of multiplying by 18 and dividing by 12. Let us now perform both upon A D. It will follow that the fourth proportional required is less than eighteen-twelfths of A D. The same thing will be true of any fractions we like to take, and we may state our result in this general form:—

[1] In modern mathematics this would be the equivalent of assuming the existence of the real number system.—J.R.N.

According as A C is greater or is less than any specified fraction of A B, so will the fourth proportional (if it exists) be greater or be less than the same fraction of A D.

But we shall now show that this property is of itself sufficient to define, without ambiguity, the fourth proportional;

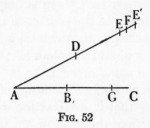

FIG. 52

that is to say, we shall show that there cannot be two different lengths satisfying this condition at the same time.

If possible, let there be two lengths, A E and A E′, each of them a fourth proportional to A B, A C, A D (Fig. 52). Then by taking a sufficient number of lengths each equal to E E′, the sum of them can be made greater than A D. Suppose for example that 500 of them just fell short of the length A D, and that 501 exceeded it; then, if we divide A D into 501 equal parts, each of these parts will be less than E E′.[1] Secondly, if we go on marking off lengths from D towards E, each equal to one of these small parts of A D, one of the points of division must fall between E and E′; since E E′ is greater than the distance between two of them. Let this point of division be at F. Then A F is got from A D by multiplying by some number or other and then dividing by 501. If we apply this same process to A B we shall arrive at a length A G, which must be either greater or less than A C. If it is less than A C, then the operation by which the length A B is made into A G is a less amount of stretching than the operation by which A B is made into A C. Consequently the operation which turns A D into A F is a less amount of stretching than that which gets

[1] To complete the proof Clifford should have considered the case where the sum of the lengths chosen was exactly equal to A D. The result as stated, however, is correct.—J.R.N.

A E, and also less than that which gets A E′ from A D. Therefore A F must be less than A E, and also less than A E′. But
this is impossible, because F lies between E and E′. And the
argument would be similar if we had supposed A G greater
than A C.

Thus we have proved that there is only one length that
satisfies the condition that the process of making A D into it
is greater than all the fractions which are less than the process
of making A B into A C, and less than all the fractions which
are greater than this same process.

Let us note more carefully the nature of this definition.

First of all we say that if any fraction whatever be taken,
and if it be greater than the ratio of A C to A B, it will also
be greater than the ratio of A E to A D, and if it be less than
the one it will also be less than the other.

This is a matter which can be tested in regard to any particular fraction. If a length A E were given to us as the fourth
proportional we could find out whether it obeyed the rule
in respect of any one given fraction. But if there is a fourth
proportional it must satisfy this rule in regard to all fractions
whatever. We cannot directly test this; but we may be able
to give a proof that the quantity which is supposed to be a
fourth proportional obeys the rule for one particular fraction, which proof shall be applicable without change to any
other fraction. It will then be proved, for this case, not only
that a fourth proportional exists, but that this particular

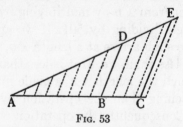

FIG. 53

quantity is the fourth proportional. This is, in fact, just what
we can do with the sides of similar triangles. If the length
A B (Fig. 53) is divided into any number of equal parts, and

lines are drawn through the points of division, making with A B the same angle that B D makes with it, they will divide A D into the same number of equal parts.

If now we set off points of division at the same distance from one another from B towards C, and through them draw lines making the same angle with the line A C that B D does, these lines will also cut off equal distances from D towards E. If any one of these lines starts from A C on the side of C towards A, it will meet A E on the side of E towards A; because the triangle which it forms with the lines A C and A E must have the same shape as A C E. So also any one of these lines which starts from A C on the side of C away from A will meet A E on the side of E away from A.

Looking then at the various fractions of A B which are now marked off, it is clear that, if one of them is less than A C, the corresponding fraction of A D is less than A E; and if greater, greater. It follows, therefore, that the line A E which is given by this construction satisfies, in the case of any fraction we choose, the condition which is necessary for the fourth proportional. Consequently, if the second assumption which we made about space be true, there always is a fourth proportional, and this process will enable us to find it.

There is, however, still one objection to be made against our definition of the fourth proportional, or rather one point in which we can make it a firmer ground-work for the study of ratios. For it assumes that quantities are continuous; that is, that any quantity can be divided into any number of equal parts, this being implied in the process of taking any numerical fraction of a quantity.

We say, for example, that if a, b, c, d, are proportionals, and if a is greater than three-fifths of b, c will be greater than three-fifths of d. Now the process of finding three-fifths of b is one or other of the following two processes. Either we divide b into five equal parts and take three of them, or we multiply b by three and divide the result into five equal parts. (We know of course that these two processes give us the same result.) But it is assumed in both cases that we can divide a given quantity into five equal parts.

Now in a definition it is desirable to assume as little as possible; and accordingly the Greek geometers in defining proportion, or (which is really the same thing) in defining the fourth proportional of three given quantities, have tried to avoid this assumption.

Nor is it difficult to do this. For let us consider the same example. We say that if a is greater than three-fifths of b, c will be greater than the same fraction of d. Now let us multiply both the quantities a and b by five. Then for a to be greater than three-fifths of b, the quantity which a has now become must be greater than three-fifths of the quantity which b has become; that is, if the new b be divided into five equal parts the new a must be greater than three of them. But each of these five equal parts is the same as the original b; and so our statement as to the relative greatness of a and b is the same as this, that five times a is greater than three times b; and similarly for c and d.

Now every fraction involves two numbers. It is a compound process made up of multiplying by one number and dividing by another, and it is clear therefore that we may, not only in this particular case of three-fifths but in general, transform our rule for the fourth proportional into this new form. According as m times a is greater or less than n times b, so is m times c greater or less than n times d, where m and n are any whole numbers whatever.

This last form is the one in which the rule is given by the Greek geometers; and it is clear that it does not depend on the continuity of the quantities considered, for whether it be true or not that we can divide a number into any given number of equal parts, we can certainly take any multiple of it that we like.

These fundamental ideas, of ratio, of the equality of ratios, and of the nature of the fourth proportional, are now established generally, and with reference to quantities of any kind, not with regard to lengths alone; provided merely that it is always possible to take any given multiple of any given quantity.

§6. *Of Areas; Stretch and Squeeze*

We shall now proceed to apply these ideas to areas, or quantities of surface, and in particular to plane areas. The simplest of these for the purposes of measurement is a rectangle. The finding of the area of a rectangle is in many cases the same process as numerical multiplication. For example, a rectangle which is 7 inches long and 5 inches broad will contain 35 square inches, and this follows from our fundamental ideas about the multiplication of numbers. But this process, the multiplication of numbers, is only applicable to the case in which we know how many times each side of the rectangle contains the unit of length, and it then tells us how many times the area of the rectangle contains the square described upon the unit of length. It remains to find a method which can always be used.

For this purpose we first of all observe that when one side of a rectangle is lengthened or shortened in any ratio, the other side being kept of a fixed length, the area of the rectangle will be increased or diminished in exactly the same ratio.

In order then to make any rectangle O P R Q out of a square O A C B (Fig. 54), we have first of all to stretch the side O A until

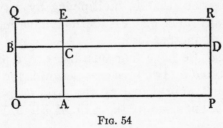

Fig. 54

it becomes equal to O P, and thereby to stretch the whole square into the rectangle O D, which increases its area in the ratio of O A to O P. Then we must stretch the side O B of this figure until it is equal to O Q, and thereby the figure O D be-

comes o R, and its area is increased in the ratio of o B to
o Q. Or we may, if we like, first stretch o B to the length o Q,
whereby the square o C becomes o E, and then stretch o A
to o P, by which o E becomes o R.

Thus the whole operation of turning the square o C into
the rectangle o R is made up of two stretches; or, as we have
agreed to call them, "multiplications"; viz. the square has
to be multiplied by the ratio of o P to o A, and by the ratio
of o Q to o B; and we may find from the result that the order
of these two processes is immaterial.

For let us represent the ratio of o P to o A by the letter a,
and the ratio of o Q to o B by b. Then the ratio of the rectangle o D to the square o C is also a; in other words, a times
o C is equal to o D. And the ratio of o R to o D is b, so that b
times o D is equal to o R; that is, b times a times o C is equal
to o R, or, as we write it, ba times o C is o R.[1]

And in the same way b times o C is equal to o E and a times
b times o C is a times o E, which is o R.

Consequently we have ba times o C giving the same result
as ab times o C; or, as we write it

$$ba = ab,$$

which means that the effect of multiplying first by the ratio
a and then by the ratio b is the same as that of multiplying
first by the ratio b and then by the ratio a.

This proposition, that in multiplying by ratios we may
take them in any order we please without affecting the result,
can be put into another form.

Suppose that we have four quantities, a, b, c, d, then I
can make a into d by two processes performed in succession;
namely, by first multiplying by the ratio of b to a, which
turns it into b, and then by the ratio of d to b. But I might

[1] It is a matter of convention which has grown up in consequence of our
ordinary habit of reading from left to right, that we always read the symbols
of a multiplication, or of any other operation, *from right to left*. Thus a b times
any quantity x, means a times b times x; that is to say, we first multiply x by
b, and then by a; that operation being first performed whose symbol comes
last.

have produced the same effect on a by first multiplying it
by the ratio of c to a, which turns it into c, and then multiplying by the ratio of d to c. We are accustomed to write
the ratio of b to a in shorthand in any of the four following
ways:—

$$b : a, \quad \frac{b}{a}, \quad b \div a, \quad b/a,$$

and so the fact we have just stated may be written thus:—

$$b/a \times d/b = c/a \times d/c.$$

Now let us assume that the four quantities, a, b, c, d, are
proportionals; that is, that the ratios b/a and d/c are equal
to one another. It follows then that the ratios c/a and d/b
are equal to one another.

This proposition may be otherwise stated in this form;
that if a, b, c, d are proportionals, then a, c, b, d will also be
proportionals: provided always that this latter statement
has any meaning, for it is quite possible that it should have
no meaning at all. Suppose, for instance, that a and b are
two lengths, c and d two intervals of time, then we understand what is meant by the ratio of b to a, and the ratio of
d to c, and these ratios may very well be equal to one another; but there is no such thing as a ratio of c to a, or of d
to b, because the quantities compared are not of the same
kind. When, however, four quantities *of the same kind* are
proportionals, they are also proportionals when taken *alter-
nately*; that is to say, when the two middle ones are interchanged.

§7. *Of Fractions*

We have seen in §3, page 92, that a ratio may be expressed
in the form of a fraction.[1] Thus, let a be represented by the

---

[1] Only where the two numbers are commensurable. The numbers representing the lengths of the side and diagonal of a square, for example, are not
commensurable.—J.R.N.

fraction $\dfrac{p}{q}$ and b by the fraction $\dfrac{r}{s}$, where p, q, r, s are numbers. Then the result on page 107 may be written—

$$\frac{p}{q} \times \frac{r}{s} = \frac{r}{s} \times \frac{p}{q}.$$

Let us examine a little more closely into the meaning of either side of this equation. Suppose we were to take a rec-

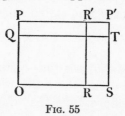

Fig. 55

tangle o q t s (Fig. 55), of which one side, o q, contained q units of length, and another, o s, s units. Then this rectangle could be obtained from the unit square by operating upon it with the two stretches q and s. Its area would thus contain qs square units. Now let us apply to this rectangle in succession the two stretches denoted by $\dfrac{p}{q}$ and $\dfrac{r}{s}$. If we stretch the rec-

tangle in the direction of the side o q in the ratio of $\dfrac{p}{q}$, we divide the side o q into q equal parts, and then take o p equal p times one of those parts. But each of these parts will be equal to unity, hence o p contains p units. We thus convert our rectangle o t into one o p', of which one side, o p, contains p and the other, o s, s units. Now let us apply to this rectangle the stretch $\dfrac{r}{s}$ parallel to the side o s (as the figure is drawn $\dfrac{r}{s}$ denotes a *squeeze*). We must divide o s into s equal parts and take r such parts, or we must measure a length o r along o s equal to r units. Thus this second stretch converts the rectangle o p' into a rectangle o r', of which the side o p contains p and the side o r contains r

units of length, or into a rectangle containing pr square units. Hence the two stretches $\frac{p}{q}$ and $\frac{r}{s}$ applied in succession to the rectangle O T convert it into the rectangle O R'. Now this may be written symbolically thus:—

$$\frac{p}{q} \times \frac{r}{s} \cdot \text{rectangle O T} = \text{rectangle O R}'$$
$$= pr \text{ unit-rectangles.}$$

Now unit-rectangle may obviously be obtained from the rectangle O T by squeezing it first in the ratio $\frac{1}{q}$ in the direction of O Q, and then in the ratio $\frac{1}{s}$ in the direction O S. Now this is simply saying that O T contains qs unit-rectangles. Hence the operation $\frac{p}{q} \times \frac{r}{s}$ applied to unit-rectangle must produce $\frac{1}{qs}$ of the result of its application to the rectangle O T. That is:—

$$\frac{p}{q} \times \frac{r}{s} \cdot \text{unit-rectangle} = \frac{1}{qs} \cdot pr \text{ unit-rectangle,}$$

or, in our notation, $= \frac{pr}{qs} \cdot$ unit-rectangle.

Hence we may say that $\frac{p}{q} \times \frac{r}{s}$ operating upon unity is equal to the operation denoted by $\frac{pr}{qs}$, or to multiplying unity by pr and then dividing the result by qs. This equivalence is termed the *multiplication of fractions*.

A special case of the multiplication of fractions arises when s equals r. We then have—

$$\frac{p}{q} \times \frac{r}{r} = \frac{pr}{qr}.$$

But the operation $\frac{r}{r}$ denotes that we are to divide unity into r equal parts, and then take r of them; in other words, we perform a *null* operation on unity. The symbol of operation may therefore be omitted, and we read—

$$\frac{p}{q} = \frac{pr}{qr}.$$

This result is then expressed in words as follows: Given a fraction, we do not alter its value by multiplying the numerator and denominator by equal quantities.

From this last result we can easily interpret the operation

$$\frac{p}{q} + \frac{r}{s}.$$

For, by the preceding paragraph—

$$\frac{p}{q} = \frac{ps}{qs}, \text{ and } \frac{r}{s} = \frac{qr}{qs}.$$

Hence—

$$\frac{p}{q} + \frac{r}{s} = \frac{ps}{qs} + \frac{qr}{qs}.$$

Or, to apply first the operation $\frac{p}{q}$ to unity and then to add to this the result of the operation $\frac{r}{s}$ is the same thing as dividing unity into qs parts, taking ps of those parts, and then adding to them qr more of the like parts. But this is the same thing as to take at once $ps + qr$ of those parts. Thus we may write—

$$\frac{p}{q} + \frac{r}{s} = \frac{ps + qr}{qs}.$$

This result is termed the *addition of fractions*. The reader will find no difficulty in interpreting addition graphically by a succession of stretches and squeezes of the unit-rectangle.

We term division the operation by which we reverse the result of multiplication. Hence when we ask the meaning of *dividing* by the fraction $\frac{p}{q}$ we put the question: What is the operation which, following on the operation $\frac{p}{q}$, just reverses its effect?

Now, $\frac{r}{s} \times \frac{p}{q} = \frac{p}{q} \times \frac{r}{s} = \frac{pr}{qs}.$

Suppose we take $r = q$, $s = p$.

Then $\frac{q}{p} \times \frac{p}{q} = \frac{pq}{qp};$

or, to multiply unity by $\frac{p}{q}$, and then by $\frac{q}{p}$, is to perform the operation of dividing unity into qp parts and then taking pq of them, or to leave unity unaltered. Hence the stretch $\frac{q}{p}$ completely reverses the stretch $\frac{p}{q}$; it is, in fact, a squeeze which just counteracts the preceding stretch. Thus multiplying by $\frac{q}{p}$ must be an operation equivalent to *dividing* by $\frac{p}{q}$. Or, to divide by $\frac{p}{q}$ is the same thing as to multiply by $\frac{q}{p}$. This result is termed the *division of fractions*.

§8. *Of Areas; Shear*

Hitherto we have been concerned with stretching or squeezing the sides of a rectangle. These operations alter its area, but leave it still of rectangular shape. We shall now describe an operation which changes its angles, but leaves its area unaltered (Fig. 56).

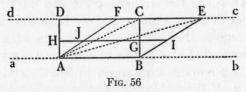

Fig. 56

Let A B C D be a rectangle, and let A B E F be a parallelogram (or a four-sided figure whose opposite sides are equal);

having the same side, A B, as the rectangle, but having the opposite side, E F (equal to A B, and therefore to C D), somewhere in the same line as C D. Then, since C D is equal to E F, the points E and F are equally distant from C and D respectively, and it follows that the triangles B C E and A D F are equal. Hence if the triangle B C E were cut off the parallelogram along B C and placed in the position A D F, we should have converted the parallelogram into the rectangle without changing its area. Thus the area of the parallelogram is equal to that of the rectangle. Now the area of the rectangle is the product of the numerical quantity which represents the length of A D into that quantity which represents the length of A B. A B is termed the *base* of the parallelogram, and A D, the perpendicular distance between its base and the opposite side E F, is termed its *height*. The area of the parallelogram is then briefly said to be "the product of its base into its height."

Suppose C D and A B were rigid rods capable of sliding along the parallel lines *cd* and *ab*. Let us imagine them connected by a rectangular elastic membrane, A B C D; then as the rods were moved along *ab* and *cd* the membrane would change its shape. It would, however, always remain a parallelogram with a constant base and height; hence its area would be unchanged. Let the rod A B be held fixed in position, and the rod C D pushed along *cd* to the position E F. Then any line, G H, in the membrane parallel and equal to A B will be moved parallel to itself into the position I J, and will not change its length. The distance through which C has moved is C E, and the distance through which G has moved is G I. Since the triangles C B E and G B I have their sides parallel they are similar, and we have the ratio of C E to G I the same as that of B C to B G; or, when the rectangle A B C D is converted into the parallelogram A B E F, any line parallel to A B remains unchanged in length, and is moved parallel to itself through a distance proportional to its distance from A B. Such a transformation of figure is termed a *shear*, and we may consider either our rectangle as being

sheared into the parallelogram or the latter as being sheared
into the former. Thus the area of a parallelogram is equal to
that of a rectangle into which it may be sheared.

The same process which converts the parallelogram A B E F
into the rectangle A B C D will convert the triangle A B E, the
half of the former, into the triangle A B C, the half of the

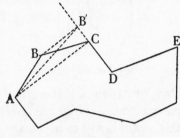

FIG. 57

latter. Hence we may shear any triangle into a right-angled
triangle, and this will not alter its area. Thus the area of any
triangle is half the area of the rectangle on the same base,
and with height equal to the perpendicular upon the base
from the opposite angle. This height is also termed the altitude, or height of the triangle, and we then briefly say: *The
area of a triangle is half the product of its base into its altitude.*

A succession of shears will enable us to reduce any figure
bounded by straight lines to a triangle of equal area, and thus
to determine the area the figure encloses by finally shearing
this triangle into a right-angled triangle (Fig. 57). For example, let A B C D E be a portion of the boundary of the
figure. Suppose A C joined; then shear the triangle A B C so
that its vertex B falls at B′ on D C produced. The area A B′ C
is equal to the area A B C. Hence we may take A B′ D E for
the boundary of our figure instead of A B C D E; that is, we
have reduced the number of sides in our figure by one. By a
succession of shears, therefore, we can reduce any figure
bounded by straight lines to a triangle, and so find its area.

§9. *Of Circles and their Areas*

One of the first areas bounded by a curved line which suggests itself is that of a *sector* of a circle, or the portion of a

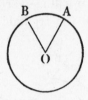

FIG. 58

circle intercepted by two radii and the arc of the circumference between their extremities (Fig. 58). Before we can consider the area of this sector it will be necessary to deduce some of the chief properties of the complete circle. Let us take a circle of unit radius and suppose straight lines drawn at the extremities of two diameters A B and C D at right angles; then the circle will appear as if drawn inside a square (see Fig. 59). The sides of this square will be each 2 and its area 4.

Now suppose the figure composed of circle and square first to receive a stretch such that every line parallel to the di-

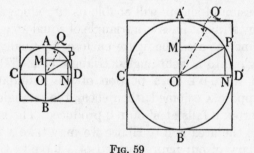

FIG. 59

ameter A B is extended in the ratio of $a : 1$, and then another stretch such that every line parallel to C D is again extended in the ratio of $a : 1$. Then it is obvious that we shall have stretched the square of the first figure into a second square whose sides will now be equal to $2a$.

It remains to be shown that we have stretched the first circle into another circle. Let O P be any radius and P M, P N perpendiculars on the diameters A B, C D. As a result of the first stretch the equal lengths O M and N P are extended into the equal lengths O′ M′ and N′ P′, which are such that $\dfrac{\text{O M}}{\text{O}'\text{ M}'} = \dfrac{\text{N P}}{\text{N}'\text{ P}'} = \dfrac{1}{a}$. Similarly as a result of the second stretch M P and O N, which remained unaltered during the first stretch, are converted into M′ P′ and O′ N′; so that $\dfrac{\text{O N}}{\text{O}'\text{ N}'} = \dfrac{\text{M P}}{\text{M}'\text{ P}'} = \dfrac{1}{a}$. During this second stretch O′ M′ and N′ P′ remain unaltered. Thus as the total outcome of the two stretches we find that the triangle O P N has been changed into the triangle O′ P′ N′. Now these two triangles are of the same shape by what was said on p. 99, for the angles at N and N′ are equal, being both right angles, and we have seen that—

$$\frac{\text{N P}}{\text{N}'\text{ P}'} = \frac{1}{a} = \frac{\text{O M}}{\text{O}'\text{ M}'}.$$

Thus it follows that the third side O P must be to the third side O′ P′ in the ratio of 1 to a; or, since O P is of unit length, O′ P′ must be equal to the constant quantity a. Further, since the angles P O N, P′ O′ N′ are equal, O′ P′ is parallel to O P. Hence the circle of unit radius has been stretched into a circle of radius a. In fact, the two equal stretches in directions at right angles, which we have given to the first figure, have performed just the same operation upon it, as if we had placed it under a magnifying glass which enlarged it uniformly, and to such a degree that every line in it was magnified in the ratio of a to 1.

It follows from this that the circumference of the second circle must be to that of the first as a is to 1. Or, the circumferences of circles are as their radii. Again, if the arc P Q is stretched into the arc P′ Q′—that is, if O′ P′, O′ Q′ are respectively parallel to O P, O Q—then the arc P′ Q′ is to the arc P Q in the ratio of the radii of the two circles. Since the arcs P Q, P′ Q′ are equal to any other arcs which subtend the same angles at the centres of their respective circles, we state generally that *the arcs of two circles which subtend equal angles at their respective centres are in the ratio of the corresponding radii.*

Since the second figure is an uniformly magnified image of the first, every element of area in the first has been magnified at the same uniform rate in the second. Now the square in the first figure contains four units of area, and in the second figure it contains $4a^2$ units of area. Hence every element of area in the first figure has been magnified in the second in the ratio of a^2 to 1. Thus the area of the circle in the first figure must be to the area of the circle in the second figure as 1 is to a^2. Or: *The areas of circles are as the squares of their radii.*

It is usual to represent the area of a circle of unit radius by the quantity π; thus the area of a circle of radius a will be represented by the quantity πa^2.

If, after stretching A B to A′ B′ in the ratio of a to 1, we had stretched or squeezed C D to C′ D′ in the ratio of b to 1, where b is some quantity different from a, our square would have become a rectangle, with sides equal to $2a$ and $2b$

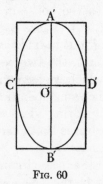

Fig. 60

respectively. It may be shown that we should have distorted our circle into the shape of that shadow of a circle which we have termed an ellipse. Furthermore, elements of area have now been stretched in the ratio of the product of a and b to 1; or, the area of the ellipse is to the area of the circle of unit radius as *ab* is to 1: whence it follows that the area of the ellipse is represented by πab, where *a* and *b* are its greatest and least radii respectively.

We shall now endeavour to connect the area of a circle of unit radius, which we have written π, with the number of linear units in its circumference. Let us take a number of points uniformly distributed round the circumference of a circle, A B C D E F (Fig. 61). Join them in succession to each other and to O, the centre of the circle, and draw the lines perpendicular to these radii (or the *tangents*) at A B C D E F; then we shall have constructed two perfectly symmetrical figures, one of which is said to be *inscribed*, the other *circumscribed* to the circle. Now the areas of these two figures differ by the sum of such triangles as A *a* B, and the area of the circle is obviously greater than the area of the inscribed and less than the area of the circumscribed figure. Thus the area of the

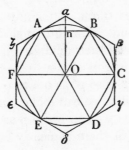

Fig. 61

circle must differ from that of the inscribed figure by something less than the sum of all the little triangles A *a* B, B *β* C, &c. Now from symmetry all these little triangles are equal, and their areas are therefore equal to one half the product of their heights, or *an*, into their bases, or such quantities as A B. Hence the sum of their areas is equal to one half of the product of *an* into the sum of the sides of the inscribed figure. Now the sum of the sides of the inscribed figure is never greater than the circumference of the circle. If we take, therefore, a great number of points uniformly distributed round the circumference of our circle, A and B may be brought as close as we please, and the nearer we bring A to B, the smaller becomes an. Hence, by taking a sufficient number of points, we can make the sum of the triangles A a B, B β C, &c. as small as we please, or the areas of the inscribed and circumscribed figures, together with the area of the circle which lies between them, can be made to differ by less than any assignable quantity. In the limit then we may say that by taking an indefinite number of points we can make these areas equal. Now the area of the inscribed figure is the sum of the areas of all such triangles as A O B, and the area of the triangle A O B is equal to half the product of its height O n into its base A B; or if we write for the "perimeter," or sum of all the sides A B, B C, &c. the quantity p, the area of the inscribed figure will equal $\frac{1}{2}p \times$ O n. Again if p' be the sum of the sides $a\beta$, $\beta\gamma$, &c. of the circumscribed figure, its area $= \frac{1}{2}p' \times$ O B.

Since the triangles O a B, O B n are of the same shape, being right-angled and again equi-angled at O, we have the ratio of B n to a B, or of their doubles A B to a β, the same as that of O n to O B. But p is obviously to p' in the same ratio as A B to a β; hence p is to p' as O n to O B. By taking a sufficient number of points we can make O n as nearly equal to O B as we please; thus we can make p as nearly equal to p', and therefore either of them as nearly equal to the circumference of the circle (which lies between them),[1] as we please. Hence in the limit p will equal the circumference of the circle, and O n its radius, and we may state that the areas of the inscribed and circumscribed figures, which approach nearer and nearer to the area of the circle as we increase the number of their sides, become ultimately equal to each other and to half the product of the circumference of the circle into its radius. This must therefore be the area of the circle. Hence we have the following equality:—The area of a circle of radius a equals one half its circumference $\times$ a. But it equals also πa^2; whence it follows that the circumference of a circle

---

[1] In the case of the circle the reader will recognize this intuitively.

equals $\pi \cdot 2a$. We may express this result in two different ways:—

(i) The ratio of the circumference of a circle to its diameter $(2a)$ is a constant quantity π.

(ii) The number of linear units (2π) in the circumference of a circle of unit-radius is twice the number of units of area (π) contained by that circumference.

The value of π, the ratio of the circumference of a circle to its diameter, is found to be a quantity which, like the ratio of the diagonal of a square to its side (see p. 95), cannot be expressed accurately by numbers; its approximate value is 3.14159.

We have now no difficulty in finding the area of the sector of a circle, for if we double the arc of a sector we obviously double its area; if we treble it, we treble its area; shortly, if we take any multiple of it, we take the same multiple of its area. Hence it follows by §5, that two sectors are to each other in the ratio of their arcs, or a sector must be to the whole circle in the ratio of its arc to the whole circumference.

If we represent by s the area of a sector of a circle of which the arc contains s units of length and the radius a units, we may write this relation symbolically—

$$\frac{s}{\pi a^2} = \frac{s}{2\pi a}.$$

Thus we deduce $s = \frac{1}{2}s \times a$; or,
The area of a sector is half the product of the length of its arc into its radius.

§10. *Of the Area of Sectors of Curves*

The knowledge of the area of a sector of a circle enables us to find as accurately as we please the area of a sector whose arc is any curve whatever. Let the arc P Q (Fig. 62) be divided into a number of smaller arcs P A, A B, B C, C D, D Q. We shall suppose that P A subtends the greatest angle at O of all these arcs. Further we shall consider only the case where the line O P diminishes continuously if P be made to pass along the

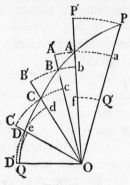

FIG. 62 [1]

arc from P to Q. If this be not the case, the sector Q O P can always be split up into smaller sectors, of which it shall be true that a line drawn from the point O to the arc continuously diminishes from one side of the sector to the other, and then for the area of each of these sectors the following investigation will hold. With O as centre describe a circle of radius O P to meet O A produced in F'; with the same centre and radius O A describe a circle to meet O B in A' and O P in a; similarly circles with radius O B to meet O A in b and O C in B', with radius O C to meet O B in c and O D in c', with radius O D to meet O C in d and O Q in D', and finally with radius O Q to meet O D in e, O A in f, and O P in Q'. Then the area of the sector obviously lies between the areas of the figure bounded by O P, O D' and the broken line P P' A A' B B' C C' D D', and of the figure bounded by O a, O Q and the broken line a A b B c C d D e Q. Hence it differs from either of them by less than their difference or by less than the sum of the areas P' a, A' b, B' c, C' d, D' e. Now since the angle at P O P' is greater than any of the other sectorial angles at O, the sum of all these areas must be less than that of the figure P P' f Q', and the area of this figure can be made as small as we please by making the angle A O P sufficiently small. This can be

---

[1] If in the diagram the areas D' D e Q, C' D d C, B' C c B, A' B b A are swung around and moved into A a f Q', there will be space left over. Thus the sum of the smaller areas < the area A a f Q.

achieved by taking a sufficient number of points like A, B, C, D, &c. We are thus able to find a series of circular sectors, the sum of whose areas differs by as small a quantity as we please from the area of the sector P O Q; in other words, we reduce the problem of finding the area of any figure bounded by a curved line to the problem already solved of finding the area of a sector of a circle. The difficulties which then arise are purely those of adding together a very great number of quantities; for, it may be necessary to take a very great number of points such as A B C D . . . in order to approach with sufficient accuracy to the magnitude of the area P O Q.

§11. *Extension of the Conception of Area*

Let A B C D be a closed curve or loop, and O a point inside it (Fig. 63).[1] Then if a point P move round the perimeter of the loop, the line O P is said to trace out the area of the loop A B C D. By this is meant that successive positions of the line O P, pair and pair, form together with the intervening elements of arc elementary sectors, the sum of the areas of which can,

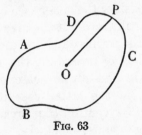

FIG. 63

by taking the successive positions sufficiently close, be made to differ as little as we please from the area bounded by the loop.

Now suppose the point O to be taken *outside* the loop A B C D (Fig. 64), and let us endeavour to find the area then traced out by the line O P joining O to a point P which moves round the loop. Let O B and O D be the extreme positions of the line O P to the left and to the right as P moves round the

[1] This must be a closed *convex* curve which does not cross itself.—J.R.N.

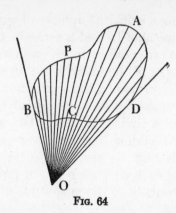

FIG. 64

loop A B C D; then as P moves along the portion of the loop
D A B, O P moves *counter-clockwise* from right to left and
traces out the area bounded by the arc D A B and the lines
O D and O B. Further, as P moves along the portion of the
loop B C D, O P moves *clockwise* from left to right and traces
out the area doubly shaded in our figure, or the area bounded
by the arc B C D and the lines O B and O D. It is the *difference*
of these two areas which is the area of the loop A B C D. If,
then, we were to consider the latter area O B C D O as *negative*,
the line O P would still trace out the area of the loop A B C D
as P moves round its perimeter. Now the characteristic difference in the method of describing the areas O D A B O and
O B C D O is, that in the former case O P moves *counter-
clockwise* round O, in the latter case it moves *clockwise*.
Hence if we make a convention that areas traced out by O P
when it is moving counter-clockwise shall be considered
positive, but areas traced out by O P when it is moving
clockwise shall be considered negative, then wherever O may
be inside or outside the loop, the line O P will trace out its
area provided P move completely round its circumference.

But it must here be noted that P may describe the loop
in two different methods, either going round it counter-
clockwise in the order of points A B C D, or clockwise in the
order of points A D C B. In the former case, according to our
convention, the greater area O D A B O is positive, in the lat-

ter it is negative. Hence we arrive at the conception that *an area may have a sign*; it will be considered positive or negative according as its perimeter is supposed traced out by a point moving counter-clockwise or clockwise. This extended conception of area, as having not only magnitude but *sense*, is of fundamental importance, not only in many branches of the exact sciences, but also for its many practical applications.[1]

Let a perpendicular o n be erected at o (which is, as we have seen, any point in the plane of the loop) to the plane of the loop, and let the length o n be taken along it containing as many units of length as there are units of area in the loop A B C D. Then o n will represent the area of the loop in magnitude; it will also represent it in *sense*, if we agree that o n shall always be measured in such a direction from o, that to a person standing with his feet at o and head at n the point P shall always appear to move counter-clockwise. Thus, for a positive area, n will be above the plane; for a negative area, in the opposite direction or below the plane. We are now able to represent any number of areas by segments of straight lines or steps perpendicular to their planes. The sum of any number of areas lying in the same plane will then be obtained by adding algebraically all the lines which represent these areas.

When the areas do not all lie in one plane the representative lines will not all be parallel. In this case there are two methods of adding areas. We may want to know the total amount of area, as, for example, when we wish to find the cost of painting or gilding a many-sided solid. In this case we add all the representative lines without regard to their direction.

In many other cases, however, we wish to find some quantity so related to the sides of a solid that it can only be found by treating the lines which represent their areas as *directed* magnitudes. Such cases, for example, arise in the discussion

[1] As in calculating the cost of levelling and embanking, in the indicator diagram, &c. It was first introduced by Möbius.

of the shadows cast by the sun or of the pressure of gases upon the sides of a containing vessel, &c. A method of combining directed magnitudes will be fully discussed in the following chapter. The conception of areas as directed magnitudes is due to Hayward.

§12. *On the Area of a Closed Tangle*

Hitherto we have supposed the areas we have talked about to be bounded by a simple loop. It is easy, however, to determine the area of a combination of loops. Thus consider the figure of eight in Fig. 65, which has two loops: if we go round it continuously in the direction indicated by the arrowheads, one of these loops will have a positive, the other a negative area, and therefore the total area will be their difference, or zero if they be equal. When a closed curve, like a figure of eight, cuts itself it is termed a *tangle*, and the points where it cuts itself are called *knots*. Thus a figure of eight is a tangle of one knot. In tracing out the area of a closed curve by means of a line drawn from a fixed point to a point moving round the curve, the area may vary according to the direction and the route by which we suppose the

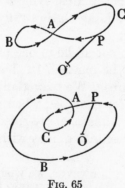

FIG. 65

curve to be described. If, however, we suppose the curve to be sketched out by the moving point, then its area will be perfectly definite for that particular description of its perimeter.

We shall now show how the most complex tangle may be split up into simple loops and its whole area determined from the areas of the simple loops. We shall suppose arrow-heads to denote the direction in which the perimeter is to be taken. Consider either of the accompanying figures. The moving line O P will trace out exactly the same area if we suppose it not to cross at the knot A but first to trace out the loop A C and then to trace out the loop A B, in both cases going round these two loops in the direction indicated by the arrow-heads. We are thus able in all cases to convert one line cutting itself in a knot into two lines, each bounding a separate loop, which just touch at the point indicated by the former knot. This dissolution of knots may be suggested to the reader by leaving a vacant space where the boundaries of the loops really meet. The two knots in the following figure (Fig. 66) are shown dissolved in this fashion:—

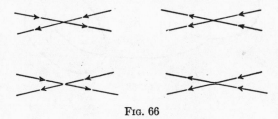

Fig. 66

The reader will now find no difficulty in separating the most complex tangle into simple loops. The positive or negative character of the areas of these loops will be sufficiently indicated by the arrow-heads on their perimeters. We append an example (Fig. 67, page 126).

In this case the tangle reduces to a negative loop a (Fig. 68), and to a large positive loop b, within which are two other positive loops c and d, the former of which contains a fifth small positive loop e. The area of the entire tangle then equals $b + c + d + e - a$. The space marked s in the first figure will be seen from the second to be no part of the area of the tangle at all.

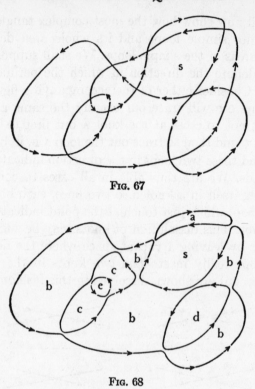

FIG. 67

FIG. 68

§13. *On the Volumes of Space-Figures*

Let us consider first the space-figure bounded by three pairs of parallel planes mutually at right angles (Fig. 69). Such a space-figure is technically termed a "rectangular parallelepiped," but might perhaps be more shortly described as a "right six-face." We may first observe that when one edge of such a right six-face is lengthened or shortened in any ratio, the other non-parallel edges being kept of a fixed length, the volume will be increased in precisely the same ratio. Hence, in order to make any right six-face out of a cube we have only to give the cube three stretches (or it may be squeezes), parallel respectively to its three sets of parallel edges. Let O A, O B, O C be the three edges of the cube which

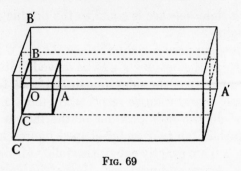

Fig. 69

meet in a corner o. Let o a be stretched to o a', so that the ratio of o a' to o a is represented by a; then if the figure is to remain right all lines parallel to o a will be stretched in the same ratio. The figure has now become a six-face whose section perpendicular to o a' only is a square. Now stretch o b to o b', so that the ratio o b' to o b be represented by b, and let all lines parallel to o b be increased in the same ratio; the figure is now a right six-face, only one set of edges of which are equal to the edge of the original square. Finally stretch o c to o c', so that o c and all lines parallel to it are increased in the ratio of o c' to o c, which we will represent by c. By a process consisting of three stretches we have thus converted our original cube into a right six-face (Fig. 70). If the cube had been of unit-volume, the volume of our six-edge would obviously be abc, and we may show as in the case of a rectangle (see p. 107) that $abc = cba = bac$, &c.; or the order of multiplying together three ratios is indifferent. If we term

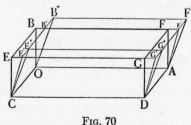

Fig. 70

the face a' c' of our right six-face its *base* and o b' its *height*, ac will represent the area of its base, and b its height, or the

volume of a right six-face is equal to the product of its base
into its height.

Let us now suppose a right six-face O A D C E B F G to receive a shear, or the face B E F G to be moved in its own plane
in such fashion that its sides remain parallel to their old
positions, and B and E move respectively along B F and E G.
If B′ E′ G′ F′ be the new position of the face B E G F, it is
easy to see that the two wedge-shaped figures B E E′ B′ O C
and F G G′ F′ A D are exactly equal; this follows from the equality of their corresponding faces. Hence the volume of the
sheared figure must be equal to the volume of the right six-
face. Now let us suppose in addition that the face B′ E′ G′ F′
is again moved in its own plane into the position B″ E″ G″ F″,
so that B′ and E′ move along B′ E′ and F′ G′ respectively.
Then the slant wedge-shaped figures B′ B″ F″ F′ A O and
E′ E″ G″ F′ D C will again be equal, and the volume of the
six-face B″ E″ G″ F″ A D C O obtained by this second shear will
be equal to the volume of the figure obtained by the first
shear, and therefore to the volume of the right six-face. But
by means of two shears we can move the face B E G F to any
position in its plane, B″ E″ G″ F″, in which its sides remain
parallel to their former position. Hence the volume of a six-
face will remain unchanged if, one of its faces, O C D A, remaining fixed, the opposite face, B E G F, be moved anywhere
parallel to itself in its own plane. We thus find that the
volume of a six-face formed by three pairs of parallel planes
is equal to the product of the area of one of its faces and the
perpendicular distance between that face and its parallel.
For this is the volume of the right six-face into which it may
be sheared; and, as we have seen, shear does not alter volume.

The knowledge thus gained of the volume of a six-face
bounded by three pairs of parallel faces, or of a so-called
parallelepiped, enables us to find the volume of an *oblique
cylinder*. A right cylinder is the figure generated by any area
moving parallel to itself in such wise that any point P moves
along a line P P′ at right angles to the area (Fig. 71). The volume of a right cylinder is the product of its height P P′ and the

generating area. For we may suppose that volume to be the sum of a number of elementary right six-faces whose bases, as at P, may be taken so small that they will ultimately completely fill the area A C B D, and whose heights are all equal to P P'.

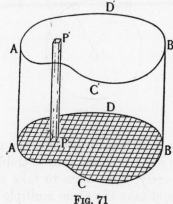

Fig. 71

We obtain an oblique cylinder from the above right cylinder by moving the face A' C' B' D' parallel to itself anywhere in its own plane. But such a motion will only shear the elementary right six-faces, such as P P', and so not change their volume. Hence the volume of an oblique cylinder is equal to the product of its base, and the perpendicular distance between its faces.

§14. *On the Measurement of Angles*

Hitherto we have been concerned with quantities of area and quantities of volume; we must now turn to quantities of *angle*. In our chapter on Space (p. 60) we have noted one method of measuring angles; but that was a merely relative method, and did not lead us to fix upon an absolute unit. We might, in fact, have taken any opening of the compasses for unit angle, and determined the magnitude of any other angle by its ratio to this angle. But there is an absolute unit which naturally suggests itself in our measurement of angles, and one which we must consider here, as we shall frequently have to make use of it in our chapter on Position.

Let o A B (Fig. 72) be any angle, and let a circle of radius a be described about o as centre to meet the sides of this angle

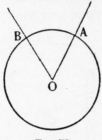

FIG. 72

in A and B. Then if we were to double the angle A O B, we should double the arc A B; if we were to treble it, we should treble the arc; shortly, if we were to take any multiple of the angle, we should take the same multiple of the arc. We may thus state that angles at the centre of a circle vary as the arcs on which they stand. Hence if θ and θ' be two angles, which are subtended by arcs s and s' respectively, the ratio of θ to θ' will be the same as that of s to s'. Now suppose θ' to represent four right angles; then s' will be the entire circumference, or, in our previous notation, $2\pi a$. We have thus—

$$\frac{\theta}{\text{four right angles}} = \frac{s}{2\pi a}.$$

Now it is extremely convenient to choose a unit angle which shall be independent of the circle upon which we measure our arcs. We should obtain such an independent unit if we took the arc subtended by it equal to the radius of the circle or if we took $s = a$. In this case our unit equals $\frac{1}{2\pi}$ of four right angles, $= \frac{1}{\pi}$ of two right angles, $= .636$ of a right angle approximately.

Thus we see that the angle subtended at the centre of any circle by an arc equal to the radius is a constant fraction of a right angle.

If this angle be chosen as the unit, we deduce from the proportion θ is to θ' as s is to s', that θ must be to unity as s is to the radius a; or:—

$$s = a\theta.$$

Thus, if we choose the above angle as our unit of angle, the measure of any other angle will be the ratio of the arc it subtends from the centre to the radius; but we have seen (p. 116) that the arcs subtended from the centre in different circles by equal angles are in the ratio of the radii of the respective circles. Hence the above measurement of angle is *independent of the radius of the circle upon which we base our measurement.* This is the primary property of the so-called *circular measurement* of angles, and it is this which renders it of such great value.

The *circular measure* of any angle is thus the ratio of the arc it subtends from the centre of any circle to the radius of the circle. It follows that the circular measure of four right angles is the ratio of the whole circumference to the radius, or equals $\dfrac{2\pi a}{a}$; that is, equals 2π. The circular measure of two right angles will then be π, of one right angle $\dfrac{\pi}{2}$, of three right angles $\dfrac{3\pi}{2}$, and so on.

§15. *On Fractional Powers*

Before we leave the subject of quantity it will be necessary to refer once more to the subject of powers which we touched upon in our chapter on Number (p. 16).

We there used a^n as a symbol signifying the result of multiplying a by itself n times. From this definition we easily deduce the following identity:—

$$a^n \times a^p \times a^q \times a^r = a^{n+p+q+r}.$$

For the left-hand side denotes that we are first to multiply a by itself n times, and then multiply this by a^p, or a multiplied by itself p times, and so on. Hence we may write the left-hand side—

$$(a \times a \times a \times a \ldots \text{to } n \text{ factors})$$
$$\times (a \times a \times a \times a \ldots \text{to } p \text{ factors})$$
$$\times (a \times a \times a \times a \ldots \text{to } q \text{ factors})$$
$$\times (a \times a \times a \times a \ldots \text{to } r \text{ factors}).$$

But this is obviously equal to $(a \times a \times a \times a \times \ldots$ to $n + p + q + r$ factors), or to $a^{n+p+q+r}$.

If b be such a quantity that $b^n = a$, b is termed an nth *root* of a, and this is written symbolically $b = \sqrt[n]{a}$. Thus, since $8 = 2^3$, 2 is a 3rd, or cube root of 8. Or, again, since $243 = 3^5$, 3 is termed a 5th root of 243.

Now we have seen at the conclusion of our first chapter that we can often learn a very great deal by extending the meaning of our terms. Let us now see if we cannot extend the meaning of the symbol a^n. Does it cease to have a meaning when n is a fraction or negative? Obviously we cannot multiply a quantity by itself a fractional number of times, nor can we do so a negative number of times. Hence the old meaning of a^n, where n is a positive integer, becomes sheer nonsense when we try to adapt it to the case of n being fractional or negative. Is then a^n in this latter case meaningless?

In an instance like this we are thrown back upon the results of our definition, and we endeavour to give to our symbol such a meaning that it will satisfy these results. Now the fundamental result of our theory of integer powers is that—

$$a^{n+p+q+r+} \ldots = a^n \times a^p \times a^q \times a^r \times \ldots$$

This will obviously be true however many quantities, n, p, q, r, we take. Now let us suppose we wish to interpret $a^{\frac{l}{m}}$ where $\frac{l}{m}$ is a fraction. We begin by assuming it satisfies the above relation, and in order to arrive at its meaning we suppose that $n = p = q = r = \ldots = \frac{l}{m}$, and that there are m such quantities.   Then

$$n + p + q + r = m \times \frac{l}{m} = l;$$

and we find $a^l = a^{\frac{l}{m}} \times a^{\frac{l}{m}} \times a^{\frac{l}{m}} \times \ldots$ to m factors

$$= (a^{\frac{l}{m}})^m.$$

Thus $a^{\frac{l}{m}}$ must be such a quantity that, multiplied by itself m times, it equals a^l. But we have defined above (p. 131, 132) an mth root of a^l to be such a quantity that, multiplied m times by itself, it equals a^l. Hence we say that $a^{\frac{l}{m}}$ is equal to an mth root of a^l; or, as it is written for shortness,—

$$a^{\frac{l}{m}} = \sqrt[m]{a^l}.$$

We have thus found a meaning for a^n when n is a fraction from the fundamental theorem of powers.

We can with equal ease obtain from the same theorem an intelligible meaning for a^n when n is a negative quantity.

We have $a^n \times a^p = a^{n+p}$. Now let us assume $p = -n$ in order to interpret a^{-n}. We find $a^n \times a^{-n} = a^{n-n} = a^0 = 1$ (by p. 29). Or dividing by a^n,

$$a^{-n} = \frac{1}{a^n};$$

that is to say, a^{-n} is the quantity which, multiplied by a^n, gives a product equal to unity. The former quantity is termed the *inverse* of the latter, or we may say that a^{-n} is the inverse of a^n. For example, what is the inverse of 4? Obviously 4 must be multiplied by $\frac{1}{4}$ in order that the product may be unity. Hence 4^{-1} is equal to $\frac{1}{4}$. Or, again, since $4 = 2^2$, we may say that 2^{-2} is the *inverse* of 4, or 2^2.

The whole subject of powers—integer, fractional, and negative—is termed the *Theory of Indices*, and is of no small importance in the mathematical investigation of symbolic quantity. Its discussion would, however, lead us too far beyond our present limits. It has been slightly considered here in order that the reader may grasp that portion of the following chapter in which fractional powers are made use of.

CHAPTER IV

Position

§1. *All Position is Relative*

THE reader can hardly fail to remember instances when he has been accosted by a stranger with some such question as: "Can you tell me where the 'George' Inn lies?"—"How shall I get to the cathedral?"—"Where is the London Road?" The answer to the question, however it may be expressed, can be summed up in the one word—*There*. The answer points out the *position* of the building or street which is sought. Practically the *there* is conveyed in some such phrase as the following: "You must keep straight on and take the first turning to the right, then the second to the left, and you will find the 'George' two hundred yards down the street."

Let us examine somewhat closely such a question and answer. "Where is the 'George'?" We may expand this into: "How shall I get from *here*" (the point at which the question is asked) "to the 'George'?" This is obviously the real meaning of the query. If the stranger were told that the "George" lies three hundred paces from the Town Hall down the High Street, the information would be valueless to the questioner unless he were acquainted with the position of the Town Hall or at least of the High Street. Equally idle would be the reply: "The 'George' lies just past the forty-second milestone on the London Road," supposing him ignorant of the whereabouts of the London Road.

Yet both these statements are in a certain sense answers to the question: "Where is the 'George'?" They would be the true method of pointing out the *there*, if the question had been asked in sight of the Town Hall or upon the London Road. We see, then, that the query, *Where?* admits of an infinite number of answers according to the infinite number of positions—or possible *heres*—of the questioner. The *where* always supposes a definite *here*, from which the desired position is to be determined. The reader will at once recognize that to ask, "Where is the 'George'?" without meaning, "Where is it with regard to some other place?" is a question which no more admits of an answer than this one: "How shall I get from the 'George' to anywhere?" meaning to nowhere in particular.

This leads us to our first general statement with regard to position. We can only describe the *where* of a place or object by describing how we can get at it from some other known place or object. We determine its *where* relative to a *here*. This is shortly expressed by saying that: All position is relative.

Just as the "George" has only position relative to the other buildings in the town, or the town itself relative to other towns, so a body in space has only position relative to other bodies in space. To speak of the position of the earth in space is meaningless unless we are thinking at the same time of the Sun or of Jupiter, or of a star—that is, of some one or other of the celestial bodies. This result is sometimes described as the "sameness of space." By this we only mean that in space itself there is nothing perceptible to the senses which can determine position.[1] Space is, as it were, a blank map into which we put our objects; it is the coexistence of objects in this map which enables us at any instant to distinguish one object from another. This process of distinguishing, which supposes at least *two* objects to be distinguished, is really determining a *this* and a *that*, a *here* and a *there*; it involves the conception of relativity of position.

[1] We shall return to this point later.

§2. *Position may be Determined by Directed Steps*

Let us turn from the question: "Where is the 'George'?" to the answer: "You must keep straight on and take the first turning to the right, then the second to the left, and you will find the 'George' 200 yards down the street."

The instruction "to keep straight on" means to keep in the street wherein the question has been asked, and in a direction ("straight on") suggested by the previous motion of the questioner, or by a wave of the hand from the questioned. Assuming for our present purpose that the streets are not curved, this amounts to: Keep a certain direction. How far? This is answered by the second instruction: Take the first turning on the right. More accurately we might say, if the first turning to the right were 150 yards distant: Keep this direction for 150 yards. Let this be represented in our figure (Fig. 73) by the step A B, where A is the position at which the

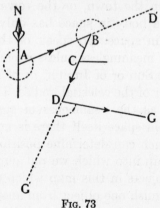

FIG. 73

question is asked. At B the questioner is to turn to the right and, according to the third instruction, he is to pass the first turning to the left at C and take the second at D. More accurately we might state the distance B D to be, say, 180 yards. Then we could combine our second and third instructions by saying: From B go 180 yards in a certain direction, namely, B D. To determine exactly what this direction B D is with regard to the first direction A B, we might use the following method. If the stranger did not change his direction at B, but went straight on for 180 yards, he would come to a point D'. Hence if we measured the angle D' B D between the street in which the question was asked and the first turning to the right, we should know the direction of B D and the position of D exactly. It would be determined by rotating B D' about B through the measured angle D' B D. If we adopt the same convention for the measurement of positive angles as we adopted for positive areas on p. 123, the angle D' B D is the angle greater than two right angles through which B D' must be rotated counter-clockwise in order to take it to the position B D. Let us term this angle D' B D for shortness β, then we may invent a new symbol $\{\beta\}$ to denote the operation: Turn the direction you are going in through an angle β counter-clockwise. If we use the symbol $\pi/2$ to denote an angle equal to a right angle, we have the following symbolic instructions:

$\{\ 0\ \}$ = Keep straight on.

$\{\ \pi/2\ \}$ = Turn at right angles to the left.

$\{\ \pi\ \}$ = Turn right round and go back.

$\{3\pi/2\}$ = Turn at right angles to the right.

Thus for a turning from A B to the left the angle of our symbolic operation will be less, for a turning from A B to the right greater, than two right angles.

If the directed person had gone to D' instead of to D, he would have walked 150 yards to B and then 180 yards to D'; he would thus have walked A B + B D', or 150 yards + 180 yards. In order to denote that he is not to continue straight on at B we introduce the operator of turning, namely $\{\beta\}$, before the 180 yards, and read $150 + \{\beta\}180$ as the instruction: Go 150 yards along some direction A B, and then, turning your direction through an angle β counter-clockwise, go 180 yards along this new direction.

We are now able to complete the symbolic expression of our instructions for finding the "George." The fourth instruction runs: Take a turning at D to the left and go 200 yards along the direction thus determined. Let D G′ represent 200 yards measured from D along B D produced, then we are to revolve D G′ through a certain angle G′ D G counter-clockwise, till it takes up the position D G. Then G will be the position of the "George." Let the angle G′ D G be represented by γ. Our final instruction may be then expressed symbolically by $\{\gamma\}200$.

Hence our total instruction may be written symbolically—

$$150 + \{\beta\}180 + \{\gamma\}200,$$

where the units are yards.

But we have not yet quite freed this symbolic instruction from any suggestion of direction as determined by streets; the first 150 yards are still to be taken along the *street* in which the question is asked. We can get rid of this street by supposing its direction determined by the angle which a clock-hand must revolve through counter-clockwise, to reach that direction, starting from some other fixed or chosen direction. For example, suppose the stranger to have a compass with him, and at A let A N be the direction of its needle. Then we might fix the position of the street A B by describing it as a direction so many degrees east of north, or still to preserve our counter-clockwise method of reckoning angles, we might determine it by the angle a which the needle would have to describe through west and south to reach the position A B. We should then interpret the notation $\{a\}150$: Walk 150 yards along a direction making an angle a with north measured through west.

Our answer expressed symbolically is now entirely cleared of any conception of streets. For,

$$\{a\}150 + \{\beta\}180 + \{\gamma\}200$$

is a definite instruction as to how to get from A to G quite independent of any local characteristics. It expresses the position of G with regard to A in a purely geometrical fashion, or by a series of *directed steps*. Expanded into ordinary English our symbols read: From a point A in a plane, take a step A B of 150 units in a direction making an angle a with a fixed direction, from B take a step B D of 180 units making an angle β with A B, and finally from D take a step D G of 200 units making an angle γ with B D. All the angles are to be measured counter-clockwise in the fashion we have described above.

§3. *The Addition of Directed Steps or Vectors*

If we now compare our figure with the symbolical instruction $\{a\}150 + \{\beta\}180 + \{\gamma\}200$, we see that $\{a\}150$ represents the step A B, when that step is considered to have not merely magnitude but also *direction*. Similarly B D and D G represent more than linear expressions for number—they are also *directed* steps. We shall then be at liberty to replace our symbolically expressed instruction

$$\{a\}150 + \{\beta\}180 + \{\gamma\}200$$

by the geometrical equivalent

$$A B + B D + D G,$$

provided we understand by the segments A B, B D, D G and the symbol + something quite different from our former con-

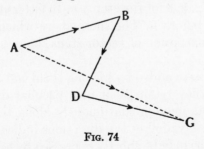

Fig. 74

ceptions (Fig. 74). We give a new and extended meaning to our quantity and to our addition.

A B + B D + D G no longer directs us to add the number of units in B D to that in A B and to the sum of these the number in D G, but it bids us take a step A B in a certain *direction*, then a step B D from the finish of the former step in another determined direction, and finally from the finish D of this second step a third directed step, D G. The entire operation brings us from A to G. Now it is obvious that we should also have got to G had we taken the directed step A G. Hence, if we give an extended meaning to the word "equal" and to its sign =, using them to mark the equivalence of the results of two operations, we may write

$$A G = A B + B D + D G,$$

and read this expression:—A G equals the sum of A B, B D and D G.

Steps such as we considered in our chapter on Quantity, which were magnitudes taken along any one straight line, are termed *scalar* steps, because they have relation only to some chosen scale of quantity. We add or subtract scalar steps by placing them end to end in *any* straight line (see §2 of Chapter III).

A step which has not only magnitude but *direction* is termed a *vector* step, because it *carries* us from one *position* in space to another. It is usual to mark by an arrow-head the sense in which we are to take this directed step. For example in Fig. 74 we are to step from A to B, and thus the arrow-head will point towards B for the step A B. In letters this is denoted by writing A before B. The method by which we have arrived at the conception of vector steps shows us at once how to add them.

Vector steps are added by placing them end to end in such fashion that they retain their own peculiar directions, and so that a point moving continuously along the zigzag thus formed will always follow the directions indicated by the arrow-heads. This may be shortly expressed by saying the steps are to be arranged in *continuous sense*. The sum of the vector steps is then the single directed step which joins the start of the zigzag thus formed to its finish. In Fig. 75 let *ab*, *cd*, *ef*, and *gh* be directed steps. Then let A B be drawn equal and parallel to *ab*; from B draw B C equal and parallel to *cd*, from C draw C D equal and parallel to *ef*, and finally from D draw D E equal and parallel to *gh*. We have drawn our zigzag so that the arrow-heads all have "a continuous sense." Hence the directed step A E is the sum of the four given vectors. If, for example, at C we had stepped C D′, equal and parallel to *ef*, but on the opposite side of B C to C D, and then taken D′ E′, equal and parallel to *gh*, the reader will

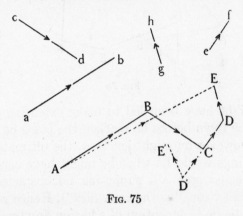

Fig. 75

remark at once that the arrow-heads in B C, C D′ and D′ E′ are not in continuous sense, or we have not gone in the proper direction at C.

Should the vector steps all have the same direction, the zigzag evidently becomes a straight line; in this case the vector steps are added precisely like scalar quantities; or, when vector steps may be looked upon as scalar, our extended conception of addition takes the ordinary arithmetical meaning.

We can now state a very important aspect of position in a plane; namely, if the position of G relative to A be denoted by the directed step or vector A G, it may also be expressed by the sum of any number of directed steps, the start of the first of such steps being at A and the finish of the last at G (see Fig. 76). We may write this result symbolically:—

$$A G = A B + B C + C D + D E + E F + F G.$$

It will be at once obvious that in our example as to finding the "George," the stranger might have been directed
by an entirely different set of instructions to his goal. In

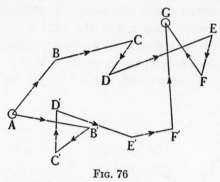

FIG. 76

fact, he might have been led to make extensive circuits in
or about the town before he reached the place he was seeking. But, however he might get to G, the ultimate result of
his wanderings would be what he might have accomplished
by the directed step A G supposing no obstacles to have
been in his way (or, "as the crow flies"). Hence we see that
with our extended conception of addition any two zigzags of
directed steps, A B C D E F G and A B′ C′ D′ E′ F′ G (which may
or may not contain the same number of component steps),
both starting in A and finishing in G, must be looked upon as
equivalent instructions; or, we must take

$$A B + B C + C D + D E + E F + F G = A G =$$
$$A B' + B' C' + C' D' + D' E' + E' F' + F' G.$$

In other words, two sets of directed steps must be held to
have an equal sum, when, their starts being the same, the
steps of both sets will, added vector-wise, have the same
finish.

Now let us suppose our stranger were unconsciously standing in front of the "George" when he asked his question as
to its whereabouts, and further let us suppose that the person who directed him gave him a perfectly correct instruction, but sent him by a properly chosen set of right and left

turnings a considerable distance round the town before bringing him back to the point A from which he had set out. In this case we must suppose the "George" not to be at the point G, but at the point A. The total result of the stranger's wanderings having brought him back to the place from which he started can be denoted by a zero step; or we must write (Fig. 76)—

$$A B + B C + C D + D E + E F + F G + G A = 0 \ldots \quad \text{(i)}$$

We may read this in words: The sum of vector steps which form the successive sides of a closed zigzag is zero. Now we have found above that—

$$A B + B C + C D + D E + E F + F G = A G \ldots \quad \text{(ii)}$$

Hence, in order that these two statements (i) and (ii) may be consistent, we must have − G A equal to A G, or

$$A G + G A = 0.$$

This is really no more than saying that if a step be taken from A to G, followed by another from G to A, the total operation will be a zero step. Yet the result is interesting as showing that if we consider a step from A to G as positive, a step from G to A must be considered *negative*. It enables us also to reduce subtraction of vectors to addition. For if we term the operation denoted by A B − D C a *subtraction* of the vectors A B and D C, since D C + C D = 0, the operation indicated amounts to adding the vectors A B and C D, or to A B + C D. Hence, to subtract two vectors, we reverse the sense of one of them and add.

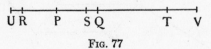

Fig. 77

The result A G + G A = 0 can at once be extended to any number of points lying on a straight line. Thus, if P Q R S T U V (Fig. 77) be a set of such points—

$$P Q + Q R + R S + S T + T U + U V + V P = 0.$$

For starting from P and taking in succession the steps indicated, we obviously come back to P, or have performed an operation whose result is equivalent to zero, or to remaining where we started.

§4. *The Addition of Vectors obeys the Commutative Law*

We can now prove that the commutative law holds for our extended addition (see p. 5). First, we can show that any two successive steps may be interchanged. Consider four successive steps, A B, B C, C D, and D E (Fig. 78). If at B instead of taking the step B C we took a step B H equal to C D in magnitude, sense, and direction, we could then get from H to D by taking the step H D. Now let B D be joined; then in the triangles B H D, D C B the angles at B and D are equal, because they are formed by the straight line B D falling on two parallel lines B H and C D; also the side B D is common, and B H is equal to C D. Hence it follows (see pp. 66–67) that these triangles are of the same shape and size, or H D is equal to B C; and again the angles B D H and D B C are equal, or H D and B C are parallel. Thus the step H D is equal to the step B C in direction, magnitude, and sense. We have then from the two methods of reaching D from B,

$$B C + C D = B D = B H + H D$$
$$= C D + B C$$

by what we have just proved.

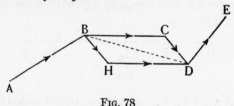

FIG. 78

Hence any two successive steps may be interchanged. By precisely the same reasoning as we have used on p. 11 we can show that if we may interchange any two successive steps of our zigzag we may interchange any two steps whatever by a series of changes of successive steps; that is, the order in which vectors are added is indifferent.

The importance of the geometry of vectors arises from the fact that many physical quantities can be represented as directed steps. We shall see in the succeeding chapter that velocities and accelerations are quantities of this character.

§5. *On Methods of Determining Position in a Plane*

It has been remarked (see p. 92) that scalar quantities may be treated as steps measured along a straight line. In this case we only require one point on this line to be given, and we can determine the relative position of any other by merely stating the magnitude of the intervening step. A line is occasionally spoken of as being a space of *one* dimension; in one-dimensioned space one point suffices to determine the relative position of all others.

When we consider, however, position in a plane, in order to determine the whereabouts of a point P with regard to another A (Fig. 79) we require to know not only the magnitude but the *direction* of the step A P. Hence what scalar steps are to one-dimensioned space, that are vector steps to plane space.

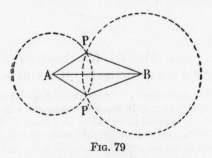

Fig. 79

In order to determine the *direction* of a step A P we must know at least one other point B in the plane. Space which requires two points to determine the position of a third is usually termed space of *two* dimensions. There are various methods in general use by which position in two-dimensioned space is determined. We shall mention a few of them, confining our remarks, however, to the plane, or to space of two dimensions which is of the same shape on both sides.[1]

(*a*) We may measure the distances between A and P and between B and P. If these distances are of scalar magnitude *r* and *r′* respectively, there will be two points corresponding to any two given values of *r* and *r′*; namely P and P′ the intersections of the two circles with centres at A and B and radii equal to *r* and *r′* respectively. We may distinguish these points as being one above, and the other below A B.[2] Only in the case of the circles touching will the two points coincide; if the circles do not meet, there will be no point.

If P moves so that for each of its positions with regard to A and B the quantities *r* and *r′* satisfy some definite relation, we shall obtain a continuous set of points in the plane or a curved line of some sort. For example, if we fasten the ends of a bit of string of length *l* to pins stuck into the plane of

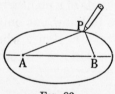

FIG. 80

the paper at A and B (Fig. 80), and then move a pencil about so that its point P always remains on the paper, and at the

---

[1] A "space of two dimensions . . . of the same shape on both sides" is essentially a meaningless concept. It becomes meaningful only when the space of two dimensions is considered as embedded in a space of three dimensions. The implications of the concept are perhaps more understandable when related to a *curved* two-dimensional space—analogous to the surface of a sphere—for in this case, quite obviously, the space is not "of the same shape on both sides": one side being concave, the other convex.—J.R.N.

[2] This sentence more correctly phrased should read "We may distinguish these points as being on opposite sides of A B." For the specifications "above" and "below" are equivocal when applied to positions in the plane.—J.R.N.

same time always keeps the string A P B taut round its point, the pencil will trace out that shadow of the circle which we have called an ellipse.

In this case $r + r' = $ A P $+$ P B $= l$, the constant length of the string. This relation $r + r' = l$ is an equation between the scalar quantities r, r' and l, which holds for every point on the ellipse, and expresses a metric property of the curve with regard to the points A and B.

If on the other hand we cause P to move so that the difference of A P and B P is a constant length $(r - r' = l)$, then P will trace out the curve we have termed the hyperbola. We can cause P to move in this fashion by means of a very simple bit of mechanism. Suppose a rod B L (Fig. 81) capable of revolving about one of its ends B; let a string of given length be fastened to the other end L and to the fixed point A. Then if, as the rod is moved round B, the string be held taut to

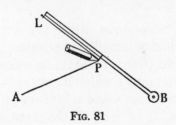

Fig. 81

the rod by a pencil point P, the pencil will trace out the hyperbola. For since L P $+$ P A equals a constant length, namely that of the string, and L P $+$ P B equals a constant length, namely that of the rod, their difference or P A $-$ P B is equal to the constant length which is the difference of the string and the rod.

The points A and B are termed in the cases of both ellipse and hyperbola the *foci*. The name arises from the following interesting property. Suppose a bit of polished watch spring were bent into the form of an ellipse so that its flat side was turned towards the foci of the ellipse; then if a hot body were placed at one focus B (Fig. 82), all the rays of heat or light radiated from B which fell upon the spring would be collected,

Fig. 82

or, as it is termed, "focussed" at A; hence A would be a much brighter and hotter point than any other within the ellipse (B of course excepted). The name *focus* is from the Latin, and means a fireplace or hearth. This property of the arc of an ellipse or hyperbola, that it collects rays radiating from one focus in the other, depends upon the fact that A P and P₍B make equal angles with the curve at P. This geometrical relation corresponds to a physical property of rays of heat and light; namely, that they make the same angle with a reflecting surface when they reach it and when they leave it.

A third remarkable curve, which is easily obtained from this our first method of considering position, is the lemniscate of James Bernoulli (from the Latin *lemniscus*, a ribbon). It is traced out by a point P which moves so that the rectangle under its distances from A and B is always equal to the area of a given square [1] ($r \cdot r' = c^2$). If the given square is greater than the square on half A B, it is obvious that P can never cross between A and B; if it is equal to the square on half A B, the lemniscate becomes a figure of eight; while if it is less, the curve breaks up into two loops.[2] In Figure 83 a series

[1] The explanation is somewhat obscure. What is meant by "the rectangle under its distances" is the area of the rectangle, the base of which is one distance and the altitude the other distance.—J.R.N.

[2] Thus if

$$r \cdot r' > \left(\frac{AB}{2}\right)^2 \quad \text{the corresponding lemniscate is}$$

$$r \cdot r' = \left(\frac{AB}{2}\right)^2 \quad " \qquad " \qquad " \qquad "$$

$$r \cdot r' < \left(\frac{AB}{2}\right)^2 \quad " \qquad " \qquad " \qquad "$$

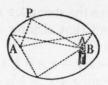

—J.R.N.

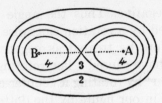

FIG. 83

of lemniscates are represented. A set of curves obtained by varying a constant, like the given square in the case of the lemniscate, is termed a *family of curves*. Such families of curves constantly occur in the consideration of physical problems.

§6. *Polar Co-ordinates*

(β) The points A and B (Fig. 84) determine a line whose direction is A B. If we know the length A P and the angle B A P, we shall have a means of finding the position of P. Let r be the number of linear units in A P and θ the number of angular units in B A P, where r and θ may of course be fractions.[1] In measuring the angle θ we shall adopt the same convention as we have employed in discussing areas (see p. 123); namely, if a line at first coincident with A B were to start

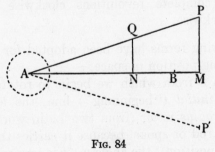

FIG. 84

from that position, and supposed pivoted at A to rotate counter-clockwise till it coincided with A P, it would trace out the angle θ. Angles traced out clockwise will like areas

---

[1] Not merely fractions, but any real number, or as Clifford says: "quantity."—J.R.N.

be considered negative. Thus the angle B A P' below A B would be obtained by a rotation clockwise from A B to A P', and must therefore be treated as negative. On the other hand, we might have caused a line rotating about A to take up the position A P' by rotating it counter-clockwise through an angle marked in our figure by the dotted arc of a circle. Further we might obviously have reached A P by a line rotating about A clockwise, and might thus represent the position of P by a negative angle. But even after we had got to P we might cause our line to rotate about A a complete number of times either clockwise or counter-clockwise, and we should still be at the end of any such number of complete revolutions in the same position A P.

We have then the following four methods of rotating a line about A from coincidence with A B to coincidence with A P:—

(i) Counter-clockwise from A B to A P.

(ii) Clockwise from A B to A P.

(iii) The first of these combined with any number of complete revolutions clockwise or counter-clockwise.

(iv) The second of these combined with any number of complete revolutions clockwise or counter-clockwise.

The following terms have been adopted for this method of determining position in space:—

The line A B from which we begin to rotate our line is termed the *initial* ("beginning") line; the length A P is termed the *radius vector* (from two Latin words signifying the carrying rod or spoke, because it carries the point P to the required position); the angle B A P is termed the *vectorial angle*, because it is traced out by the radius vector in moving from A B to the required position A P; A is termed the *pole*, because it is the end of the axis about which we may suppose the spoke to turn. Finally A P $(= r)$ and the angle B A P $(= \theta)$ are termed the *polar co-ordinates* of the point P, because they regulate the position of P relative to the pole A and the initial line A B.

§7. *The Trigonometrical Ratios*

If P M be a perpendicular dropped from P on A B, the ratios of the sides of the right-angled triangle P A M have for the purpose of abbreviation been given the following names:—

$\dfrac{P\,M}{A\,P}$, or the ratio of the perpendicular to the hypothenuse,

is termed the *sine* of the angle B A P.

$\dfrac{A\,M}{A\,P}$, or the ratio of the base to the hypothenuse, is termed

the *cosine* of the angle B A P.

$\dfrac{P\,M}{A\,M}$, or the ratio of the perpendicular to the base, is termed

the *tangent* of the angle B A P.

$\dfrac{A\,M}{P\,M}$, or the ratio of the base to the perpendicular, is termed

the *cotangent* of the angle B A P.

If θ be the scalar magnitude of the angle B A P these ratios are written for shortness, *sin θ, cos θ, tan θ*, and *cot θ*, respectively. Let us take any other point Q on A P, and drop Q N perpendicular to A B, then the triangles Q A N, P A M are of the same shape (see p. 99), and thus the ratios of their corresponding sides are equal. It follows from this that the ratios sine, cosine, tangent, and cotangent for the triangles Q A N and P A M are the same. Hence we see that sin θ, cos θ, tan θ, and cot θ are independent of the position of P in A P; they are ratios which depend only on the magnitude of the *angle* B A P or θ. They are termed (from two Greek words meaning *triangle-measurement*) the trigonometrical ratios of the angle θ. The discussion of trigonometrical ratios, or

Trigonometry, forms an important element of pure mathematics. The names of the trigonometrical ratios themselves are derived from an older terminology which connected these ratios with the figure supposed to be presented by an archer whose bow string was placed against his breast.[1]

§8. *Spirals*

Let us suppose the spoke A P (Fig. 85) to revolve about the pole A, and as it revolves let the point P move along the spoke in such fashion that the magnitude *r* of A P is always definitely related in some chosen manner to the magnitude θ of B A P. Then if P be taken as the point of a pencil it will mark out a curved line on the plane of the paper. Such a curved line is

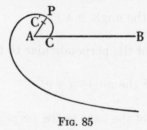

Fig. 85

termed a *polar curve* or *spiral,* the latter name from a Greek word denoting the coil, as of a snake, to which some of these curves may be considered to bear resemblance.

One of the most interesting of these spirals was invented by Conon of Samos (*fl.* b.c. 250), but its chief properties having been discussed by Archimedes, it is usually called by his name. The spiral of Archimedes is defined in the following simple manner. As the spoke A P moves uniformly round the pole the point P moves uniformly along the spoke. Let

---

[1] In our figure the angle B A P has been taken *less* than a right angle, it may have any magnitude whatever. It has been found useful to establish a convention with regard to the *signs* of the perpendicular P M and the base A M. P M is considered positive when it falls above, but negative when it falls below the initial line A B; A M is considered positive when M falls to the right, but negative when it falls to the left of A. The reader will understand the value of this convention better after examining §§ 11, 12.

c be the position of P when the spoke coincides with the
starting line A B, and let A C contain a units of length. Then
if P be the position of the pencil-point when the spoke has
described an angle B A P containing θ units of angle, and if
A c′ be measured along A P equal to A C, the point will have
described the distance c′ P while the spoke was turning
through the angle C A P. But since the point and spoke are
moving uniformly, the distance c′ P must be proportional
to the angle C A P, or their ratio must be an unchangeable
quantity for all distances and angles. Let b be the distance
traversed by the point along the spoke while it turns through
unit angle, then c′ P must be equal to the number of units
in C A P multiplied by b. Using r to denote the magnitude of
A P we have

$$c′\ P = b \times \theta, \text{ but } c′\ P = r - a;$$

thus:
$$r = a + b\theta.$$

This relation between r and θ is termed the polar *equation*
to the spiral.

The following easily constructed apparatus will enable us
to draw a spiral of Archimedes. D E F (Fig. 86) is a circular disc

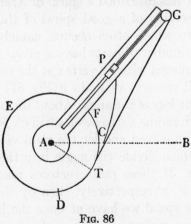

FIG. 86

of chosen radius; upon the edge of this disc is cut a groove. To
the centre A of the disc is attached a rod or spoke which can
be revolved about A as a pole; at the other end of this rod is

a small grooved wheel or pulley G. A string is then fastened to some point D in the groove of the disc, and passing round the pulley G is attached to a small block P which holds a pencil and is capable of sliding in a slot in the spoke. If this block be fastened by a piece of elastic to A, the string from P to G and then from G to the groove on the disc will remain taut. Now supposing the disc to be held firmly pressed against the paper, and the spoke A G to be turned about A counter-clockwise, the pencil P will describe the required spiral. For the string touching the disc in the point T the figure G A T always remains of the same size and shape as we turn the spoke about the pole; hence the length of string G T is constant. Thus if a length of string represented by the arc D T be wound on to the disc as we turn the spoke from the position A B to the position A P, the length P G (since the length G T always remains the same) must lose a length equal to D T as P moves from C to P. But the amount of string D T wound on to the disc is proportional to the angle through which the spoke A P has been turned; hence the point P must have moved towards G through a distance proportional to this angle, or it has described a spiral of Archimedes.

Once in possession of a good spiral of this kind we can solve a problem which often occurs, namely to divide an angle into any number of parts having given ratios.[1] Let the given angle be placed with its vertex at the pole of the spiral and let the radii vectores A C and A P (Fig. 87) be those which coincide with the legs of the angle. About the pole A describe a circular arc with radius A C to meet A P in C'. Now let us suppose the problem solved and let the radii vectores A D, A E, A F be those which divide the angle into the required proportional parts. If these radii vectores meet the circular arc C C' in D', E', F' respectively, then by the fundamental property of the spiral we have at once the lines D' D, E' E, F' F, C' P in the same ratio as the angles C A D, C A E, C A F,

---

[1] It is interesting to note that the trisection of an angle, one of the famous problems of classical antiquity, while not possible using ruler and compass, can be accomplished with the aid of the spiral of Archimedes.—J.R.N.

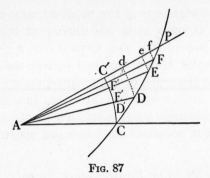

FIG. 87

C A P. Thus if we measure lengths A d, A e, A f equal to A D,
A E, A F respectively along A P, C' P will be divided in $d\,e\,f$ into
lengths which are proportional to the required angles. Conversely, if we were to divide C' P into segments C' d, $d\,e$, $e\,f$,
and f P in the same ratio as the required angular division, we
should obtain lengths A d, A e, A f, which would be the radii
of circles with a common centre A cutting the spiral in the
required points of angular division. The spiral of Archimedes
thus enables us to reduce the division of an angle in any
fashion to the like division of a line.

Now the division of a line in any fashion, that is, into a set
of segments in any given ratio, is at once solved so soon as we
have learnt by the aid of a pair of compasses or a "set square"
to draw parallel lines. Thus suppose we require to divide
the line C' P (Fig. 88) into segments in the ratio of 3 to 5 to 4;
we have only to mark off along any line through C', say C' Q,
steps C' R, R S, S T placed end to end and containing 3, 5, and
4 units of any kind respectively. If the finish of the last step

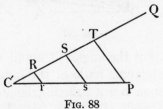

FIG. 88

T be joined to P and the parallels R r, S s to T P through R and
S be drawn to meet C' P in r and s, then C' P will be divided

in r and s into segments in the required ratio of 3 to 5 to 4. This follows at once from our theory of triangles of the same shape (see p. 99). For, since R c′ r, s c′ s, and T c′ P are such triangles, they have their corresponding sides proportional, and the truth of the proposition is obvious.

A spiral of Archimedes accurately cut in a metal or ivory plate is an extremely useful addition to the ordinary contents of a box of so-called mathematical instruments.

§9. *The Equiangular Spiral*

Another important spiral was invented by Descartes, and is termed from two of its chief properties either the *equiangular* or the *logarithmic spiral.*

Let B O A (Fig. 89) be a triangle with a small angle at O, and whose sides O A and O B are of any not very greatly different lengths. Upon O B and upon the opposite side of it to A construct a triangle B O C of the same shape as the triangle A O B,

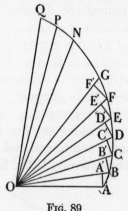

FIG. 89

and in such wise that the angles at B and A are equal. Then upon O C place a triangle C O D of the same shape as either B O C or A O B; upon O D a fourth triangle D O E, again of the same shape; upon O E a fifth triangle, and so on. We thus ultimately form a figure consisting of a number of triangles A O B, B O C, C O D, D O E, &c., of the same shape, all placed with one of their equal angles at o, and in such fashion that each pair has a common side consisting of two non-corresponding sides (that is, of sides not opposite to equal angles). The points A B C D E, &c., will form the angles of a polygonal line, and if the angles at o are only taken small enough, the sides of this polygon will appear to form a continuous curved line. This curved line, to which we can approach as closely as we please by taking the angles at o smaller and smaller, is termed an *equiangular spiral*. It derives its name from the following property,—A B, B C, C D, &c., being corresponding sides of triangles of the same shape, make equal angles O B A, O C B, O D C, &c., with the corresponding sides O B, O C, O D, &c.; but when the angles at o are taken very small A B, B C, C D, &c., will appear as successive elements of the curved line or spiral. Hence the arc of the spiral meets all rays from the pole o at the same constant angle.

Let us now endeavour to find the relation between any radius vector O P $(= r)$ and the vectorial angle A O P $(= \theta)$.

Since all our triangles A O B, B O C, C O D, &c., are of the same shape, their corresponding sides must be proportional (see p. 99); or,

$$\frac{O B}{O A} = \frac{O C}{O B} = \frac{O D}{O C} = \frac{O E}{O D} = \frac{O F}{O E} = \&c.$$

Each of these equal ratios will therefore have the same scalar value; let us denote that value by the symbol μ. Then we must have

$$O B = \mu \cdot O A; \quad O C = \mu \cdot O B; \quad O D = \mu \cdot O C; \quad \&c.$$

Or, $O B = \mu \cdot O A$; $O C = \mu^2 \cdot O A$; $O D = \mu^3 \cdot O A$, and so on. Hence if O N be the radius vector which occurs after n equal angles are taken at o, we must have

$$O N = \mu^n \cdot O A.$$

Now let the very small angles at o be each taken equal to some small part of the unit angle; thus we might take them

$\frac{1}{100}$ or $\frac{1}{1000}$ of the unit angle. We will represent this fraction of the unit angle by $1/b$, where we may suppose b a
whole number for greater simplicity. Further let us use
λ to denote the bth power of μ, or $\lambda = \mu^b$. With the notation
explained on p. 131 we then term μ a bth root of λ, and write
$\mu = \lambda^{1/b}$.

Hence finally we have $\text{O N} = \text{O A} \cdot \lambda^{n \times 1/b}$, or in words: The
base of the $(n + 1)^{\text{th}}$ equal-shaped triangle placed about O
is equal to the base of the first multiplied by a certain quantity λ raised to the power of n-times the quantity $1/b$ which
expresses the magnitude of the equal angles at O in units of
angle.

Now let the spoke or ray O P fall within the angle which is
formed by the successive rays O N and O Q of the system of
equal-shaped triangles round O. Then O N makes an angle
n-times $1/b$, and O Q an angle $(n + 1)$-times $1/b$ with O A.
Hence the angle A O P, or θ, must lie in magnitude between
n/b and $(n + 1)/b$. Similarly the magnitude of O P must lie
between those of O N and O Q. Now by sufficiently decreasing
the angles at O we can approach nearer and nearer to the
form of the spiral, and the ray O P must always lie between
two successive rays of our system of triangles. The angle θ,
which will thus always lie between n/b and $(n + 1)/b$, can
only differ from either of them by a quantity less than $1/b$.
If then b be taken large enough, or the equal angles at O
small enough fractions of the unit angle, this difference $1/b$
can be made vanishingly small. In this case we may say
that *in the limit* the angle θ becomes equal to n/b and the
ray O P equal to O N or O Q, which will thus be ultimately
equal. Hence $\text{O P} = \text{O A} \cdot \lambda^{n/b} = \text{O A} \cdot \lambda^\theta$, or in words: If a
ray O P of the equiangular spiral make an angle A O P with
another ray O A, the ratio of O P to O A is equal to a certain
number λ raised to the power of the quantity θ which expresses the magnitude of the angle A O P in units of angle.

If a and r be the numbers which express the magnitudes
of O A and O P, we have $r = a\lambda^\theta$. This is termed the *polar
equation* of the spiral.

We proceed to draw some important results from a consideration of this spiral. The reader will at once observe that the ratio of any pair of rays O P and O Q (Fig. 90) is equal to the ratio of any other pair which include an equal angle, for the ratio of any pair of rays depends only on the included angle. Further, if we wanted to multiply the ratio of any two quantities p and q by the ratio of two other quantities r and s we might proceed as follows: Find rays of the equiangular spiral O P, O Q, O R, O S containing the same number of linear units as p, q, r, s contain units of quantity (see p. 91) and,

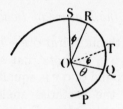

FIG. 90

let θ be the angle between the first pair, ϕ the angle between the second pair.

Then

$$\frac{O Q}{O P} = \lambda^\theta, \text{ and } \frac{O S}{O R} = \lambda^\phi;$$

whence it follows that $\frac{O Q}{O P} \times \frac{O S}{O R} = \lambda^\theta \times \lambda^\phi = \lambda^{\theta+\phi}$, or is equal to the ratio of any pair of rays which include an angle $\theta + \phi$. Thus if the angle Q O T be taken equal to ϕ, and O T be the corresponding ray of the spiral, $\frac{O T}{O P} = \lambda^{\theta+\phi}$, and is a ratio equal to the product of the given ratios. Hence to find the product of ratios we have only to add the angles between pairs of rays in the given ratios, and the ratio of any two rays including an angle equal to the sum will be equal to the required product. Thus the equiangular spiral enables us to *replace multiplication by addition*. This is an extremely valuable substitution, as it is much easier to add than to multiply.

Since $\dfrac{O\,Q}{O\,R}$ divided by $\dfrac{O\,S}{O\,R} = \lambda^\theta$ divided by $\lambda^\phi = \lambda^{\theta-\phi}$, it is obvious that we may in like fashion replace the division of two ratios by the subtraction of two angles. A set of quantities like the angles at the pole of an equiangular spiral which enables us to replace multiplication and division by addition and subtraction is termed a *table of logarithms*. Since the equiangular spiral acts as a graphical table of logarithms, it is frequently termed the *logarithmic spiral*.

§10. *On the Nature of Logarithms*

Since in the logarithmic spiral $O\,P = O\,A \times \lambda^\theta$, where θ is equal to the angle A O P, we note that as θ increases, or as the ray O P revolves round O, O P is equally multiplied during equal increments of the vectorial angle A O P. When one quantity depends upon another in such fashion that the first is equally multiplied for equal increments of the second, it is said to *grow at logarithmic rate*. This logarithmic rate is measured by the ratio of the growth of the first quantity for unit increment of the second quantity to the magnitude of the first quantity before it started this growth.

Let us endeavour to apply this to our equiangular spiral. Suppose A O B, B O C, C O D, &c. to be as before the triangles by means of which we construct it (see Fig. 89), the angles at O being all equal and very small. Along O B measure a length O A' equal to O A; along O C, a length O B' equal to O B; along O D, a length O C' equal to O C, and so on. Then A' B, B' C, C' D, &c., will be the successive growths as a ray is turned successively from O A to O B, from O B to O C, and so on. Join A A', B B', C C', &c. Now the triangles A O B, B O C, C O D, &c., are all of the same shape; so too are the isosceles triangles A O A', B O B', C O C', &c. Hence the differences of the corresponding members of these sets, A A' B, B B' C, C C' D, &c., must also be of equal shape, and thus their corresponding sides proportional. It follows then that the lengths

A′ B, B′ C, C′ D, &c., are in the same ratio as the lengths
A′ A, B′ B, C′ C, &c., or again as the lengths
O A, O B, O C, &c.

Whence we deduce that

$$\frac{A'\,B}{O\,A} = \frac{B'\,C}{O\,B} = \frac{C'\,D}{O\,C} = \&c.$$

Or, the growth A′ B is always in a constant ratio to the growing quantity O A.

Now, if the angles at O be very small, the line A A′ will
practically coincide with the arc of a circle with centre O
and radius equal to O A. Hence (see pp. 130, 131) A A′ will ultimately equal O A × the angle A O A′, while the angle at A′
will ultimately be equal to a right angle.

Further, the ratio of A′ B to A A′ remains the same for all
the little triangles A A′ B, B B′ C, C C′ D, &c. It is in each case
the ratio of the *base* to the *perpendicular* when we look upon
these triangles with regard to the equal angles A B A′, B C B′,
C D C′, &c. Now these are the angles of the triangles which
give the spiral its name. Let any one of them, and therefore
all of them, be equal to *a*. By definition the cotangent of an
angle (see p. 151) is equal to the ratio of the base to the perpendicular.

Hence

$$\cot a = \frac{A'B}{A\,A'} = \frac{A'\,B}{O\,A \times \text{angle}\,A\,O\,A'},$$

or

$$\frac{A'\,B}{O\,A} = \text{angle}\ A\,O\,A' \times \cot a.$$

Now A B denotes the growth for an angle A O A′, supposed
very small; whence it follows that the *logarithmic rate*, or
the ratio of the growth to the growing quantity for *unit* angle,
is equal to cot *a*. Thus the logarithmic rate for the growth of
the ray of the equiangular or logarithmic spiral, as it describes equal angles about the pole, is equal to the cotangent
of the angle which gives its name to the spiral.

Let us suppose O A to be unit of length, then, since O P

$= \mathrm{O}\,\mathrm{A} \times \lambda^{\theta}$, the result $\mathrm{O}\,\mathrm{P}$ of revolving the ray $\mathrm{O}\,\mathrm{A}$ through an angle θ equal to unity will be λ, or λ is the result of making unity grow at logarithmic rate cot a.

Now let us denote by the symbol e the result of making unity grow at logarithmic rate unity during the description of unit angle. Then e will have some definite numerical value. This value is found, by a process of calculation into which we cannot enter here, to be nearly equal to 2.718. This means that, if while unit ray were turned through unit angle it grew at logarithmic rate unity, its total growth (1.718) would lie between eight and nine-fifths of its initial length. Since e is the result of turning unit ray through unit angle, and since the ray is equally multiplied for equal multiples of angle, e^{γ} must represent the result of turning unit ray through γ unit angles. Hitherto we have been concerned with unit ray growing at logarithmic rate unity; now let us suppose unity to grow at logarithmic rate γ; then it grows γ times as much as if it grew at logarithmic rate unity, or the result of turning unit ray through unit angle, while it grows at logarithmic rate γ, must be the same as if we spread $1/\gamma$ of this rate of growth over γ unit angles; that is, as if we caused unity to grow at logarithmic unity for γ unit angles, or e^{γ}. Hence e^{γ} denotes the result of making unit ray grow at logarithmic rate unity while it describes γ unit angles, or again of making unit ray grow at logarithmic rate γ while it describes a unit of angle.

Let us inquire what is the meaning of e^{γ} when γ is a commensurable fraction equal to s/t, s and t being integers. Let x be the as yet unknown result of turning unit ray through an angle equal to γ while it grows at unit logarithmic rate; then x^{t} will be the result of turning unit ray through t angles equal to γ while it grows at unit rate; but t angles equal to γ form an angle containing s units, or this result must be the same as the result of turning unity through an angle s while it grows at logarithmic rate unity. Thus we have $x^{t} = e^{s}$. That is, x is a t-th root of e^{s}, or, as we write it, equal to $e^{s/t} = e^{\gamma}$. Thus e^{γ}, if γ be a commensurable fraction, is the result of

causing unit ray to grow at logarithmic rate unity through
an angle equal to γ, or as we have seen at logarithmic rate γ
through unit angle.

Now let us suppose it possible to find a commensurable
fraction γ equal to cot a; then the result of making unity
grow at logarithmic rate cot a as it is turned through unit
angle must be e^{γ}. But we have seen (see p. 162) that it is
equal to λ. Hence

$$\lambda = e^{\gamma}.$$

Further, the result of making unity grow at logarithmic
rate cot a as it is turned through an angle θ is λ^{θ}; or,

$$\lambda^{\theta} = e^{\gamma\theta}.$$

Thus we may write

$$\mathrm{O\,P} = \mathrm{O\,A} \cdot \lambda^{\theta} = \mathrm{O\,A} \cdot e^{\gamma\theta},$$

or with our previous symbols,

$$r = a \cdot e^{\gamma\theta}.$$

This is therefore the equation to our equiangular spiral
expressed in terms of the quantity e.

If we take a spiral in which a is the unit of length, and in
which cot a or γ is also unity, we find

$$r = e^{\theta}.$$

The symbol e^{θ} is then read the *exponential* of θ, and θ is
termed the *natural logarithm* of r. It is denoted symbolically
thus:—

$$\theta = \log_e r.$$

The quantity e is termed the *base* of the natural system of
logarithms. Our spiral would in this case form a graphical
table of *natural logarithms*.

Returning to the equation

$$r = a \cdot e^{\gamma\theta},$$

let us suppose γ so chosen that $e^{\gamma} = 10$; then γ will represent the angle through which unit ray must be turned in
order that, growing at unit logarithmic rate, it may in-

crease to ten units. Again taking a to be of unit length we find $r = e^{\gamma\theta} = 10^{\theta}$. θ is in this case termed the logarithm of r to the base 10, and this is symbolically expressed thus:—

$$\theta = \log_{10} r.$$

The spiral obtained in this case would form a graphical table of logarithms to the base 10. Such logarithms are those which are usually adopted for the purposes of practical calculation.

Natural logarithms were first devised by John Napier, who published his invention in 1614.[1] Logarithms to the base 10 are now used in all but the simplest numerical calculations which it is needful to make in the exact sciences; their value arises solely from the fact that addition and subtraction are easier operations than multiplication and division.

§11. *The Cartesian Method of Determining Position*

(γ) In order to determine the position of a point P_1 in space of two dimensions, we may draw the line B A B' (Fig. 91),

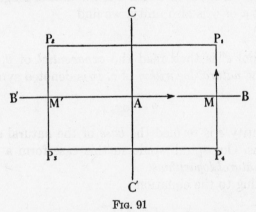

FIG. 91

joining the given points A B and another line C A C' at right angles to this through A. These will divide the plane into

---

[1] *Logarithmorum Canonis Descriptio*. 4to. Edinburgh, 1614.

four equal portions termed *quadrants*. Let P₁ M be a line drawn from the point P₁ (the position of which relative to A we wish to determine), parallel to C A and meeting B′ A B in M. Then we may state the following rule to get from A to P₁: Take a step A M from A on the line B′ A B, and then a step to the left at right angles to this equal to M P₁. Now a step like A M may be taken either forwards along A B or backwards along A B′. Precisely as before (see p. 92) we shall take + A M to mean a step *forwards* along A B, and − A M to mean a step A M′ *backwards* along A B′ through the same distance A M. Let us use the letter i to denote the operation, which we have represented by $(\pi/2)$ on p. 137. Thus applied to unit step it will signify: Step *forwards* in the direction of the previous step and from its finish unit distance, and then rotate this unit distance through a right angle counter-clockwise about the finish of the previous step. The operator i placed before a step, thus $i \cdot$ M P₁, will then be interpreted as follows: Step from M in the direction A B a distance equal to the length M P₁, and then rotate this step M P₁ about M counter-clockwise through a right angle. We are thus able to express symbolically the position of P₁ relative to A, or the step A P₁, by the relation

$$A\,P_1 = A\,M + i \cdot M\,P_1.$$

If we had to get to a point P₄ in the quadrant B A C′, instead of to P₁, we should have, instead of stepping forwards from M, to step *backwards* a distance M P₄, and then rotate this through a right angle counter-clockwise. The step backwards would be denoted by inserting a − sign as a reversing operation (see pp. 35, 36), and we should have

$$A\,P_4 = A\,M - i \cdot M\,P_4.$$

Next let us see how we should get to a point like P₂ in the quadrant C A B′, where P₂ is at a perpendicular distance P₂ M′ from A B′. First, we must take a step, A M′, backwards; this is denoted by − A M′; secondly, we must step *forwards* from M′ a distance M′ P₂; since this step is *forwards*, it will be towards A; thirdly, by applying the operation i to this step, we rotate it about M′ counter-clockwise through a right angle, and so reach P₂. Hence

$$\text{A P}_2 = -\text{ A M}' + i \cdot \text{M}' \text{ P}_2.$$

Finally, if we wish to reach P₃ in the quadrant B′ A C′, we must step backwards A M′, and then still further backwards a step M′ P₃, and lastly rotate this step counter-clockwise through a right angle. This will be expressed by

$$\text{A P}_3 = -\text{ A M}' - i \cdot \text{M}' \text{ P}_3.$$

Now let us suppose P₁, P₂, P₃, P₄, to be the four corners of a rectangular figure whose centre is at A and whose sides are parallel to B A B′ and C A C′. Let the number of units in A M be x, and the number in M P₁ be y, then we may represent the four steps which determine the positions of the P's relative to A as follows:—

$$\text{A P}_1 = x + iy \qquad\qquad \text{A P}_2 = -x + iy$$
$$\text{A P}_3 = -x - iy \qquad\qquad \text{A P}_4 = x - iy.$$

Here x and y are mere numbers, but, when we represent these numbers by steps on a line, the y-numbers are to be taken on a certain line at right angles to that line on which the x-numbers are taken. Thus the moment we represent our x and y numbers by lengths, they give us a means of determining position.

The quantities x and y might thus be used to determine the position of a point, if we supposed them to carry with them proper signs. Our general rule would then be to step forwards from A along A B a distance x, and then from the end of x a distance forwards equal to y; rotate this step y about the end of x counter-clockwise through a right angle, and the finish of y will then be the point determined by the quantities x, y. If x or y be negative, the corresponding forwards must be read: Step forwards a negative quantity, that is, step backwards. Thus:—

P₁, or position in the quadrant B A C is determined by x, y.

P₂	.	.	.	.	C A B′	.	.	$-x, y.$
P₃	.	.	.	.	B′ A C′	.	.	$-x, -y.$
P₄	.	.	.	.	C′ A B	.	.	$x, -y.$

The quantities x and y are termed the *Cartesian co-ordinates* of the point P, this method of determining the position

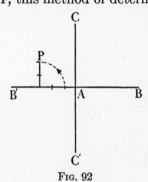

FIG. 92

of a point having been first used by Descartes. B A B′ (Fig. 92) and C A C′ are termed the co-ordinate *axes* of x and y respectively, while A is called the *origin* of co-ordinates. For example, let the Cartesian co-ordinates of a point be $(-3, 2)$. How shall we get at it from the origin A? If P be the point, we have A P $= -3 + i \cdot 2$. Hence we must step backwards 3 units; from this point step forwards 2 and rotate this step 2 about the extremity of the step 3 through a right angle counter-clockwise; we shall then be at the required point.

If P be determined by its Cartesian co-ordinates x and y, we might find a succession of points, P, by always taking a step y related in a certain invariable fashion to any step x which has been previously made.

Such a succession of points P, obtained by giving x every possible value, will form a line or curve, and the relation between x and y is termed its *Cartesian equation*.

As an instance of this, suppose that for every step x, we take a step y equal to the double of it. Then we shall have for our relation $y = 2x$, and our instructions to reach any point P of the series are $x + i \cdot 2x$. Suppose the quadrant

B A C (Fig. 93) divided into a number of little squares by lines parallel to the axes, and let us take the sides of these squares to

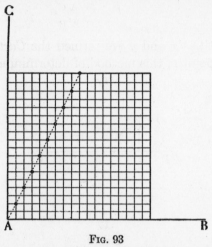

FIG. 93

be of unit length. Then if we take in succession $x = 1, 2, 3$, &c., we can easily mark off our steps. Thus: 1 along A B and then 2 to the left; 2 along A B and 4 to the left; 3 along A B and then 6 to the left; 4 along A B and then 8 to the left; 5 along A B and then 10 to the left, and so on. It will be obvious (by pp. 98, 99) that our points all lie upon a straight line through A, and however many steps we take along A B, followed by double steps perpendicular to it, we shall always arrive at a point on the same line. If we gave x negative values we should obtain that part of the line which lies in the third quadrant B' A C'. Hence we see that $y = 2x$ is the equation to a straight line which passes through A.

Let us take another example. Suppose that the rectangle

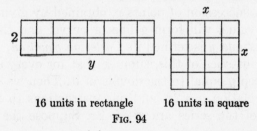

16 units in rectangle   16 units in square

FIG. 94

contained by y and a length of 2 units, always contains as many units of area as there are square units in x^2 (Fig. 94). Our relation in this case may be expressed by $2y = x^2$, and we have the following series of steps from A to points of the series:—

$$1 + i \cdot \tfrac{1}{2}, \qquad 2 + i \cdot 2, \qquad\qquad 3 + i \cdot \tfrac{9}{2},$$
$$4 + i \cdot 8, \qquad 5 + i \cdot \tfrac{25}{2}, \qquad 6 + i \cdot 18, \text{ &c.}$$

We can by means of our little squares easily follow out the operations above indicated; we thus find a series of points like those in the quadrant B A C of the figure. (See Fig. 95.) If, however, we had taken x equal to the negative quantities $-1, -2, -3, -4, -5, -6$, &c., we should have found precisely the same values for y, because we have seen that $(-a) \times (-a) = a^2 = (+a) \times (+a)$. These negative values for x give us a series of points like those in the quad-

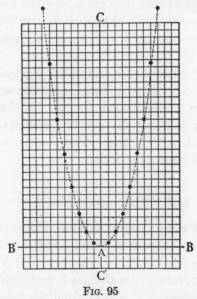

FIG. 95

rant B′ A C of the figure. It is impossible that any points of the series should lie below B A B′, because both negative and positive values for x give when squared a positive value for the step y, so that no possible x-step would give a negative y-step. The series of points obtained in this fashion are

found to lie upon a curve which is one of those shadows of a
circle which we have termed parabolas.

Hence we may say that $2y = x^2$ is the equation to a
parabola.

This method of plotting out curves is of great value, and
is largely used in many branches of physical investigation.
For example, if the differences of successive x-steps denote
successive intervals of time, and y-steps the corresponding
heights of the column of mercury in a barometer above some
chosen mean position, the series of points obtained will, if
the intervals of time be taken small enough, present the appearance of a curve. This curve gives a graphical representation of the variations of the barometer for the whole period
during which its heights have been plotted out. Barometric
curves for the preceding day are now given in several of the
morning papers. Heights corresponding to each instant of
time are in this case generally registered automatically by
means of a simple photographic apparatus.

The plotting out of curves from their Cartesian equations,
usually termed *curve tracing*, forms an extremely interesting
portion of pure mathematics. It may be shown that any
relation, which does not involve higher powers of x and y
than the second, is the equation to some one of the forms
taken by the shadow of a circle.

§12. *Of Complex Numbers*

We shall now return to our symbol of operation i, and inquire a little closer into its meaning. Let the point P (Fig. 96)
be denoted as before by A M $+ i \cdot$ M P, so that we should read
this result: Step from A to M along A B, and from M to P′ along
the same line (where M P′ = M P), finally rotate M P′ about M
counter-clockwise through a right angle; M P′ will then take
up the position M P. Now let M Q′ be taken equal to A P′,
then A M $+ i \cdot$ M Q′ will mean: Step from A to M and then
from M perpendicular to A M to the left through a distance,
M Q′, equal to A P′. Since however M Q′ = A P′ = A M + M P

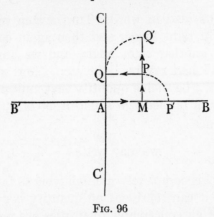

Fig. 96

$= \text{M P} + \text{P Q}'$, P Q$'$ must be equal to A M and we can read our operation

$$\text{A M} + i \cdot (\text{M P} + \text{P Q}')$$

which denotes two successive steps at right angles to A M, namely M P followed by the step P Q$'$. Suppose now we wished to rotate this latter step through a right angle counter-clockwise, we should have to introduce before it the symbol i, and M P $+ i \cdot$ P Q$'$ would signify the step M P followed by the step P Q at right angles to it to the left. Now P Q$'$ is equal to A M, and hence the result of this operation must bring us to Q, a point on A C which might have been reached by the simple operation $0 + i \cdot$ A Q. Thus we may put

$$0 + i \cdot \text{A Q} = \text{A M} + i \cdot (\text{M P} + i \cdot \text{P Q})$$
$$= \text{A M} + i \cdot \text{M P} + i \cdot i \cdot \text{P Q};$$

or, since the quantities A Q, A M, M P, and P Q here merely denote numerical magnitudes, and since as such A Q = M P and A M = P Q, we must have

$$0 = \text{A M} + i \cdot i \cdot \text{A M},$$

or $\qquad - \text{A M} = i \cdot i \cdot \text{A M}.$

Thus the operation i is of such a character that repeated twice it is equivalent to a mere reversor, or, as we may express it symbolically,

$$- 1 = i^2.$$

This may be read in words: Turn a step counter-clockwise through a right angle, and then again counter-clockwise through another right angle, and we have the same result as if we had reversed the step. Now we have seen (p. 132) that if x be such a quantity that multiplied by itself it equals a, x is termed the square root of a, and written $\sqrt{a}$. Hence since

$$i^2 = -1, \text{ we may write } i = \sqrt{-1}.$$

This symbol is completely unintelligible so far as *quantity* is concerned; it can represent no quantity conceivable, for the squares of all conceivable quantities are positive quantities. For this reason $\sqrt{-1}$ is sometimes termed an *imaginary quantity*. Treated however as a *symbol of operation* $\sqrt{-1}$ has a perfectly clear and real meaning; it is here an instruction to step forwards a unit length and then rotate this length counter-clockwise through a right angle.

Any expression of the form $x + \sqrt{-1}\, y$ is termed a *complex number*.

Let P be any point determined by the step A P = A M $+ \sqrt{-1}$ M P, and let r, x, y be the numerical values of the lengths A P, A M, and P M. It follows from the right-angled triangle P A M that $r^2 = x^2 + y^2$. The quantity r is then termed the *modulus* of the complex number $x + \sqrt{-1}\, y$.

Further let the angle M A P contain θ units of angle; then

$$\sin\theta = \frac{\text{P M}}{\text{A P}} = \frac{y}{r}, \quad \cos\theta = \frac{\text{A M}}{\text{A P}} = \frac{x}{r},$$

$$\text{or} \quad y = r\sin\theta, \quad x = r\cos\theta.$$

The angle θ is termed the *argument* of the complex number. Here r and θ are the polar co-ordinates of P, and we are thus able to connect them with the Cartesian co-ordinates; they are respectively the modulus and argument of the complex number which may be formed from the Cartesian coordinates. Since r is merely numerical we may write the complex number $x + \sqrt{-1}\, y$ in the form $r \cdot (\cos\theta + \sqrt{-1}$ $\sin\theta)$, or as the product of its modulus and the operator

$$\cos\theta + \sqrt{-1}\, \sin\theta,$$

which depends solely on its argument θ. Hence we may interpret the step

$$\text{A P} = r \cdot (\cos\theta + \sqrt{-1}\, \sin\theta)$$

as obtained in the following fashion: Rotate unit length from A B (Fig. 97) through an angle θ, and then stretch it in the ratio of $r : 1$. The latter part of this operation will be signified by the

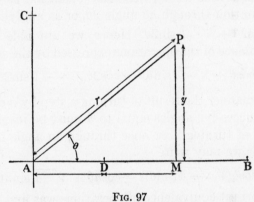

FIG. 97

modulus r, the former by the operator $(\cos\theta + \sqrt{-1}\, \sin\theta)$. Thus if A D be of unit length and lying in A B, we may read—

$$\text{A P} = r \cdot (\cos\theta + \sqrt{-1}\, \sin\theta) \cdot \text{A D},$$

and we look upon our complex number as a symbol denoting the combination of two operations performed on a unit step A D.

Starting then from the idea of a complex number as denoting position, we have been led to a new operation represented by the symbol $\cos\theta + \sqrt{-1}\, \sin\theta$. This is obviously a generalized form of our old symbol $\sqrt{-1}$. The operator $\cos\theta + \sqrt{-1}\, \sin\theta$ applied to any step bids us turn the step through an angle θ. We shall see that this new conception has important results:

§13. *On the Operation which turns a Step through a given Angle*

Suppose we apply the operator $(\cos\theta + \sqrt{-1}\,\sin\theta)$ twice to a unit step. Then the symbolic expression for this operation will be

$$(\cos\theta + \sqrt{-1}\,\sin\theta)(\cos\theta + \sqrt{-1}\,\sin\theta),$$

or $\qquad\qquad (\cos\theta + \sqrt{-1}\,\sin\theta)^2.$

But to turn a step first through an angle θ and then through another angle θ is clearly the same operation as turning it by one rotation through an angle 2θ, or as applying the operator $\cos 2\theta + \sqrt{-1}\,\sin 2\theta$. Hence we are able to assert the equivalence of the operations expressed by the equation—

$$(\cos\theta + \sqrt{-1}\,\sin\theta)^2 = \cos 2\theta + \sqrt{-1}\,\sin 2\theta.$$

In like manner the result of turning a step by n operations through successive angles equal to θ must be identical with the result of turning it at once through an angle equal to n times θ, or we may write

$$(\cos\theta + \sqrt{-1}\,\sin\theta)^n = \cos n\theta + \sqrt{-1}\,\sin n\theta.$$

This important equivalence of operations was first expressed in the above symbolical form by De Moivre, and it is usually called after him De Moivre's Theorem.

We are now able to consider the operation by means of which a step A P can be transformed into another A Q. We must obviously turn A P about A counter-clockwise till it coincides in position with A Q; in this case P will fall on P′, so that A P′ = A P. Then we must stretch A P′ into A Q; this will be a process of multiplying it by some quantity ρ, which is equal to the ratio of A Q to A P′.

Expressing this symbolically, if ϕ be the angle P A Q, we have

$$(\cos\phi + \sqrt{-1}\,\sin\phi) \cdot \text{A P} = \text{A P}′.$$
$$\rho \cdot (\cos\phi + \sqrt{-1}\,\sin\phi) \cdot \text{A P} = \rho \cdot \text{A P}′ = \text{A Q}.$$

This last equation we can interpret in various ways:

(i) $\rho \cdot (\cos\phi + \sqrt{-1} \sin\phi)$ is a complex number of which ρ is the modulus and ϕ the argument. Hence we may say that to multiply a step by a complex number is to turn the step through an angle equal to the argument and to alter its length by a stretch represented by the modulus.

(ii) Or, again, we may consider the step A P (Fig. 98) as itself representing a complex number, $x + \sqrt{-1}\, y$, or if r be the

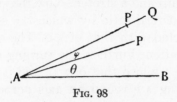

FIG. 98

scalar value of A P and θ the angle B A P, we may put A P = $r(\cos\theta + \sqrt{-1} \sin\theta)$. Similarly A Q will be a complex number, and its scalar magnitude $(= \rho \cdot$ A P$' = \rho r)$ will be its modulus, while the angle B A Q = $\theta + \phi$ will be its argument. We have then the following identity—

$$\rho(\cos\phi + \sqrt{-1}\sin\phi) \cdot r(\cos\phi + \sqrt{-1}\sin\theta) =$$
$$\rho r \cdot (\cos\overline{\theta + \phi} + \sqrt{-1}\cos\overline{\phi + \theta}).$$

This may be read in two ways:

First, the product of two complex numbers is itself a complex number, and has the product of the moduli for its modulus, the sum of the arguments for its argument.

Or secondly, if we turn unit step through an angle θ and give a stretch r, and then turn the result obtained through an angle ϕ and give it a stretch ρ, the result will be the same as turning unit step through an angle $\theta + \phi$ and giving it a stretch equal to $\rho\, r$.

Thus we see that any relation between complex numbers may be treated either as an algebraical fact relating to such numbers, or as a theorem concerning operations of turning and stretching unit steps.

(iii) We may consider what answer the above identity gives to the question: What is the ratio of two *directed* steps

A Q and A P? Or, using the notation suggested on p. 41, we ask: What is the meaning of the symbol $\frac{AQ}{\lfloor AP}$? A step like A P (or A Q) which has magnitude, direction, and sense is, as we have noted, termed a vector. We therefore ask: What is the ratio of two vectors, or what operation will convert one into the other? The answer is: An operation which is the product of a turning (or spin) and a stretch. Now the stretch is a scalar quantity, a numerical ratio by which the scalar magnitude of A P is connected with that of A Q. The stretch therefore is a scalar operation. Further, the turning or spin converts the direction of A P into that of A Q, and it obviously takes place by spinning A P round an axis perpendicular to the plane of the paper in which both A P and A Q lie. Thus the second part of the operation by which we convert A P into A Q denotes a spin (counter-clockwise) through a definite angle about a certain axis. The amount of the spin might be measured by a step taken along that axis. Thus, for instance, if the spin were through 6 units of angle, we might measure 6 units of length along the axis to denote its amount. We may also agree to take this length along one direction of the axis ("out from the face of the clock") if the spin be counter-clockwise, and in the opposite direction ("behind the face of the clock") if the spin be clockwise. Thus we see that our spinning operation may be denoted by a line or step having magnitude, direction, and sense; that is, by a *vector*. We are now able to understand the nature of the ratio of two vectors; it is an operation consisting of the product of a scalar and a vector. This product was termed by Sir William Hamilton a *quaternion*, and made the foundation of a very powerful calculus.

Thus a quaternion is primarily the operation which converts one vector step into another. It does this by means of a spin and a stretch. If we have three points in plane space, the reader will now understand how the position of the third with regard to the first can be made identical with that of the second by means of a spin and a stretch of the step joining the first to the third, that is, by means of a quaternion.[1]

§14. *Relation of the Spin to the Logarithmic Growth of Unit Step*

Let us take a circle of unit radius and endeavour to find how its radius grows in describing unit angle about the centre. Hitherto we have treated of growth only in the direction of length; and hence it might be supposed that the radius of a circle does not "grow" at all as it revolves about the centre. But our method of adding vector steps suggests at once an obvious extension of our conception of growth. Let a step A P (Fig. 99) become A Q as it rotates about A through the angle P A Q, then if we marked off A Q a distance A P' equal to A P, P' Q would be the *scalar* growth of A P; that is, its

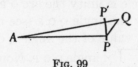

Fig. 99

growth in the direction of its length. But if A P be treated as a vector (see p. 139)

$$A\,Q = A\,P + P\,Q,$$

or the *directed* step P Q must be added to A P in order to convert it into A Q; P Q may be thus termed the directed growth of A P. If we join P P', we shall have P Q equal to the sum of P P' and P' Q. Now if the angle P A P' be taken very small P P' will be ultimately perpendicular to A P, and this part of the growth P Q might be represented by $\sqrt{-1} \cdot$ P P'. Hence we are led to represent a growth perpendicular to a rotating line by a scalar quantity multiplied by the symbol $\sqrt{-1}$.

We can now consider the case of our circle of unit radius.

---

[1] The term "stretch" must be considered to include a squeeze or a stretch denoted by a scalar quantity ρ less than unity.

Let O P (Fig. 100) be a radius which has revolved through an angle θ from a fixed radius O A, and let O Q be an adjacent position of O P such that the angle Q O P is very small. Then P Q will be a small arc sensibly coincident with the straight line

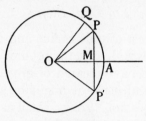

FIG. 100

P Q, and the line P Q will be to all intents and purposes at right angles to O P. Hence to obtain O Q we must take a step P Q at right angles to O P. This we represent by $\sqrt{-1}$ Q P. Since the radius of the circle is unity the arc Q P, which equals the radius multiplied by the angle Q O P (see pp. 130, 131), must equal the numerical value of the angle Q O P. Or the growth of O P is given by $\sqrt{-1} \times$ angle Q O P. Now since O P remains of constant length as it revolves about O, it is equally multiplied (*i.e.*, by the factor unity) in describing equal angles. It thus satisfies our definition of growth at logarithmic rate (see p. 160). In this case what value shall we give to the rate for unit angle?

It must equal $\frac{P Q}{O P}$ divided by the ratio of the angle Q O P

to unit angle $= \dfrac{P Q}{O P \times \text{angle Q O P}} = \sqrt{-1}$ since O P is unity.

Thus O P is growing at logarithmic rate $\sqrt{-1}$ as it describes unit angle; that is to say, the result of turning O P through unit angle might be *symbolically* expressed by $e^{\sqrt{-1}}$. Hence the result of turning O P through an angle θ must be $e^{\sqrt{-1}\theta}$. We may then write

$$O P = O A \cdot e^{\sqrt{-1}\theta}.$$

Drop P M perpendicular to O A and produce it to meet the circle again in P', then by symmetry M P = M P', and we have

$$O P = O M + \sqrt{-1} \, M P.$$
$$O P' = O M - \sqrt{-1} \, M P'.$$

Now since O P and O P' are of unit magnitude,

$$\cos\theta = \frac{O M}{O P} = O M, \quad \sin\theta = \frac{P M}{O P} = P M.$$

Also the angle P' O M equals the angle M O P, but, according to our convention as to the measurement of angles, it is of opposite sense, or equals $-\theta$. Thus we must write

$$O P' = O A \cdot e^{-\sqrt{-1}\theta}.$$

Substituting their values, we deduce the symbolical results

$$\left.\begin{array}{l} e^{\sqrt{-1}\theta} = \cos\theta + \sqrt{-1}\,\sin\theta \\ e^{-\sqrt{-1}\theta} = \cos\theta - \sqrt{-1}\,\sin\theta \end{array}\right\} \text{(i)}$$

Further,

$$O P - O P' = 2\sqrt{-1}\,P M$$
$$O P + O P' = 2\,O M$$

that is,

$$\left.\begin{array}{l} e^{\sqrt{-1}\theta} - e^{-\sqrt{-1}\theta} = 2\sqrt{-1}\,\sin\theta \\ e^{\sqrt{-1}\theta} + e^{-\sqrt{-1}\theta} = 2\cos\theta \end{array}\right\} \text{(ii)}$$

These values for $\cos\theta$ and $\sin\theta$ in terms of the exponential e were first discovered by Euler. They are meaningless in the form (ii) when $\cos\theta$ and $\sin\theta$ are interpreted as mere numerical ratios; but they have a perfectly clear and definite meaning when we treat each side of the equation in form (i) as a symbol of operation. Thus $\cos\theta + \sqrt{-1}\,\sin\theta$ applied to unit step directs us to turn that step without altering its length through an angle θ; on the other hand, $e^{\sqrt{-1}\theta}$ applied to the same step causes it to grow at logarithmic rate unity *perpendicular* to itself, while it is turned through the angle θ. The two processes give the same result.

§15. *On the Multiplication of Vectors*

We have discussed how vector steps are to be added, and
proved that the order of addition is indifferent; we have also
examined the operation denoted by the ratio of two vectors.
The reader will naturally ask: Can no meaning be given to
the product of two vectors?

If both the vectors be treated as complex numbers, or as
denoting operations, we have interpreted their product (see
p. 175) as another complex number or as a resultant operation. Or again we have interpreted the product of two
vectors when one denotes an operation and the other a step
of position; the product in this case is a direction to spin the
step through a certain angle and then stretch it in a certain
ratio. But neither of these cases explains what we are to
understand by the product of two steps of position.

Let A P, A Q (Fig. 101) be two such steps: What is the meaning of the product A P · A Q? Were A P and A Q merely scalar

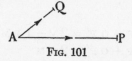

Fig. 101

quantities then their product would be purely scalar, and we
should have no difficulty in interpreting the result A P · P Q as
another scalar quantity. But when we consider the steps A P,

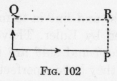

Fig. 102

P Q to possess not only magnitude but *direction*, the meaning
of their product is by no means so obvious.

If A Q were at right angles to A P (see Fig. 102), we should
naturally interpret the product A P · A Q as the area of the
rectangle on A Q and A P, or as the area of the figure Q A P R.
Now let us see how this area might be generated. Were we
to move the step A Q parallel to itself and so that its end A

always remained in the step A P, it would describe the rectangle Q A P R while its foot A described the step A P. Hence if A P and A Q are at right angles we might interpret their product as follows:

The product A P · A Q bids us move the step A Q parallel to itself so that its end A traverses the step A P; the area traced out by A Q during this motion is the value of the product A P · A Q.

It will be noted at once that this interpretation, although suggested by the case of the angle Q A P being a right angle, is entirely independent of what that angle may be. If Q A P be not a right angle the area traced out according to the above rule would be the parallelogram on A P, A Q as sides. Hence the interpretation we have discovered for the product A P · A Q gives us an intelligible meaning, whatever be the angle Q A P.

There is, however, a difficulty which we have not yet solved. An area is a *directed* quantity (see p. 123), and its direction depends on how we go round its perimeter. Now the area Q A P R (Fig. 103) will be positive if we go round its perimeter counter-clockwise, or from A to P; that is, in the direction

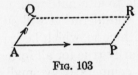

Fig. 103

of the first step of the product or in the direction of motion of the second or moving step. Thus the product A P · A Q will be the area Q A P R taken with the sign suggested by the step A P. The product A Q · A P will be formed by causing the step A P to move parallel to itself along A Q, and it is therefore also the area of the parallelogram on A Q and A P; but it is to be taken with the sign suggested by A Q, or it is the area P A Q R.

By our convention as to the sign of areas,

$$P A Q R = - Q A P R,$$

or $$A Q \cdot A P = - A P \cdot A Q.$$

Hence we see that, with the above interpretation, the product of two vectors does not follow the commutative law (see p. 41).

If we suppose the angle Q A P to vanish, and the vector A Q to become identical with A P, the area of the enclosed parallelogram will obviously vanish also. Thus, if a vector step be multiplied by itself, the product is zero; that is,

$$A P \cdot A P = (A P)^2 = 0.$$

If we take a series of vector steps, a, β, γ, δ, &c. then relations of the following types will hold among them:

$$a^2 = 0, \qquad \beta^2 = 0, \qquad \gamma^2 = 0, \qquad \delta^2 = 0, \text{ &c.}$$
$$a\beta = -\beta a, \qquad a\gamma = -\gamma a, \qquad \beta\gamma = -\gamma\beta,$$
$$\delta\gamma = -\gamma\delta, \text{ &c.}$$

A series of quantities for which these relations hold was first made use of by Grassmann, and termed by him *alternate units*.

The reader will at once observe that alternate units have an algebra of their own. They dispense with the commutative law, or rather replace it by another in which the sign of a product is made to alternate with the alternation of its components. Their consideration will suggest to the reader that the rules of arithmetic, which he is perhaps accustomed to assume as necessarily true for all forms of symbolic quantity, have only the comparatively small field of application to scalar magnitudes. It becomes necessary to consider them as mere conventions, or even to lay them aside entirely as we proceed step by step to enlarge the meaning of the symbols we are employing.

Although $2 \times 2 = 0$ and $2 \times 3 = -3 \times 2$ may be sheer nonsense when 2 and 3 are treated as mere numbers, it yet becomes downright common sense when 2 and 3 are treated as directed steps in a plane.

Let us take two alternate units a, β and interpret the quantity $aa + b\beta$, where a and b are merely scalar magnitudes. If O A (Fig. 104) be the vector a, aa signifies that we are to

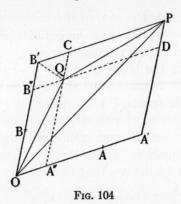

Fig. 104

stretch o a to o a' in the ratio of 1 to a. To this o a' we are
to add the vector o b' derived from o b by giving it the
stretch b. Hence if a' p = o b' the vector o p represents the
quantity $aa + b\beta$, which is termed an *alternate number*. Let
o q represent a second alternate number $a'a + b'\beta$, obtained
by adding the results of applying two other stretches a' and
b' to the alternate units a and β. In the same way we might
obtain, by adding the results of stretching three alternate
units (a, β, γ), alternate numbers with three terms (of the
form $aa + b\beta + c\gamma$), and so on. If we take the *product* of as
many alternate numbers as we have used alternate units in
their composition, we obtain a quantity called a *determinant*,
which plays a great part in the modern theory of quantity.
We shall confine ourselves here to the consideration of a
determinant formed from two alternate units. Such a determinant will be represented by the product o p · o q, which
according to our convention as to the multiplication of
vectors equals the area of the parallelogram on o p, o q as
sides, or (by p. 113) twice the triangle q o p. Through q
draw c q a'' parallel to o b, and d q b'' parallel to o a, then
o a'' = a' a and o b'' = b' β. Join b' q, then twice the triangle
b' q p equals the parallelogram b'' p. Hence, adding to both
these the parallelogram a' b'' we have the parallelogram
a' b'' together with twice the triangle b' q p equal to the
parallelogram b' a', or to twice the triangle b' o p. But the

triangle B′ O P equals the sum of the triangles O Q B′, B′ Q P, and O P Q. It follows then that the parallelogram A′ B″ must equal twice the triangle O P Q together with twice the triangle O Q B′. Now twice the latter equals B′ A″. Hence the difference of the parallelograms A′ B″ and B′ A″ is equal to twice O P Q. The parallelogram A′ B″ is obtained from the parallelogram A B by giving it two stretches a and b' parallel to its sides, and therefore its area equals ab' times the area A B. Similarly B′ A″ equals ba' times the area A B; but the area A B itself is $a\beta$. Thus we see that the identity

$$O P \cdot O Q = A' B'' - B' A''$$

may be read

$$(a\alpha + b\beta)(a'\alpha + b'\beta) = (ab' - ba')a\beta.$$

Or, the determinant is equal to the parallelogram on the alternate units magnified in the ratio of 1 to $ab' - ba'$. It obviously vanishes if $ab' - ba' = 0$, or if $a/b = a'/b'$. In this case P and Q lie, by the property of similar triangles, on the same straight line through O, and therefore, as we should expect, the determinant O P · O Q is zero.

The reader will find little difficulty in discovering like properties for a determinant formed from three alternate units. In this case there will be a geometrical relation between certain volumes, which may be obtained by stretches in the manner explained on p. 127.[1]

We have in this section arrived at a legitimate interpretation of the product of two directed steps or vectors. We find that their product is an area, or according to our previous convention (see p. 123), also a directed step or vector whose direction is perpendicular to the plane which contains both steps of the product.

---

[1] I have to thank my friend Mr. J. Rose-Innes for suggesting the introduction of the above remarks as to determinants. I may, perhaps, be allowed to add that by treating the alternate units, like Grassmann, as points, and the alternate number as their loaded centroid, a determinant of the second order is represented geometrically by a length, and we thus obtain for one of the *fourth* order a geometrical interpretation as a volume.

§16. *Another Interpretation of the Product of Two Vectors*

The reader must remember, however, that the result of the preceding paragraph has only been obtained *by means of a convention*; namely, by adopting the area of a certain parallelogram as the interpretation of the vector product. Only as long as we observe that convention will our deductions with regard to the multiplication of vectors be true. We might have adopted a different convention, and should then have come to a different result. It will be instructive to follow out the results of adopting another convention, if only by so doing we can impress the reader with the fact that the fundamental axioms of any branch of exact science are based rather upon conventions than upon universal truths.

Suppose then that in interpreting the product A P · A Q we consider A P to be a directed step which represents the area

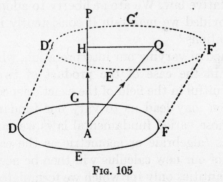

FIG. 105

D E F G (Fig. 105). This area will be perpendicular to the direction of A P, and we might assume as our convention that the product A P · A Q shall mean the volume traced out by the step A Q, moving parallel to itself and in such wise that its end A takes up every possible position in the plane D E F G. This volume will be the portion of an oblique cylinder on the base D E F G intercepted by a plane parallel to that base through Q. We have seen (p. 129) that the volume of this

cylinder is the product of its base into its height, viz. the
perpendicular distance A H between the two planes. Now
let r and ρ be the scalar magnitudes of A P and A Q respectively, and θ = the angle P A Q. Then A H = $\rho \cos\theta$, and the
volume = A P $\cdot$ A Q = $r \rho \cos\theta$, for r represents the number
of units of area in D E F G. Hence, since a volume is a purely
numerical quantity having only magnitude and no direction, we find that with this new convention the product of
two vectors is a purely *scalar* quantity, or our new convention leads to a totally different result from the old.

Further, since r and ρ are merely numbers, $r \rho = \rho r$, and
thus A P $\cdot$ A Q = $r \rho \cos\theta = \rho r \cos\theta$ = A Q $\cdot$ A P, if A Q be
treated as the directed step which represents an area con-
taining ρ units of area. Thus in this case the vector product
obeys the commutative law, which again differs from our
previous result. We can then treat the product of two vectors either as a vector and as a quantity not obeying the
commutative law, or as a *scalar* and as a quantity obeying
the commutative law. We are at liberty to adopt either convention, provided we maintain it consistently in our resulting investigations.[1]

The method of varying our interpretation, which has been
exemplified in the case of the product of two vectors, is
peculiarly fruitful in the field of the exact sciences. Each new
interpretation may lead us to vary our fundamental laws,
and upon those varied fundamental laws we can build up a
new calculus (algebraic or geometric as the case may be).
The results of our new calculus will then be necessarily true
for those quantities only for which we formulated our fundamental laws. Thus those laws which were formulated for
pure number, and which, like the postulates of Euclid with
regard to space, have been frequently supposed to be the
only conceivable basis for a theory of quantity, are found to
be true only within the limits of scalar magnitude. When we

---

[1] In the mathematical treatment of physical problems both conventions are
often adopted together. Thus in a single equation scalar and vector products
may be combined.—J.R.N.

extend our conception of quantity and endow it with direction and position, we find those laws are no longer valid. We are compelled to suppose that one or more of those laws cease to hold or are replaced by others of a different form. In each case we vary the old form or adopt a new one to suit the wider interpretation we are giving to quantity or its symbols.

§17. *Position in Three-Dimensioned Space*

Hitherto we have been considering only position in a plane; very little alteration will enable us to consider the position of a point P relative to a point A as determined by a step A P taken in space.

We may first remark, however, that while two points A and B are sufficient to determine in a plane the position of any third point P, we shall require, in order to fix the position of a point P in space, to be given three points A, B, C not lying in one straight line. If we knew only the distances of P from two points A and B, the point P might be anywhere on a certain circle which has its centre on the line A B and its plane perpendicular to that line; to determine the position of P on this circle, we require to know its distance from a third point C. Thus position in space requires us to have at least three non-collinear points (or such geometrical figures as are their equivalent) as basis for our determination of position. Space in which we live is termed space of three dimensions; it differs from space of two dimensions in requiring us to have three and not two points as a basis for determining position.

Three points will fix a plane, and hence if we are given three points A, B, C in space, the plane through them will be a definite plane separating all space into two halves. In one of these any point P whose position we require must lie. We may term one of these halves *below* the plane and the other *above* the plane. Let P N (Fig. 106) be the perpendicular from P upon the plane; then if we know how to find the point N

in the plane A B C, the position of P will be fully determined
so soon as we have settled whether the distance P N is to be
measured above or below the plane. We may settle by convention that all distances above the plane shall be considered *positive*, and all below *negative*. Further, the position
of the point N, upon which that of P depends, may be deter-

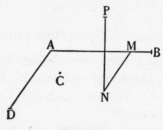

FIG. 106

mined by any of the methods we have employed to fix position in a plane. Thus if N M be drawn perpendicular to A B,
we have the following instruction to find the position of P:
Take a step A M along A B, containing, say, x units; then take
a step M N to the right and perpendicular to A B, but still
in its plane, containing, say, y units; finally step *upwards*
from N the distance N P perpendicular to the plane A B C,
say, through z units. We shall then have reached the same
point P as if we had taken the directed step A P. If x had
been negative we should have had to step backwards from
A; if y had been negative, perpendicular to A B only to the
left; if z had been negative, perpendicular to the plane but
downwards. The reader will easily convince himself that by
observing these rules as to the sign of x, y, z he could get
from A to any point in space.

Let i denote unit step along A B, j unit step to the right
perpendicular to A B, but in the plane A B C, and k unit step
perpendicular to the plane A B C upwards, from foot to
head. Then we may write

$$A P = x \cdot i + y \cdot j + z \cdot k,$$

where x, y, z are scalar quantities possessing only magnitude and sign; but i, j, k are vector steps in three mutually rectangular directions.

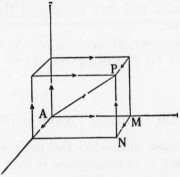

Fig. 107

The step A P (Fig. 107) may be regarded as the diagonal of a solid rectangular figure (a *right six-face*, as we termed it on p. 126), and thus we shall get to the same point P by traversing any three of its non-parallel sides in succession starting from A. But this is equivalent to saying that the order in which we take the directed steps $x \cdot i$, $y \cdot j$, and $z \cdot k$ is indifferent.

The reader will readily recognize that the sum of a number of successive steps in space is the equivalent to the step which joins the start of the first to the finish of the last; and thus a number of propositions concerning steps in space similar to those we have proved for steps in a plane may be deduced. By dividing all space into little cubes by three systems of planes mutually at right angles, we may plot out surfaces just as we plotted out curves. Thus we shall choose any values we please for x and y, and suppose the magnitude of the third step related in some constant fashion to the previous steps. For example, if we take the rectangle under z and some constant length a, always equal to the differences of the squares on x and y. or symbolically if we take $az = x^2 - y^2$, we shall reach P by taking the step

$$\text{A P} = x \cdot i + y \cdot j + \frac{x^2 - y^2}{a} \cdot k.$$

The series of points which we should obtain in this way would be found to lie upon a surface resembling the saddle-back we have described on pp. 82, 83. The above relation between z, x, and y will then be termed the *equation* to a saddleback surface.

We cannot, however, enter fully on the theory of steps in space without far exceeding the limits of our present enterprise.

§18. *On Localized Vectors or Rotors*

Hitherto we have considered the position of a point P relative to a point A, and compared it with the position of another point Q relative to the same point A. Thus we have considered the ratio and product of two steps A P and A Q.

We have thereby assumed either that the two steps we were considering had a common extremity A, or at least were capable of being moved parallel to themselves till they had such a common extremity. Such steps are, as we have re-marked, termed *vector* steps.

Suppose, however, that instead of comparing the position of two points P and Q relative to the same point A, we com-pared their positions relative to two different points A and B. (See Fig. 108.) The position of P relative to A will then be

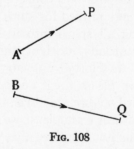

FIG. 108

determined by the step A P and the position of Q relative to B by the step B Q.

Now it will be noted that these steps A P and B Q have not only direction and magnitude, but have themselves *posi-*

tion in space. The step A P has itself position in space relative to the step B Q. It is no longer a step merely indicating the position of P with regard to A, but taken as a whole it has itself attained position when considered with regard to the step B Q. This *localizing*, not of a point P relative to a point A, but of a step A P with regard to another step B Q, is a new and important conception. Such a localized vector is termed a *rotor* from the part it plays in the theory of rotating or spinning bodies.

Let us try and discover what operation will convert the rotor B Q into the rotor A P; in other words: What is the operation $\dfrac{A\ P}{B\ Q}$? In order to convert B Q into A P we must make the magnitude and position of B Q the same as that of A P. Its magnitude may be made the same by means of a stretching operation which stretches B Q to A P. This stretch, as we have seen in the case of a quaternion (see p. 176), may be represented by a numerical ratio or a mere *scalar* quantity. Next let C D (Fig. 109) be the shortest distance

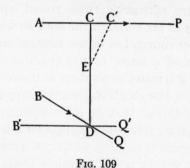

FIG. 109

between the rotors A P and B Q; then C D will be perpendicular to both of them.[1] B Q may then be made to coincide in position with A P by the following process:

[1] That the shortest distance between two lines is perpendicular to both of them may be proved in the following manner. Let us suppose the lines replaced by perfectly smooth and very thin rods, and let two rings, one on either rod, be connected by a stretched elastic string. Obviously the rings will slide along the rods till the elastic string takes up the position of the shortest distance;

First turn B Q about the shortest distance, C D, through some angle, Q D Q', till it takes up the position B' Q' parallel to A P; then slide B' Q' along the shortest distance parallel to itself till its position coincides with A P. If we wished B' Q' to coincide point for point with A P, we should further have to slide it along A P till B' and A were one.

Now the two operations of turning a line about another line at right angles to it, and moving it along that line, are just akin to the operations which are applied to the groove in the head of a screw when we drive the screw into a block of wood; or again to the handle of a corkscrew when we twist the screw into a cork. The handle in the one case and the groove in the other not only spin round, but go forward in the direction of the screw axis. Such a movement along an axis, and at the same time about it, is termed a *twist*. The ratio of the forward space described to the angle turned through during its description by the head of the screw is termed the *pitch* of the screw. This pitch will remain constant for all forward spaces described if the thread of the screw be uniform. Thus turn an ordinary corkscrew twice round, and it will have advanced twice as far through the cork as when it has been turned only once round. Let us see whether we cannot apply this conception of a screw to the operations by which we bring the rotor B Q into the position of the rotor A P. Upon a rod placed at C D, the shortest distance, suppose a fine screw cut with such a thread that its pitch equals the ratio of C D to the angle Q D Q'. Then if we suppose B Q attached to a nut upon this screw at D, when we turn B Q through the angle Q D Q', the nut with B Q will advance (owing to the pitch we have chosen for the screw) through the distance D C. In

---

for that will correspond to the least possible tension of the string. Suppose that the string is then not at right angles to one of the rods, say, at the point C. By holding the string firmly at E, we might shift the ring at C along the rod to C', so that the angle E C' C should be a right angle. Then since C' is a right angle C E would be greater than C' E, being the side opposite the greatest angle of the triangle E C' C. Hence the length of string C' E + E D is less than the length C D, or C D cannot be the shortest distance which we have supposed it to be. Thus the shortest distance must be at right angles to both lines.

other words, B Q will have been brought up to A P and coincide with it in position and direction.

Hence the operations by means of which B Q can be made to coincide with A P are a stretch followed by a twist along a certain screw.[1] A screw involves direction, position, and pitch; a twist (as of a nut) about this axis involves something additional, namely a magnitude, viz. that of the angle through which the nut is to be turned. Magnitude associated with a screw has been termed by the author of the present book a *motor* [2] (since it expresses the most general instantaneous motion of a rigid body). Hence the operation by which one rotor is converted into another may be described as a motor combined with a stretch. This operation stands in the same relation to two rotors as the quaternion to two vectors. The motor plays such an important part in several branches of physical inquiry that the reader will do well to familiarize himself with the conception.

The sum of two vector steps is, as we have seen (p. 139), a third vector; but unlike vector steps the sum of two rotors is in general a motor; only in special cases does it become either a rotor or a vector. The geometry of rotors and motors, which we have only here been able to hint at, forms the basis of the whole modern theory of the relative rest (Static) and the relative motion (Kinematic and Kinetic) of invariable systems.

§19. *On the Bending of Space*

The peculiar topic of this chapter has been position, position namely of a point P relative to a point A. This relative position led naturally to a consideration of the geometry of steps. I proceeded on the hypothesis that all position is relative, and therefore to be determined only by a stepping process. The relativity of position was a postulate deduced

---

[1] In general the screw must be followed by a slide, unless the single perpendicular (C D) to both rotors (B Q and A P) bisects them.—J.R.N.

[2] "Preliminary Sketch of Biquaternions," *Proceedings of the London Mathematical Society*, vol. iv. p. 383.

from the customary methods of determining position, such methods in fact always giving relative position. *Relativity of position is thus a postulate derived from experience.* The late Professor Clerk-Maxwell fully expressed the weight of this postulate in the following words:—

All our knowledge, both of time and place, is essentially relative. When a man has acquired the habit of putting words together, without troubling himself to form the thoughts which ought to correspond to them, it is easy for him to frame an antithesis between this relative knowledge and a so-called absolute knowledge, and to point out our ignorance of the absolute position of a point as an instance of the limitation of our faculties. Any one, however, who will try to imagine the state of a mind conscious of knowing the absolute position of a point will ever after be content with our relative knowledge.[1]

It is of such great value to ascertain how far we can be certain of the truth of our postulates in the exact sciences that I shall ask the reader to return to our conception of position albeit from a somewhat different standpoint. I shall even ask him to attempt an examination of that state of mind which Professor Clerk-Maxwell hinted at in his last sentence.

Suppose we had a tube of exceedingly small bore bent into a circular shape, and within this tube a worm of length A B (Fig. 110). Then in the limiting case when we make the bore

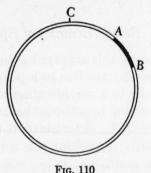

FIG. 110

[1] *Matter and Motion* (London: Society for Promoting Christian Knowledge, 1876; p. 20. New York: The Macmillan Co., 1920; p. 12).—J.R.N.

of the tube and the worm infinitely fine, we shall be considering space of one dimension. For so soon as we have fixed *one* point, c, on the tube, the length of arc c a suffices to determine the position of the worm. Assuming that the worm is incapable of recognizing anything outside its own tube-space, it would still be able to draw certain inferences as to the nature of the space in which it existed were it capable of distinguishing some mark c on the side of its tube. Thus it would notice when it returned to the point c, and it would find that this return would continually recur as it went round in the bore; in other words, the worm would readily postulate the finiteness of space. Further, since the worm would always have the same *amount of bending*, since all parts of a circle are of the same shape, it might naturally assume the *sameness* of all space, or that space possessed the same properties at all points. This assumption is precisely akin to the one we make when we assert that the postulates of Euclidian geometry, which, experience teaches us, are practically true for the space immediately about us, are also true for all space; we assume the sameness of our three-dimensioned space. The worm would, however, have better reason for its postulate than we have, because it would have visited every part of its own one-dimensioned space.

Besides the finiteness and sameness of its space the worm might assert the relativity of position, and determine its position by the length of the arc between c and a. Let us now make a variation in our problem and suppose the worm incapable either of making or of recognizing any mark on the tube. Then it would clearly be impossible for the worm to ascertain whether its space were limited or not; it would never know when it had made a complete revolution in its tube. In fact, since the worm would always possess the same amount of bending, it would naturally associate *that bending with its physical constitution, and not with the space which it was traversing*. It might thus very reasonably suppose its space was infinite, or that it was moving in an infinitely long tube. If the worm thus associated bending with its physical condition it would find no difference between motion in space of constant bend (a circle) and motion in what is termed *homaloidal* or flat space (a straight line); if suddenly transferred from one to the other it would attribute the feeling arising from difference of bending to some change which had taken place in its physical constitution. Hence in one-dimensioned space of constant bend all position is necessarily relative, and the finite or infinite character of space will be postulated according as it is possible or not to fix a point in it.[1]

Let us now suppose our worm moving in a different sort of tube; for example, that shadow of a circle we have called an ellipse. In such a tube the degree of bending is not everywhere the same; the worm as it passes from the place of least bending C to the place of most bending D, will pass through a succession of bendings, and each point H between C and D will have its own degree of bending (Fig. 111). Hence there is

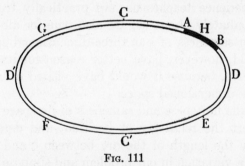

FIG. 111

something quite apart from the position of H relative to C which characterizes the point H; namely, associated with H is a particular degree of bending, and the position of the point H in C D is at once fixed if we know the degree of bending there. Thus the worm might determine *absolute* position in its space by the degree of bending associated with its position. The worm is now able to appreciate differences of bend,

[1] This supposes the one-dimensioned space of constant bend to lie in a plane; the argument does not apply to space like that of a *helix* (or the form of a corkscrew), which is of constant bend, but yet not finite.

and might even form a scale of bending rising by equal differences. The zero of such scale might be anywhere the
worm pleased, and degrees of greater and less bend might be
measured as positive and negative quantities from that zero.
This zero might in fact be purely imaginary; that is, represent a degree of bending non-existent in the worm's space;
for example, in the case of an ellipse, absolute straightness,
a conception which the worm might form as a limit to its
experience of degrees of bend.[1] Thus it would seem that in
space of "varying bend," or space which is not same, position is not necessarily relative. The relativity has ceased to
belong to position in space; it has been transferred to the
scale of bending formed by the worm; it has become a *relativity of physical feeling*. In the case of an elliptic tube there
are owing to its symmetry four points of equal bend, as H,
E, F, and G, but there is the following distinction between
H, F and E, G. If the worm be going round in the direction
indicated by the letters C H D E, at H or F it will be passing
from positions of less to positions of greater bending, but at
E or G from positions of greater to positions of less bending.
Thus the worm might easily draw a distinction between H,
F and E, G. It would only be liable to suppose the point H

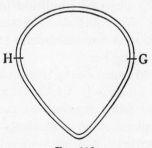

H   G

Fɪɢ. 112

and F identical because they possess the same degree of
bending. We might remove even this possible doubt by supposing the worm to be moving in a pear-shaped tube, as in
Fig. 112; then there will only be two points of equal bend,

[1] Physicists may be reminded of the absolute zero of temperature.

like H and G, which are readily distinguished in the manner mentioned above.

We might thus conclude that in one-dimensioned space of variable bend position is not necessarily relative. There is, however, one point to be noted with regard to this statement. We have assumed that the worm will associate change of bending with change of position in its space, but the worm would be sensible of it as a change of physical state or as a change of feeling. Hence the worm might very readily be led into the error of postulating the sameness of its space, and attributing all the changes in its bend, really due to its position in space, to some periodic (if it moves uniformly round its tube) or irregular (if it moves in any fashion backwards and forwards) changes to which its physical constitution was subject. Similar results might also arise if the worm were either moving in space of the same bend, which bend could be changed by some external agency as a whole, or if again its space were of varying bend, which was also capable of changing in any fashion with time. The reader can picture these cases by supposing the tube made of flexible material. The worm might either attribute change in its degree of bend to change in the character of its space or to change in its physical condition not arising from its position in space. We conclude that the postulate of the relativity of position is not necessarily true for one-dimensioned space of varying bend.

When we proceed from one- to two-dimensioned space, we obtain results of an exactly similar character. If we take perfectly even (so called *homaloidal*) space of two dimensions, that is, a plane, then a perfectly flat figure can be moved about anywhere in it without altering its shape. If by analogy to an infinitely thin worm we take an infinitely thin flat-fish, this fish would be incapable of determining position could it leave no landmarks in its plane space. So soon as it had fixed two points in its plane it would be able to determine *relative* position.

Now, suppose that instead of taking this homaloidal space

of two dimensions we were still to take a perfectly same space but one of finite bend, that is, the surface of a sphere. Then let us so stretch and bend our flat-fish that it would fit on to some part of the sphere. Since the surface of the sphere is everywhere space of the same shape, the fish would then be capable of moving about on the surface without in any way altering the amount of bending and stretching which we had found it necessary to apply to make the fish fit in any one position. Were the fish incapable of leaving landmarks on the surface of the sphere, it would be totally unable to determine position; if it could leave at least two landmarks it would be able to determine *relative* position. Just as the worm in the circular tube, the fish without landmarks might reasonably suppose its space infinite, or even look upon it as perfectly flat (homaloidal) and attribute the constant degree of bend and stretch to its physical nature.

Let us now pass to some space of two dimensions which is not same—to some space, for example, like the saddleback surface we have considered on pages 82, 83, which has a varying bend. In this case the fish, if it fitted at one part of the surface, would not necessarily fit at another. If it moved about in its space, it would be needful that a continual process of bending and stretching should be carried on. Thus every part of this two-dimensioned space would be defined by the particular amount of bend and stretch necessary to make the fish fit it, or, as it is usually termed, by the *curvature*. In surfaces with some degree of symmetry there would necessarily be parts of equal curvature, and in some cases the fish might perhaps distinguish between these points in the same fashion as the worm distinguished between points of equal curvature in the case of an elliptic tube. In irregular surfaces, however, it is not necessary that such points of equal curvature should arise. We are thus led to conclusions like those we have formed for one-dimensioned space, namely: Position in space of two dimensions which is not same might be determined *absolutely* by means of the curvature. Our fish has only to carry about with it a scale of degrees of bending and stretching corresponding to various positions on the surface in order to determine absolutely its position in its space. On the other hand, the fish might very readily attribute all these changes of bend and stretch to variations of its physical nature in nowise dependent on its position in space. Thus it might believe itself to have a most varied physical life, a continual change of physical feeling quite independent of the geometrical character of the space in which it dwelt. It might suppose that space to be perfectly same, or even degrade it to the "dreary infinity of a homaloid." [1]

As a result, then, of our consideration of one- and two-dimensioned space we find that, if these spaces be not same (à fortiori not homaloidal), we should by reason of their curvature have a means of determining absolute position. But we see also that a being existing in these dimensions would most probably attribute the effects of curvature to changes in its own physical condition in nowise connected with the geometrical character of its space.

What lesson may we learn by analogy for the three-dimensioned space in which we ourselves exist? To begin with, we assume that all our space is perfectly same, or that solid figures do not change their shape in passing from one position in it to another. We base this postulate of sameness upon the results of observation in that somewhat limited portion of space of which we are cognizant.[2] Supposing our observations to be correct, it by no means follows that because the portion of space of which we are cognizant is

[1] In this case of two-dimensioned space assume it to be a plane. Cf. Clifford's *Lectures and Essays*, vol. i. p. 323.

[2] It may be held by some that the postulate of the sameness of our space is based upon the fact that no one has hitherto been able to form any geometrical conception of space-curvature. Apart from the fact that mankind habitually assumes many things of which it can form no geometrical conception (mathematicians the circular points at infinity, theologians transubstantiation), I may remark that we cannot expect any being to form a geometrical conception of the curvature of his space till he views it from space of a higher dimension, that is, practically, never.

for practical purposes same, that therefore *all* space is same.[1]
Such an assumption is a mere dogmatic extension to the
unknown of a postulate, which may perhaps be true for the
space upon which we can experiment. To make such dogmatic assertions with regard to the unknown is rather characteristic of the mediæval theologian than of the modern
scientist. On the like basis with this postulate as to the
sameness of our space stands the further assumption that it
is homaloidal. When we assert that our space is everywhere
same, we suppose it of constant curvature (like the circle
as one- and the sphere as two-dimensioned space); when we
suppose it homaloidal we assume that this curvature is zero
(like the line as one- and the plane as two-dimensioned
space). This assumption appears in our geometry under the
form that two parallel planes, or two parallel lines in the
same plane—that is, planes, or lines in the same plane, which
however far produced will never meet—have a *real* existence
in our space. This real existence, of which it is clearly impossible for us to be cognizant, we postulate as a result built
upon our experience of what happens in a limited portion of
space. We may postulate that the portion of space of which
we are cognizant is practically homaloidal, but we have
clearly no right to dogmatically extend this postulate to
all space. A constant curvature, imperceptible for that
portion of space upon which we can experiment, or even a
curvature which may vary in an almost imperceptible manner with the time, would seem to satisfy all that experience has taught us to be true of the space in which we
dwell.

But we may press our analogy a step further, and ask,
since our hypothetical worm and fish might very readily at-

[1] Yet it must be noted that, because a solid figure *appears* to us to retain
the same shape when it is moved about in that portion of space with which
we are acquainted, it does not follow that the figure *really* does retain its shape.
The changes of shape may be either imperceptible for those distances through
which we are able to move the figure, or if they do take place we may attribute
them to "physical causes"—to heat, light, or magnetism—which may possibly
be mere names for variations in the curvature of our space.

tribute the effects of changes in the bending of their spaces
to changes in their own physical condition, whether we may
not in like fashion be treating merely as physical variations
effects which are really due to changes in the curvature of
our space; whether, in fact, some or all of those causes which
we term physical may not be due to the geometrical construction of our space. There are three kinds of variation in
the curvature of our space which we ought to consider as
within the range of possibility.

(i) Our space is perhaps really possessed of a curvature
varying from point to point, which we fail to appreciate
because we are acquainted with only a small portion of
space, or because we disguise its small variations under
changes in our physical condition which we do not connect
with our change of position. The mind that could recognize
this varying curvature might be assumed to know the ap-
solute position of a point. For such a mind the postulate of
the relativity of position would cease to have a meaning. It
does not seem so hard to conceive such a state of mind as
the late Professor Clerk-Maxwell would have had us believe.
It would be one capable of distinguishing those so-called
physical changes which are really geometrical or due to a
change of position in space.

(ii) Our space may be really same (of equal curvature),
but its degree of curvature may change as a whole with the
time. In this way our geometry based on the sameness of
space would still hold good for all parts of space, but the
change of curvature might produce in space a succession of
apparent physical changes.

(iii) We may conceive our space to have everywhere a
nearly uniform curvature, but that slight variations of the
curvature may occur from point to point, and themselves
vary with the time. These variations of the curvature with
the time may produce effects which we not unnaturally
attribute to physical causes independent of the geometry
of our space. We might even go so far as to assign to
this variation of the curvature of space "what really hap-

pens in that phenomenon which we term the motion of matter." [1]

We have introduced these considerations as to the nature of our space to bring home to the reader the character of the postulates we make in the exact sciences. These postulates are *not*, as too often assumed, necessary and universal truths; they are merely axioms based on our experience of a certain limited region. Just as in any branch of physical inquiry we start by making experiments, and basing on our experiments a set of axioms which form the foundation of an exact science, so in geometry our axioms are really, although less obviously, the result of experience. On this ground geometry has been properly termed at the commencement of Chapter II a *physical* science. The danger of asserting dogmatically that an axiom based on the experience of a limited region holds universally will now be to some extent apparent to the reader. It may lead us to entirely overlook, or when suggested at once reject, a possible explanation of phenomena. The hypotheses that space is not homaloidal, and again, that its geometrical character may change with the time, may or may not be destined to play a great part in the physics of the future; yet we cannot refuse to consider them

---

[1] This remarkable *possibility* seems first to have been suggested by Professor Clifford in a paper presented to the Cambridge Philosophical Society in 1870 (*Mathematical Papers*, p. 21). I may add the following remarks: The most notable physical quantities which vary with position and time are heat, light, and electro-magnetism. It is these that we ought peculiarly to consider when seeking for any physical changes, which may be due to changes in the curvature of space. If we suppose the boundary of any arbitrary figure in space to be distorted by the variation of space-curvature, there would, by analogy from one and two dimensions, be no change in the volume of the figure arising from such distortion. Further, if we *assume* as an axiom that space resists curvature with a resistance proportional to the change, we find that waves of "space-displacement" are precisely similar to those of the elastic medium which we suppose to propagate light and heat. We also find that "space-twist" is a quantity exactly corresponding to magnetic induction, and satisfying relations similar to those which hold for the magnetic field. It is a question whether physicists might not find it simpler to assume that space is capable of a varying curvature, and of a resistance to that variation, than to suppose the existence of a subtle medium pervading an invariable homaloidal space.

as possible explanations of physical phenomena, because they may be opposed to the popular dogmatic belief in the universality of certain geometrical axioms—a belief which has arisen from centuries of indiscriminating worship of the genius of Euclid.

CHAPTER V

Motion

§1. *On the Various Kinds of Motion*

WHILE the chapters on Space and Position considered the sizes, the shapes, and the distances of things, the present chapter on Motion will treat of the changes in these sizes, shapes, and distances, which take place from time to time.

The difference between the ordinary meaning attached to the word "change" in everyday life and the meaning it has in the exact sciences is perhaps better illustrated by the subject of this chapter than by any other that we have yet studied. We attained exactness in the description of quantity and position by substituting the method of representing them by straight lines drawn on paper for the method of representing them by means of numbers; though this, at first sight, might easily seem to be a step backwards rather than a step forwards, since it is more like a child's sign of opening its arms to show that its stick is so long, than a process of scientific calculation.

It is, however, by no means an easy thing to give an accurate description of motion, even although it is itself as common and familiar a conception as quantity or position.

Let us take a simple case. Suppose that a man, on a railway journey, is sitting at one end of a compartment with his face towards the engine; and that, while the train is going along, he gets up and goes to the other end of the compartment and sits down with his back to the engine. For ordinary purposes this description is amply sufficient, but it is very far indeed from being an exact description of the motion of the man during that time. In the first place, the train was moving, and it is necessary to state in what direction, and how fast it was going at every instant during the interval considered. Next, we must describe the motion of the man relatively to the train; and, for this purpose, we must neglect the motion of the train and consider how the man would have moved if the train had been at rest. First of all, he changes his position from one corner of the compartment to the opposite corner; next, in doing this he turns round; and, lastly, as he is walking along or rising up or sitting down, the size and shape of many of his muscles are altered. We should thus have to say, first, exactly how fast and in what direction he was moving at every instant, as we had to do in the case of the train; then, how quickly he was turning round; and, lastly, what changes of size or shape were taking place in his muscles, and how fast they were occurring.

It may be urged that this would be a very troublesome operation, and that nobody wants to describe the motion of the man so exactly. This is quite true; the case which has been taken for illustration is not one which it is necessary to describe exactly, but we can easily find another case which is very analogous to this, and which it is most important to describe exactly. The earth moves round the sun once in every year; it is also rotating on its own axis once every day; the floating parts of it—the ocean and the air— are constantly undergoing changes of shape and state which we can observe and which it is of the utmost importance that we should be able to predict and calculate; even the solid nucleus of the earth is constantly subject to slight changes in size and shape, which, however, are not large enough to admit of accurate observation. Here, then, is a problem whose complexity is quite as great as that of the former, and whose solution is of pressing practical importance.

The method which is adopted for attacking this problem of the accurate description of motion is to begin with the simplest cases. By the simplest cases we mean those in which certain complicating circumstances do not arise. We

may first of all restrict ourselves to the study of the motions
of those bodies in which there is no change of size or shape.
A body which preserves its size and shape unaltered during
the interval of time considered is called a *rigid* body. The
word "rigid" is here used in a technical sense belonging to
the science of dynamic, and does not mean, as in ordinary
language, a body which resists alteration of size and shape,
but merely a body which, during a certain time, happens
not to be altered in those respects. Then, as the first and
simplest case, we should study that motion of a rigid body
in which there is no turning round, and in which therefore
every line in the body keeps the same direction (though of
course not the same position) throughout the motion. We
state this by saying that every line "rigidly connected"
with the body remains parallel to itself. Such a motion is
called a *motion of translation*, or simply a *translation*; and so
the first and simplest case we have to study is the translation of rigid bodies. After that we must proceed to consider
their turning round, or *rotation*; and then we have to describe the changes of size or shape which bodies may undergo, these last changes being called *strains*. The study of
motion therefore requires the further study of translations,
of rotations, and of strains, and further, the art of combining these together. When we have studied all this we shall
be able to describe motions exactly; and then, but not till
then, will it be possible to state the exact circumstances
under which motions of a given kind occur. The exact circumstances under which motions of a given kind occur we
call a *law of nature*.

§2. *Translation and the Curve of Positions*

Let us talk, to begin with, of the translation of a rigid
body.

Suppose a table to be taken from the top to the bottom of
a house in such a manner that the surface of it is always kept
horizontal, and that its length is made always to point due

north and south; it may be taken down a staircase of any
form, but it is not to be turned round or tilted up. The
table will then undergo a translation. If we now consider
a particular corner of the table, or the end of one of its legs,
or any other point, this point will have described a certain
curve in a certain manner; that is to say, at every point of
this curve it will have been going at a certain definite rate.
Now the important property of a motion of translation,
which makes it more easy to deal with than any other motion, is that for all points of the body this curve is the same
in size and shape and mode of description. That this is so
in the case of the table is at once seen from the fact that the
table is never turned round nor tilted up during the motion,
so that the different points of it must at any instant be
moving in the same direction and at the same rate. In order
therefore to describe this motion of the table it will be sufficient to describe the motion of any point of it, say the end
of one of its legs. And so, in general, the problem of describing the motion of translation of any rigid body is reduced
to the problem of describing the motion of a point along a
curve.

Now this is a very much easier task than our original problem of describing the motion of the earth or the motion of
the man in the train; but we shall see that, by properly studying this, it will be easy to build up out of it other more
complicated cases. Still, even in this form our problem is
not quite simple enough to be directly attacked. What we
have to do, it must be remembered, is to state exactly where
a certain point was, and how fast it was going at every instant of time during a certain interval. This would require
us first to describe exactly the shape of the curve along
which the point moved; next, to say now far it had travelled
along the curve from the beginning up to any given instant;
and lastly, how fast it was going at that instant. To deal
with this problem we must first take the very simplest case
of it, that, namely, in which the point moves along a straight
line, and leave for the present out of account any descrip-

tion of the rate of motion of the point; so that we have only
to say where the point was on a certain straight line at every
instant of time within a given interval.

But we have already considered what is the best way of
describing the position of a point upon a straight line. It is
described by means of the step which is required to carry it
to that position from a certain standard place, viz. a step
from that place so far to the right or to the left. To specify
the length of the step, if we are to describe it exactly, we
must not make use of any words or numbers, but must draw
a line which will represent the length corresponding to every
instant of time within a certain interval, so that we may
always be able to answer the question, Where was the point
at this particular instant? But a question, in order to be
exactly answered, must first be exactly asked; and to do
this it is necessary that the instant of time about which the
question is asked should be accurately specified.

Now time, like length, is a continuous quantity which
cannot in general be described by words or numbers, but
can be by the drawing of a line which shall represent it to a
certain scale. Suppose, then, that the interval of time during
which the motion of a point has to be described is the interval from twelve o'clock to one o'clock. We must mark on
a straight line a point to represent twelve o'clock and another point to represent one o'clock; then every instant between twelve o'clock and one o'clock will be represented by
a point which divides the distance between these two
marked points in the same ratio in which that instant
divides the interval between twelve o'clock and one o'clock.
Then for every one of these points it is necessary to assign a
certain length, representing (to some definite scale) the distance which the point has travelled up to that instant; and
the question arises, In what way shall we mark down these
lengths?

Let us first of all observe the difficulty of answering this
question. If we could be content with an approximate solution instead of an exact one, we might make a table and put

down in inches and decimals of an inch the distances travelled, making an entry for every minute, or even perhaps
for every second during the hour. Such tables are in fact
constructed and published in the "Nautical Almanac" for
the positions of the moon and of the planets. The labour of
making this table will evidently depend upon its degree of
minuteness; it will of course take sixty times as long to make
a table showing the position of the point at every second as
to make one showing the position at every minute, because
there will be sixty times as many values to calculate. But
the problem of describing exactly the motion of the point
requires us to make a table showing the position of the point
at every instant; that is, a table in which are entered an
infinite number of values. These values moreover are to be
shown, not in inches and decimals of an inch, but by lengths
drawn upon paper. Yet we shall find that this pictorial
mode of constructing the table is in most cases very much
easier than the other. We have only to decide where we
shall put the straight lines which represent the distances
that the point has travelled at different instants.

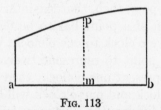

FIG. 113

Let *ab* (Fig. 113) be the length which represents the interval
of time from twelve o'clock to one o'clock, and let *m* be the
point representing any intermediate instant. Then if we draw
at *m* a line perpendicular to *ab* whose length shall represent
(to any scale that we may choose) the distance that the
point has up to this instant travelled, then *p*, the extremity
of this line, will correspond to an entry in our table. But if
such lines be drawn perpendicular to *ab* from every point in
it, all the points *p*, which are the several extremities of these
lines, will lie upon some curve; and this curve will represent

an infinite number of entries in our table. For, when once
the curve is drawn, if a question is asked: What was the
position of the point at any instant between twelve o'clock
and one o'clock? (this instant being specified in the right
way by marking a point between a and b which divides that
line in the same ratio as the given instant divides the hour),
then the answer to this question is obtained simply by drawing a line through the marked point perpendicular to ab,
until it meets the curve; and the length of that line will
represent, to the scale previously agreed upon, the distance
travelled by the point.

Such a curve is called the *curve of positions* for a given
motion of the point; and we arrive at this result, that the
proper way of specifying exactly a translation along a
straight line is to draw the curve of positions.

We have now learned to specify, by means of a curve, the
positions of a body which has motion of translation along a
straight line; and we have not only represented an infinite
number of positions instead of a finite number, which is all
a numerical table would admit, but have also represented
each position with absolute exactness instead of approximately. It is important to notice that in this and in all
similar cases the exactness is ideal and not practical; it is
exactness of conception and not of actual measurement. For
though it is not possible to measure a given length and to
state that measure any more accurately by drawing a line
than it is by writing it down in inches and decimals of an
inch, yet the representation by means of a line enables us
to reason upon it with an exactness which would be impossible if we were restricted to numerical measurement.

§3. *Uniform Motion*

Hitherto we have supposed our point to be moving along
a straight line, but were it to move along a curve the construction given for the curve of positions would still hold
good, only the distance traversed at any instant must now

be measured from some standard position *along the curve.*
Hence any motion of a point, or any motion of translation
whatever, can be specified by a properly drawn curve of
positions, and the problem of comparing and classifying different motions is therefore reduced to the problem of comparing and classifying curves. Here again it is advisable and
even necessary to begin with a simple case. Let us take the
case of uniform motion, in which the body passes over equal
distances in equal times; and then, as we may easily see,
the curve of positions is a straight line. Uniform motion
may also be described as that in which a body always goes
at the same rate, and not quicker at one time and slower at
another. It is obvious that in this case any two equal distances would require equal times for traversing them, so that
the two descriptions of uniform motion are equivalent.

It was shown by Archimedes (the proof is an easy one,
depending upon the definition of the fourth proportional)
that whenever equal distances are traversed in equal times,
different distances will be traversed in times proportional
to them. Assuming this proposition, it becomes clear that
the curve of positions must be a straight line, for a straight
line is the only curve which has the property that the height
of every point of it is proportional to its horizontal distance
from a fixed straight line.

We may also see in the following manner the connection
between the straight line and uniform motion.

Suppose we walk up a hill so as always to get over a horizontal distance of four miles in an hour. The rate at which
we go up will clearly depend on the steepness of the hill; and
if the hill is a plane, *i.e.* is of the same steepness all the way
up, then our rate of ascent will be the same at every instant,
or our upward motion will be uniform. If the hill be four
miles long and one mile high, then, since the four miles of
horizontal distance will be traversed in an hour, the one mile
of vertical distance will also be traversed in an hour, and we
shall be gaining height at the uniform rate of one mile an
hour. If the hill were two miles high, or, as we say twice as

steep, then we should have been gaining height at the rate of two miles an hour. But now if we suppose a hill of varying steepness, so that the outline of it seen from one side is a curve, then it is clear that the rate at which we go up will depend upon the part of the hill where we are, assuming that the rate at which we go forward horizontally remains always the same. This "elevation" of the hill may be taken as the curve of positions for our vertical motion; for the horizontal distance that we have gone over, being always proportional to the time, may be taken to represent the time, and then the curve will have been constructed according to our rule, viz. a horizontal distance will have been taken proportional to the time elapsed, and from the end of this line a perpendicular will have been raised indicating the height which we have risen in that time. Uniform motion then has for its curve of positions a straight line, and the rate of the motion depends on the steepness of the line. Variable motion, on the other hand, has a curved line for its curve of positions, and the rate of motion depends upon its varying steepness.

In the case of uniform motion it is very easy indeed to understand what we mean by the rate of the motion. Thus, if a man walks uniformly six miles an hour, we know that he walks a mile in ten minutes, and the tenth part of a mile in one minute, and so on in proportion. It may not, however, be possible to specify this rate by means of numbers; that is to say, the man may not walk any definite number of miles in the hour, and the exact distance that he walks may not be capable of representation in terms of miles and fractions of a mile. In that case we shall have to represent the velocity or rate at which the man walks in much the same way as we have represented other continuous quantities. We must draw to scale upon paper a line representing the length that he has walked in an hour, or a minute, or any other interval of time that we decide to select; thus, for example, a uniform rate of walking might be specified by marking points corresponding to particular hours upon an

Ordnance map. The rate of motion, or *velocity*, is then a continuous quantity which can be exactly specified, as we specify other continuous quantities, but which can be only approximately described by means of numbers.

§4. *Variable Motion*

Let us now suppose that the motion is not uniform, and inquire what is meant in that case by the rate at which a body moves.

A train, for example, starts from a station and in the course of a few minutes gets up to a speed of 30 miles an hour. It began by being at rest, and it ends by having this large velocity. What has happened to it in the meantime? We can understand already in a rough sort of way what is meant by saying that at a certain time between the two moments the train must have been going at 15 miles an hour, or at any other intermediate rate; but let us endeavour to make this conception a little more exact. Suppose, then, that a second train, which is indefinitely long, is moving in the same direction at a uniform rate of 15 miles an hour on a pair of rails parallel to that on which the first train moves; thus, when our first train is at rest the second one will appear to move past it at the rate of 15 miles an hour. When the first train starts an observer seated in it will see the second train going apparently rather more slowly than before, but it will still seem to be moving forwards. As the first train gets up its speed, this apparent forward motion will gradually decrease until the second train will appear to be going so slowly that conversation may be held between the two; this will take place when the rate of the first train has amounted to something nearly but not quite equal to 15 miles an hour, which we supposed to be the constant rate of the second train. But as the rate of the first train continues to increase there will come a certain instant at which the second train will appear to stop gaining upon the first and to begin to lose. At that particular instant it will be neither gaining nor losing, but will be going at the same rate; at that particular instant, therefore, we must say that the first train is going at the rate of 15 miles an hour. And it is at that instant only, for the equality of the rates does not last for any fraction of a second, however small; the very instant that the second train appears to stop gaining it also appears to begin losing. The two trains then run exactly together for no distance at all, not even for the smallest fraction of an inch, and yet we have to say that at one particular instant our first train is going at the rate of 15 miles an hour, although it does not continue to go at that rate during the smallest portion of time. There is no way of measuring this instantaneous velocity except that which has just been described of comparing the motion with a uniform motion having that particular velocity.

Upon this we have to make the very important remark that the rate at which a body is going is a property as purely instantaneous as is the precise position which it has at that instant. Thus, if a stone be let fall to the ground, at the moment that it hits the ground it is going at a certain definite rate; and yet at any previous moment it was not going so fast, since it does not move at that rate for the smallest fraction of a second. This consideration is somewhat difficult to grasp thoroughly, and in fact it has led many people to reject altogether the hypothesis of continuity; but still we may be helped somewhat in understanding it by means of our study of the curve of positions, wherein we saw that to a uniform motion corresponds a straight line and that the rate of the motion depends on the steepness of the line.

Let us now suppose a motion in which a body goes at a very slow but uniform rate for the first second, during the next second uniformly but somewhat faster, faster again during the third second, and so on. The curve of positions will then be represented by a series of straight lines becoming steeper and steeper and forming part of a polygon. From a sufficient distance off this polygon will look like a curved line; and if, instead of taking intervals of a second during which the rates of motion are severally considered uniform, we had taken intervals of a tenth of a second, then the polygon would look like a curved line without our going so far away as before. For the shorter the lengths of the sides of our polygon, the more will it look curved, and if the intervals of time are reduced to one-tenth the sides will be only one-tenth as long. The rate at which the body under consideration is moving when it is in the position to which any point of the polygon corresponds, is obtained by prolonging that side of the polygon which passes through the point; the rate will then depend on the steepness of this line, since, where the line is a side of the polygon, it represents the uniform motion which the body has during a certain interval. When the polygon looks like a curve the sides are very short, and any side, being prolonged both ways, will look like a tangent to the curve.

Now in considering the general case of varying motion we should have, instead of the above polygon which looks like a curve, an actual curve; the difference between them being that, if we look at the curve-like polygon with a sufficiently strong microscope, we shall be able to see its angles, but however powerful a microscope we may apply to the curve it will always look like a curve. But there is this property in common, that if we draw a tangent to the curve at any point, then, since the steepness of this tangent will be exactly the same as the steepness of the curve at that particular point, it will give the rate for the motion represented by the curve, just as before the steepness of the prolonged small side of the polygon gave the rate for the motion represented by the polygon. That is to say, the instantaneous velocity of a body in any position may be learnt from its curve of positions by drawing a tangent to this curve at the point corresponding to the position; for the steepness of this tangent will give us the velocity or rate which we want, since the tangent itself corresponds to a uniform motion of the same velocity as that belonging to the given varying motion at the particular instant. From this means of representing the rate we can see how it is that the instantaneous velocity of a body generally belongs to it only at an instant and not for any length of time however short; for the steepness of the curve is continually changing as we go from one part of it to another, and the curve is not straight for any portion of its length however small.

The problem of determining the instantaneous velocity in a given position is therefore reduced to the problem of drawing a tangent to a given curve. We have a sufficiently clear general notion of what is meant by each of these things, but the notion which is sufficient for purposes of ordinary discourse is not sufficient for the purposes of reasoning, and it must therefore be made exact. Just as we had to make our notion of the ratio of two quantities exact by means of a definition of the fourth proportional, or of the equality of two ratios which were expressed in terms of numbers, so here we shall have to make our idea of a velocity exact by expressing it in terms of measurable quantities which do not change.

We have no means of measuring the instantaneous velocity of a moving body; the only thing that we can measure is the space which it traverses in a given interval of time. In the case in which a body is moving uniformly, its instantaneous velocity, being always the same, is completely specified as soon as we know how far the body has gone in a definite time. And, as we have already observed, the result is the same whatever this interval of time may be; the rate of four miles an hour is the same as eight miles in two hours, or two miles in half an hour, or one mile in a quarter of an hour. But if a body be moving with a velocity which is continually changing, the knowledge of how far it has gone in a given interval of time tells us nothing about the instantaneous velocity for any position during that interval. To say, for instance, that a man has travelled a distance of four miles during an hour, does not give us any information about the actual rate at which he was going at any moment during the hour, unless we know that he has been going at a uni-

form rate. Still we are accustomed to say that in such a case
he must have been going *on an average* at the rate of four
miles an hour; and, as we shall find it useful to speak of this
rate as an "average velocity," its general definition may be
given as follows:—

If a body has gone over a certain distance in a certain
time its *mean* or *average velocity* is that with which, if it
travelled uniformly, it would get over the same distance in
the same time.

This mean velocity is very simply represented by the help
of the curve of positions. Let a and b (Fig. 114) be two points

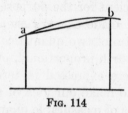

FIG. 114

on the curve of positions; then the mean velocity between the
position represented by a and that represented by b is given
by the steepness of the straight line $a\,b$. This, moreover,
enables us to make some progress towards a method of
calculating instantaneous velocity, for we showed that the
problem of finding the instantaneous velocity of a body is,
in the above method of representation, the problem of drawing a tangent to a curve. Now the mean velocity of a body
is defined in terms of quantities which we are already able
to measure, for it requires the measurement of an interval
of time and of the distance traversed during that interval;
and further the *chord* of a curve, *i.e.* the line joining one
point of it to another, is a line which we are able to draw. If
then we can find some means of passing from the chord of a
curve to the tangent, the representation we have adopted
will help us to pass from the mean to the instantaneous
velocity.

§5. *On the Tangent to a Curve*

Now let us suppose the chord *a b* (Fig. 115) joining the points on the curve to turn round the point *a*, which remains fixed; then *b* will travel along the curve towards *a*; and if we

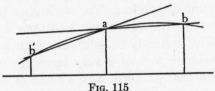

FIG. 115

suppose *b* not to stop in this motion until it has got beyond *a* to a point such as *b'* on the other side, the chord will have turned round into the position *a b'*. Now, looking at the curve which is drawn in the figure, we see that the tangent to the curve at *a* obviously lies between *a b* and *b' a*. Thus if *a b* turn round *a* so as to move into the position *a b'* it will at some instant have to pass over the position of the tangent. At the instant when it passes over this position where is the point *b*? We can at once see from the figure that it cannot be anywhere else than at *a*, and yet we cannot attach any definite meaning to a line described as joining two coincident points. If we could, the determination of the tangent would be very easy, for in order to draw the tangent to the curve at *a*, we should merely say, Take any other point *b* on the curve; join *a b* by a straight line; then make *b* travel along the curve towards *a*, and the position of the line *a b* when *b* has got to *a* is that of the tangent at *a*. Here however arises the difficulty which we have already pointed out, namely, that we cannot form any distinct conception of a line joining two coincident points; two separate points are necessary in order to fix a straight line. But it is clear that, although it is not yet satisfactory, there is still something in the definition that is useful and correct; for if we make the chord turn from the position *a b* to the position of the tangent at *a*, the point *b* does during this motion move along the curve up to the point *a*.

This difficulty was first cleared up and its explanation made a matter of common sense by Newton. The nature of his explanation is as follows:—Let us for simplicity take the curve to be a circle. If a straight stick be taken and bent so as to become part of a circle, the size of this circle will depend upon the amount of bending. The stick may be bent completely round until the ends meet, and then it will make a very small circle; or it may be bent very slightly indeed, and then it will become part of a very large circle. Now, conversely, suppose that we begin with a small circle, and, holding it fast at one point, make it get larger and larger, so that the piece we have hold of gets less and less bent; then, as the circle becomes extremely large, any small portion of it will more and more nearly approximate to a straight line. Hence a circle possesses this property, that the more it is magnified the straighter it becomes; this property likewise belongs to all the curves which we require to consider. It is sometimes expressed by saying that the curve is straight in its elements, or in its smallest parts; but the statement must be understood to mean only this, that the smaller the piece of a curve is taken the straighter it will look when magnified to a given length.

Now let us apply this to the problem of determining the position of a tangent. Let us suppose the tangent *a t* of a circle to be already drawn, and that a certain convenient length is

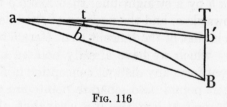

Fig. 116

marked off upon it (Fig. 116); from the end of this T let a perpendicular be drawn to meet the circle in B, and let *a* be joined to B by a straight line. We have now to consider the motion of the point B along the circle as the chord *a* B is turning round *a* towards the position *a* T; and the difficulty in

our way is clearly that figures like *a* B T get small, as for
example *a b t*, and continue to decrease until they cease to
be large enough to be definitely observed. Newton gets over
this difficulty by supposing that the figure is always magnified to a definite size; so that instead of considering the
smaller figure *a b t* we magnify it throughout until *a t* is
equal to the original length *a* T. But the portion *a b* of the
circle with which we are now concerned is less than the
former portion *a* B; consequently when it is magnified to
the same length (or nearly so) it must appear straighter.
That is to say, in the new figure *a b′* T, which is *a b t* magnified, the point *b′* will be nearer to the point T than B in the
old one *a* B T; consequently, also, as *b* moves along to *a* the
chord *a b* will get nearer to the tangent *a* T, or, what is the
same thing, the angle *t a b* will get smaller. This last result
is clear enough, because, as we previously supposed, the
chord *a b* is always turning round towards the position *a t*.

But now the important thing is that, by taking *b* near
enough to *a*, we can make the curve in the magnified figure
as straight as we please; that is to say, we can make *b′* ap-

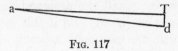

proach as near as we like to T. If we were to measure off from
T perpendicularly to *a* T any length, however small, say T *d*
(Fig. 117), then we can always draw a circle which shall have
a T for a tangent and which shall pass between T and *d*; and,
further, if we like to draw a line *a d* making a very small angle
with *a* T, then it will still be possible to make *b* go so close to *a*
that in the magnified figure the angle *b′ a* T shall be smaller
than the angle *d a* T which we have drawn.

Now mark what this process, which has been called Newton's microscope, really means. While the figure which we
wish to study is getting smaller and smaller, and finally
disappears altogether, we suppose it to be continually magnified, so as to retain a convenient size. We have one point

moving along a curve up towards another point, and we
want to consider what happens to the line joining them when
the two points approach indefinitely near to one another.
The result at which we have arrived by means of our microscope is that, by taking the points near enough together, the
line may be made to approach as near as we please to the
tangent to the curve at the point a. This, therefore, gives us
a definition of the tangent to a curve in terms only of measurable quantities. If at a certain point a of a curve there is
a line $a\,t$ possessing the property that by taking b near enough
to a on the curve the line $a\,b$ can be brought as near as we
like to $a\,t$ (that is, the angle $b\,a\,t$ made less than any assigned
angle, however small), then $a\,t$ is called the tangent to the
curve at the point a. Observe that all the things supposed
to be done in this definition are things which we know can
be done. A very small angle can be assigned; then, this
angle being drawn, a position of the point b can be found
which is such that $a\,b$ makes with $a\,t$ an angle smaller than
this. A supposition is here made in terms of quantities which
we already know and can measure. We only suppose in addition that, however small the assigned angle may be, the
point b can always be found; and if this is possible, then in
the case in which the assigned angle is extremely small,
the line $a\,b$ or $a\,t$ (for they now coincide) is called a tangent.

It is worth while to observe the likeness between this
definition and the one that we previously discussed of the
fourth proportional or of the equality of ratio. In that definition we supposed that, a certain fraction being assigned,
if the first ratio were greater than this fraction, so also was
the second ratio, and if less, less; and the question whether
these ratios were greater or less is one that can be settled
by measurement and comparison. We then made the further
supposition that whatever fraction were assigned the same
result would hold good; and we said that in that case the
ratios were equal. Now in both of these definitions, applying
respectively to tangents and to ratios, the difficulty is that
we cause a particular supposition to be extended so as to be

general; for we assume that a statement which can be very easily tested and found true in any one case is true in an infinite number of cases in which it has not been tested. But although the test cannot be applied individually to all these cases in a practical way, yet, since it is true in any individual case, we know on rational grounds that it must be satisfied in general; and therefore, justified by this knowledge, we are able to reason generally about the equality of ratios and about the tangents to curves.

Let us now translate the definition at which we have thus arrived from the language of curves and tangents into the language of instantaneous and mean velocities. The steepness of the chord of the curve of positions indicates the mean velocity, while the steepness of the tangent to the curve at any point indicates the instantaneous velocity at that point. The process of making the point *b* move nearer and nearer to the point *a* corresponds to taking for consideration a smaller and smaller interval of time after that moment at which the instantaneous velocity is wanted.

Suppose, then, the velocity of a body, viz. a railway train, to be varying, and that we want to find what its value is at a given instant. We might get a very rough approximation to it, or in some cases no approximation at all, by taking the mean velocity during the hour which follows that instant. We should get a closer approximation by taking the mean velocity during the minute succeeding that instant, because the instantaneous velocity would have less time to change. A still closer approximation would be obtained were we to take the mean velocity during the succeeding second. In all motions we should have to consider that we could make the approximation as close as we like by taking a sufficiently small interval. That is to say, if we choose to name any very small velocity, such as one with which a body going uniformly would move only an inch in a century, then, by taking the [time] interval small enough, it will be possible to make the mean velocity differ from the instantaneous velocity by less than this amount. Thus, finally, we shall have the following definition of instantaneous velocity: If there is a certain velocity to which the mean velocity during the interval succeeding a given instant can be made to approach as near as we like by taking the interval small enough, then that velocity is called the instantaneous velocity of the body at the given instant.

In this way then we have reduced the problem of finding the velocity of a moving body at any instant to the problem of drawing a tangent to its curve of positions at the corresponding point; and what we have already proved amounts to saying that, if the position of the body be given in terms of the time by means of a curve, then the velocity of the body will be given in terms of the time by means of the tangent to this curve.

Now there are many curves to which we can draw tangents by simple geometrical methods, as, for example, to the ellipse and the parabola; so that, whenever the curve of positions of a body happens to be one of these, we are able to find by geometrical construction the velocity of the body at any instant. Thus in the case of a falling body the curve of positions is a parabola, and we might find by the known properties of the tangent to a parabola that the velocity in this case is proportional to the time. But in the great majority of cases the problem of drawing a tangent to the curve of positions is just as difficult as the original problem of determining the velocity of a moving body, and in fact we do in many cases solve the former by means of the latter.[1]

§6. *On the Determination of Variable Velocity*

What is actually wanted in every case will be apparent from the consideration of the problem we have just mentioned—that of a body falling down straight. We note, from the experience of Galilei, that the whole distance which the body has fallen from rest at any instant is proportional to the square of the time; in fact, to obtain this distance in feet

[1] The method is due to Roberval (1602–1675).

we must multiply the number of seconds by itself and the result by a number a little greater than sixteen. Thus, for instance, in five seconds the body will have fallen rather more than twenty-five times sixteen feet, or 400 feet. Now what we want is some direct process of proving that when the distance traversed is proportional to the square of the time the velocity is always proportional to the time. In the present case we can find the velocity at the end of a given number of seconds by multiplying that number by thirty-two feet; thus at the end of five seconds the velocity of the body will be 160 feet per second.[1] Now as a matter of fact a

---

[1] The following may be taken as a proof. Let a be the distance from rest moved over by the body in t seconds, b that moved over by it in $t + t'$ seconds, so that t' seconds is the interval we take to find out the mean velocity. Now by our rule just quoted, since a feet are passed over in t seconds, we have

$$a = 16t^2,$$

and similarly $\qquad b = 16(t + t')^2 = 16(t^2 + 2tt' + t'^2).$

Hence we have $b - a = 16(t^2 + 2tt' + t'^2) - 16t^2$

$$= 16(2tt' + t'^2)$$
$$= 16t'(2t + t'),$$

giving the distance moved over in the interval t'. But the mean velocity during this interval is obtained by dividing the distance moved over by the time taken to traverse it; hence the mean velocity in our case for the interval of t' seconds immediately succeeding the t seconds

$$= \frac{b - a}{t'}$$

$$= \frac{16t'(2t + t')}{t'}$$

$$= 16(2t + t')$$
$$= 32t + 16t'.$$

Now if we look at this result, which we have obtained for the mean velocity, we see that there are two terms in it. The first, viz. $32t$, is quite independent of the interval t' which we have taken; the second, viz. $16t'$, depends directly on it, and will therefore change when we change the interval. Now the distance per second represented by $16t'$ feet can be made as small as we like by taking t' small enough; so that the mean velocity during the interval t' seconds succeeding the given instant can be made to approach $32t$ feet per second as near as we like by taking t' small enough. Recurring to our definition of instantaneous velocity, it is now evident that the instantaneous velocity of our falling body at the end of t seconds is $32t$ feet per second.

process (of which there is a simple example in the footnote) has been worked out, by which from any algebraical rule telling us how to calculate the distance traversed in terms of the time we can find another algebraical rule which will tell us how to calculate the velocity in terms of the time. One case of the process is this: If the distance traversed is at any instant a times the nth power of the time, then the velocity at any instant will be na times the $(n-1)$th power of the time. It is by means of this process of altering one algebraical rule so as to get another from it that both of the problems which we have shown to be equivalent to one another are solved in practice.

There is yet another problem of very great importance in the study of natural phenomena which can be made to depend on these two. When a point moves along a straight line the distance of it from some fixed point in the line is a quantity which varies from time to time. The rate of change of this distance is the same thing as the velocity of the moving point; and the rate of change of any continuous quantity can only be properly represented by means of the velocity of a point.

Thus, for instance, the height of the tide at a given port will vary from time to time during the day, and it may be indicated by a mark which goes up and down on a stick. The rate at which the height of the tide varies will obviously be the same thing as the velocity with which this mark goes up and down. Again the pressure of the atmosphere is indicated by means of the height of a mercury barometer. The rate at which this pressure changes is obviously the same thing as the velocity with which the surface of the mercury moves up and down. Now whenever we want to describe the changes which take place in any quantity in terms of the time, we may indeed roughly and approximately do so by means of a table. But this is also the most troublesome way; the proper way of describing them is by drawing a curve in which the *abscissa*, or horizontal distance, at any point represents the time, while the height of the curve at that point represents the value of the quantity at that time (see p. 167). Whenever this is done we practically suppose the variation of the quantity to be represented by the motion of the point on a curve. The quantity can only be adequately represented by marking off a length proportional to it on a line; so that if the quantity varies then the length marked off will vary, and consequently the end of this length will move along the curve. The rate at which the quantity varies is the rate at which this point moves; and when the values of the quantity for different times are represented by the perpendicular distances of points on a curve from the line which represents the time, its rate of variation is determined by the tangent to that curve.

§7. *On the Method of Fluxions*

Hence we have three problems which are practically the same. First, to find the velocity of a moving point when we know where it is at every instant; secondly, to draw a tangent to a curve at any point; thirdly, to find the rate of change of a quantity when we know how great it is at every instant. And the solution of them all depends upon that process by which, when we take the algebraical rule for finding the quantity in terms of the time, we deduce from it another rule for finding its rate of change in terms of the time.

This particular process of deriving one algebraical rule from another was first investigated by Newton. He was accustomed to describe a varying quantity as a *fluent*, and its rate of change he called the *fluxion* of the quantity. On account of these names, the entire method of solving these problems by means of the process of deriving one algebraical rule from another was termed the *Method of Fluxions*.

In general the rate of variation of a quantity will itself change from time to time; but if we consider only an interval very small as compared with that required for a considerable variation of the quantity, we may legitimately suppose that

it has not altered much during that interval. This is practically equivalent to supposing that the law of change has
been uniformly true during that interval, and that the rate
of change does not differ very much from its mean value.
Now the mean rate of change of a quantity during an interval
of time is just the difference between the values of the quantity at the beginning and at the end divided by the interval.
If any quantity increased by one inch in a second, then, although it may not have been increasing uniformly, or even
been increasing at all during the whole of that second, yet
during the second its mean rate of increase was one inch per
second. Now if the rate of increase only changes slowly we
may, as an approximation, fairly suppose it to be constant
during the second, and therefore to be equal to the mean
rate; and, as we know, the smaller the interval of time is, the
less is the error arising from this supposition. This is, as a
matter of fact, the way in which that process is established
by means of which a rule for calculating position is altered
into a rule for calculating velocity. The difference between
the distances of the moving point from some fixed point on
the line at two different times is divided by the interval between the times, and this gives the mean rate of change
during that interval. If we find that, by making the interval
smaller and smaller, this mean rate of change gets nearer
and nearer to a certain value, then we conclude that this
value is the actual rate of change when we suppose the interval to shrink up into an instant, or that it is, as we call it,
the instantaneous rate of change.

Because two differences are used in the argument which
establishes the process for changing the one rule into the
other, this process was called, first in other countries and
then also in England, the *Differential Calculus*. The name is
an unfortunate one, because the rate of change which is
therein calculated has nothing to do with differences, the
only connection with differences being that they are mentioned in the argument which is used to establish the process.
However this may be, the object of the differential calculus

or of the method of fluxions (whichever name we choose to give it) is to find a rule for calculating the rate of change of a quantity when we have a rule for calculating the quantity itself; and we have seen that when this can be done the problem of drawing a tangent to a curve and that of finding the velocity of a moving point are also solved.

§8. *Of the Relationship of Quantities, or Functions*

But we not only have rules for calculating the value of a quantity at any time, but also rules for calculating the value of one quantity in terms of another quite independently of the time. Of the former class of rules an example is the one mentioned above for calculating the rise of the tide. We may either write down a formula which will enable us to calculate it at a given instant, or we may draw a curve which shall represent its rise at different times of the day. Of the second kind of rule a good example is that in which the pressure of a given quantity of gas is given in terms of its volume when the temperature is supposed to be constant; the algebraical statement of the rule giving the relation between them is that the two things vary inversely as one another, or that the product representing them is constant.

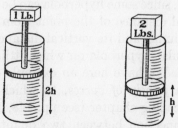

FIG. 118

Thus if we compress a mass of air to one-half of its natural volume the pressure will become twice as great, or will be, as it is called, two "atmospheres." And so if we compress it to one-fifth of the volume the pressure will become five times as great, or five atmospheres (Fig. 118).

If we like to represent this by a figure (see Fig. 119) we shall draw a curve in which the abscissa, or horizontal distance from the starting point, will represent the volume, and a vertical line drawn through the extremity of this abscissa will represent the pressure. For any particular temperature the curve traced out by the extremity of the line representing the pressure will be a hyperbola having one asymptote vertical and the other horizontal; and for different temperatures we shall have different hyperbolas with the same asymptotes.

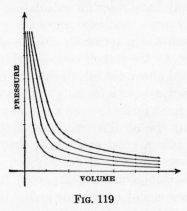

Fig. 119

Thus every point in the plane will represent a particular state of the body, since some hyperbola can be drawn through it; the horizontal distance of the point from the origin will represent the volume, and its vertical distance the pressure, while the particular hyperbola on which it lies will indicate the temperature. We have here an example of the physical importance of a *family of curves*, to which reference was made in the preceding chapter (see pp. 148, 149).

When the connection between two quantities has to be found out by actual observation, this is done by properly plotting down points on paper (as in §11, Chap. IV) to represent successive observations. Thus in the case of air the pressure would be observed for different values of the volume. For each of these observed pairs of values a point would be marked in the plane; and when a sufficient number had been marked it would become obvious to the eye that, roughly speaking, the point lay on a hyperbolic curve. But it is to be noticed that it is only roughly that this result holds, because observations are never so accurate that the curve does not require to be drawn pretty freely in passing through the points. But directly the geometer has seen that the shape of the curve is hyperbolic he recognizes the law that pressure varies inversely as volume.

We have here the relation between two quantities expressed by means of a curve. Whenever two quantities are related in some such way, so that one of them being given the other can be calculated or found, each is said to be a *function* of the other. Now a function may be supposed to be given either by an algebraical rule or by a curve. Thus to find the pressure corresponding to a given volume we might say that a certain number was to be divided by the number representing the volume, and the result would be the number of units of pressure; or we might say that from the given point of the horizontal line which represented the volume a perpendicular was to be drawn and continued till it met the curve, and that the ordinate (or the part of this between the horizontal line and the curve) represented the pressure. We have thus a connection established between the science of geometry and the science of quantity, as, for example, the relation between the two quantities, volume and pressure, is expressed by means of a certain curve.

Now every connection between two sciences is a help to both of them. When such a connection is established we may both use the known theorems about quantities in order to investigate the nature of curves (and this is, in fact, the method of co-ordinates introduced by Descartes), or we may make use of known geometrical properties of curves in order to find out theorems about the way in which quantities depend upon one another. For the first purpose the relation between the two quantities is regarded as an equation. Thus, instead of saying that a pressure varies inversely as a volume we should prefer to say that the product of the pressure and the volume is equal to a certain constant, the temperature being supposed unaltered; or, paying attention only to the geometrical way of expressing this, we should say that, for points along the curve we are considering, the product of the abscissa and the ordinate is equal to a certain fixed quantity. This is written for shortness

$$xy = c^2,$$

and from such an equation all the properties of a hyperbola may be deduced.

But we may also make use of the properties of known curves in order to study the ways in which quantities can depend on one another. Thus the perpendicular distance P M from the

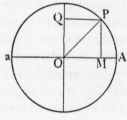

Fig. 120

point P of the circle to a fixed diameter A O a (Fig. 120) is a quantity whose ratio to the radius O P depends in a certain definite way upon the magnitude of the angle P O A, or, what is the same thing (p. 131), upon the length of the arc A P. The ratio is in fact what we have termed the sine of the angle, or, as it is sometimes called, the sine of the arc. If the arc A P is made proportional to the time, or, what is the same thing, if P is made to move uniformly round the circle, then the length of the line P M will represent the distance from the centre O of a point Q oscillating according to a law which is defined by this geometrical construction. This particular kind of oscillation, which is called *simple harmonic motion*, occurs when the air is agitated by sound, or the ether by light, or when any elastic body is set into a tremor. Relations such as that which we have just mentioned between arcs of a circle and straight lines drawn according to some simple constructions in the circle give rise to what are often termed *circular* functions. Thus the trigonometrical ratios considered in §7 of Chapter IV are functions of this kind. We have also *hyperbolic* functions, depending on the hyperbola in somewhat the same way in which circular functions depend upon the circle, and *elliptic* functions, so called because by means of them the length of the arc of an ellipse can be calculated.

But the most valuable method of studying the properties of functions is derived from the considerations of which we have been treating in this chapter, viz. considerations of the rate of change of quantities. When the relation between two quantities is known, the relation between their rates of change can be found by a known algebraical process; and we have shown that the problem of finding this relation ultimately comes to the same thing as the problem of drawing a tangent to the curve which expresses the relation between the two original quantities. Thus, in the case we previously considered of two quantities whose product is constant or which vary inversely as one another, it is clear that one must increase when the other decreases; it is found that the ratio of these rates of change is equal to the ratio of the quantities themselves. Thus the rate of change of the volume of a gas is to the rate of change of the pressure (the temperature being kept constant) as the volume is to the pressure, it being always remembered that an increase of the one implies a decrease of the other.

The consideration of this ratio of the rates of change is of great importance in determining one of the fundamental changeable properties of a body, namely, its *elasticity*. We define the elasticity of a gas as the change of pressure which will produce a given *contraction*; where by the term contraction is meant the change in the volume divided by the whole volume before change. Thus if the volume of a gas diminished one per cent., it would experience a contraction of $\frac{1}{100}$th. If then, in accordance with our definition, we divide the pressure necessary to produce this contraction by $\frac{1}{100}$, or, what is the same thing, multiply it by 100, we shall get what is called the elasticity. Now in our case the change of pressure divided by the whole pressure is equal to what we have called the contraction, that is, to $\frac{1}{100}$; and therefore the change of pressure is equal to $\frac{1}{100}$th of the whole pressure. But we have just proved that the elasticity is 100 times the change of pressure necessary to produce the contraction we have been considering, and it is therefore equal to the whole pressure. Consequently the elasticity of a gas is measured by the pressure of the gas.

§9. *Of Acceleration and the Hodograph*

We may then consider the rate of change of any measurable quantity as another quantity which we can find; and we have derived our notion of it from the velocity of a moving point. In the simplest case, when this point is moving along a straight line, the rate at which it is going is the rate of change of its distance from a point fixed in the line. But in the general case, when the point is moving not on a straight line, but along any sort of curve, we shall not give a complete description of its state of motion if we only say how fast it is going; it will be necessary to say in addition in what direction it is going. Hence we must not only measure the quantity of a velocity, but also a certain quality of it, viz. the direction. Now we do as a matter of fact contrive to study these two things together, and the method by which we do so is perhaps one of the most powerful instruments by which the scope of the exact sciences has been extended in recent times. Defining the velocity of a moving point as the rate of change of its position, we are met by the question, What is its position?

This question has been answered in the preceding chapter. The position of a moving point is determined when we know the directed step or vector which connects it with a fixed point. If then the velocity of the moving point means

the rate of change of its position, and if this position is determined by the vector which would carry us from some
fixed point to the moving point, in order to understand
velocity we shall have to get a clear conception of what is
meant by the rate of change of a vector.

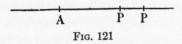

FIG. 121

Let us go back for a moment to the simpler case of a point
moving along a straight line; its position is determined by
means of the step A P from the point A fixed in the straight
line to the moving point P (Fig. 121). Now this step alters
with the motion of the point; so that if the point comes to P'
the step is changed from A P to A P'. How is this change made
in the step? Clearly by adding to the original step A P the new
step P P', and we specify the velocity of P by saying at what
rate this addition is made.

Now let us resume the general case. We have the fixed
point A given; and the position of the moving point P is
determined by means of the step A P. As P moves about, this
step gets altered, so that when P comes to P' this step is A P';
it is therefore obvious that it is altered not only in magnitude
but also in direction. Now the change may be made by adding to the original step A P the new step P P'; and it is quite
clear that if we go from A to P and then from P to P' the result is exactly the same as if we had gone directly from A to

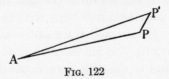

FIG. 122

P' (Fig. 122). The question then is: At what rate does this
addition take place, or what step per second is added to the
position? The answer as before is of the nature of a step or
vector—that is, the change of position of the moving point
has not only magnitude but direction. We shall therefore

have to say that the rate of change of a step or vector is always so many feet per second in a certain direction.

To sum up, then, we state that the velocity of a moving point is the rate of change of the step which specifies the position; and that in order to describe accurately this velocity, we must draw a line of given length in a given direction; we observe also that the rate of change of a directed quantity is itself a directed quantity. This last remark is of the utmost importance, and we shall now apply it to a consideration of the velocity itself.

If a point is moving uniformly in a straight line its velocity is always the same in magnitude and the same in direction; and consequently a line drawn to represent it would be unaltered during the motion. But if a point moves uniformly round a circle its velocity, although always the same in magnitude, will be constantly changing in direction, and the line which specifies this velocity will thus be always of the same length, but constantly turning round so as always to keep parallel with the direction of motion of the moving point. And so, generally, when a point is moving along any kind of curve let us suppose that through some other point, which is kept fixed, a line is always drawn which represents the velocity of the moving point both in magnitude and direction. Since the velocity of the moving point will in general change, this line will also change both in size and in direction, and the end of it will trace out some sort of curve. Thus in the case of the uniform circular motion, since the velocity remains constant, it is clear that the end of the line representing the velocity will trace out a circle; in the case of a body thrown into the air the end of the corresponding line would be found to describe a vertical straight line. This curve described by the end of the line which represents the velocity at any instant may be regarded as a map of the motion, and was for that reason called by Hamilton the *hodograph*. If we know the path of the moving point and also the hodograph of the motion, we can find the velocity of the moving point at any particular position in its path.

All we have to do is to draw through the centre of reference of the hodograph a line parallel to the tangent to the path at the given position; the length of this line will give the rate of motion, or the velocity of the point as it passes through that position in its path. Hamilton proved that in the case of the planetary orbits described about the sun the hodograph is always a circle. In this case it possesses other interesting properties, as, for example, that the amount of light and heat received by the planet during a given interval of time is proportional to the length of the arc of the hodograph between the two points corresponding to the beginning and end of that interval.

But the great use of the hodograph is to give us a clear conception of the rate of change of the velocity. This rate of change is called the *acceleration*. Now, it must not be supposed that acceleration always means an *increase* of velocity, for in this case, as in many others, mathematicians have adopted for use one word to denote a change that may have many directions; thus a decrease of velocity is called a negative acceleration. This mode of speaking, although rather puzzling at first, becomes a help instead of a confusion when one is accustomed to it. Now a velocity may be changed in magnitude without altering its direction— that is to say, it may be changed by adding it to a velocity parallel to itself. In this case we say that the acceleration is in the direction of motion. But a velocity may also be changed in direction without being changed in magnitude, and we have seen that then the hodograph is a circle. The velocity is altered by adding to it a velocity perpendicular to itself, for the tangent at any point to a circle is at right angles to the radius drawn to that point, and in this case we may say that the acceleration is at right angles to the direction of motion. But in general both the magnitude and the direction of the velocity will vary, and then we shall see that the acceleration is neither in the direction of motion nor at right angles to it, but that it is in some intermediate direction.

If we consider the motion in the hodograph of the end of

the line representing the velocity, we observe the motion of a point whose position is defined by the step to it from the centre of the hodograph. Now this step is just the velocity of the point P in the original curve, for the line o q is supposed to be drawn at every instant to represent the velocity

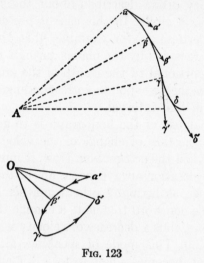

FIG. 123

of P in magnitude and direction. Now we saw that the rate of change of the step from some fixed point A to P was the velocity of P. Hence, since the step o q drawn from the fixed point o to Q defines the position of Q, it is obvious that the rate of change of the step o q is the velocity of Q. Since o q represents the velocity of P, it follows that the velocity of the point Q describing the hodograph is the rate of change of the velocity of P; that is to say, it is the acceleration of the motion of P. This acceleration being the velocity of Q, and a velocity being as we have seen a vector, it at once follows that the acceleration is a vector or directed quantity.

In changing the magnitude and direction of the velocity of a moving point we may consider that we are pouring in, as it were, velocity of a certain kind at a certain rate. In the case of a stone thrown up obliquely and allowed to fall again the path described is a parabola, and the direction of motion, which originally pointed obliquely upwards, turns round and becomes horizontal, and then gradually points more and more downwards. But what has really been happening the whole time is that velocity straight downwards has been continually added at a uniform rate during every second, so that the original velocity of the stone is compounded with a velocity vertically downwards, increasing uniformly at the rate of thirty-two feet a second. In this case, then, we say that the acceleration, or rate of change per second of the velocity of the stone, is constant and equal to thirty-two feet a second vertically downwards.

If we whirl anything round at the end of a string we shall be continually pouring in velocity directed towards the end of the string which is held in the hand; and since the velocity of the body which is being whirled is perpendicular to the direction of the string, the added velocity is always perpendicular to the existing velocity of the body. And so also when a planet is travelling round the sun there is a continual pouring in of velocity towards the sun, or, as we say, the acceleration is always in the line joining the planet to the sun. In addition it is in this case found to vary inversely as the square of the distance from the sun.

§10. *On the Laws of Motion*

These examples prepare us to understand that law of motion which is the basis of all exact treatment of physics. When a body is moving let us consider what it is that depends upon the circumstances, meaning by the "circumstances" the instantaneous position relative to it of other bodies as well as the instantaneous state of the body itself irrespective of its motion. We might at first be inclined to say that the velocity of the body depends on the circumstances, but very little reflection will show us that in the same circumstances a body may be moving with very different velocities. At a given height above the earth's surface, for example, a stone may be moving upwards or downwards, or horizontally, or at any inclination, and in any of these modes with any velocity whatever; and there is nothing contrary to nature in supposing a motion of this sort. Yet we should find that, no matter in what way the stone may move through a given position, the rate of change per second of its velocity will always be the same, viz. it will be thirty-two feet per second vertically downwards. When we push a chair along the ice, in order to describe the circumstances we must state the compression of those muscles which keep our hands against the chair. Now the rate at which the chair moves does not depend simply upon this compression; for a given amount of push may be either starting the chair from rest or may be quickening it when it is going slowly, or may be keeping it up at a high rate.

What is it, then, which does depend upon the circumstances? In whichever of these ways, or in whatever other way this given amount of push is used, its result in every case is obviously to change the rate of motion of the chair; and this change of the rate of motion will vary with the amount of push. Hence it is the rate of change of the velocity, or the acceleration of the chair which depends upon the circumstances, and these circumstances are partly the compression of our muscles and partly the friction of the ice; the one is increasing and the other is diminishing the velocity in the direction in which the chair is going.

The law of motion to which allusion has just been made is this:—The acceleration of a body, or the rate of change of its velocity depends at any moment upon the position relative to it of the surrounding bodies, but not upon the rate at which the body itself is going. There are two different ways in which this dependence takes place. In some cases, as when a hand is pushing a chair, the rate of change of the velocity depends on the state of compression of the bodies in contact; in other cases, as in the motion of the planets about the sun, the acceleration depends on the relative position of bodies at a distance.

The acceleration produced in a body by a particular set

of surrounding circumstances must in each case be determined by experiment, but we have learnt by experience a general law which much simplifies the experiments which it is necessary to make. This law is as follows:—If the presence of one body alone produces a certain acceleration in the motion of a given body, and the presence of a second body alone another acceleration; then, if both bodies are present at the same time, the one has in general no effect upon the acceleration produced by the other. That is, the total acceleration of the moving body will be the combination of the two simple accelerations; or, since accelerations are directed quantities, we have only to combine the simple accelerations, as we did vector steps in §3 of the preceding chapter, in order to find the result of superposing two sets of surrounding circumstances.

Now while this great law of nature simplifies extremely our consideration of the motion of the *same* body under different surrounding circumstances, it does not enable us to state anything as to the motion of *different* bodies under the same surrounding circumstances. This case, however, is amply provided for by another comprehensive law which experience also has taught us. We may thus state this third all-important law of motion:—The ratio of the accelerations which any two bodies produce in each other by their mutual influence is a constant quantity, quite independent of the exact physical characteristics of that influence. That is to say, however the two bodies influence one another, whether they touch or are connected by a thread or being at a distance still alter one another's velocities, this ratio will remain in these and all other cases the same.

§11. *Of Mass and Force*

Let us see how we can apply this law. Suppose we take some standard body P and any other Q, and note the ratios of the accelerations they produce in each other under any of the simplest possible circumstances of mutual influence.

Let the ratio determined by experiment be represented by *m*, or *m* expresses the ratio of the acceleration of the standard body P to that of the second body Q. This quantity *m* is termed the *mass* of the body Q. Let *m′* be the ratio of the accelerations produced in the standard body P and a third body R by their mutual influence. Now the law as it stands above enables us to treat only of the ratio of the accelerations of P and Q, or again of P and R under varied circumstances of mutual influence. It does not tell us anything about the ratio of the accelerations which Q and R might produce in each other. Experience, however, again helps us out of our difficulties and tells us that if Q and R mutually influence each other, the ratio of the acceleration of Q to that of R will be *inversely* as the ratio of *m* to *m′*. If then we choose to term unity the *mass* of our standard body, we may state generally that *mutual accelerations are inversely as masses*. Hence, when we have once determined the masses of bodies we are able to apply our knowledge of the effect of any set of circumstances on *one* body, to calculate the effect which the same circumstances would produce upon any other body.[1]

The reader will remark that mass as defined above is a ratio of accelerations, or in other words a mere numerical constant experimentally deducible for any two bodies. It is found that for two bodies of the same uniform substance, their masses are proportional to their volumes. This relation of mass to volume has given rise to much obscurity. An indescribable something termed *matter* has been associated with bodies. Bodies are supposed to consist of matter filling

---

[1] Without considering the body R, the same conclusion may be arrived at thus:

1. The acceleration of P (due to Q) is proportional to the mass of Q.
2. The acceleration of Q (due to P) is proportional to the mass of P.

∴ dividing 1 by 2

i.e. $\dfrac{\text{Acc. P (due to Q)}}{\text{Acc. Q (due to P)}} = \dfrac{m\text{Q}}{m\text{P}}$

or in other words the mutual accelerations are inversely as the masses.—J.R.N.

space, and the mass of a body is defined as the amount of matter in it. An additional conception termed *force* has been introduced and is supposed to be in some way resident in matter. The force of a body P on a body Q of mass m is a quantity proportional to the mass m of Q and to the acceleration which the presence of P produces in the motion of Q. It will be obvious to the reader that this conception of force no more explains why the presence of P tends to change the velocity of Q, than the conception of matter explains why mutual accelerations are inversely as masses. The custom of basing our ideas of motion on these terms "matter" and "force" has too often led to obscurity, not only in mathematical, but in philosophical reasoning. We do not know *why* the presence of one body tends to change the velocity of another; to say that it arises from the force resident in the first body acting upon the matter of the moving body is only to slur over our ignorance. All that we do know is that the presence of one body may tend to change the velocity of another, and that, if it does, the change can be ascertained from experiment, and obeys the above laws.

To calculate by means of the laws of motion from the observed effects on a simple body of a simple set of circumstances the more complex effects of any combination of circumstances on a complex body or system of bodies is the special function of that branch of the exact sciences which is termed *Applied Mathematics*.

BIBLIOGRAPHY
OF THE MAJOR WRITINGS
OF WILLIAM KINGDON CLIFFORD

L. and E. = Lectures and Essays, edited by Leslie Stephen and F. Pollock (London: Macmillan and Co.; 1879). *M.P.* = *Mathematical Papers* by William Kingdon Clifford, edited by Robert Tucker (London: Macmillan and Co.; 1882).[1]

1863
"On Jacobians and Polar Opposites." *M.P.*
"Analogues of Pascal's Theorem." *M.P.*

1864
"Analytical Metrics." *M.P.*
"Geometrical Theorem." *M.P.*

1865
"On Triangular Symmetry." *M.P.*

1866
"On Some Extensions of the Fundamental Proposition in M. Chasles's Theory of Characteristics." *M.P.*
"On the General Theory of Anharmonics." *M.P.*
"Bitangent Circles of a Conic." *M.P.*
"Of Power-coordinates in General." *M.P.*

1867
"On the Principal Axes of a Rigid Body." *M.P.*

1868
"On Some of the Conditions of Mental Development." *L. and E.*
"On Some Porismatic Problems." *M.P.*
"On a General Investigation of the Theory of Polars." *M.P.*
"On the Powers of Spheres." *M.P.*

[1] The data for this bibliography are drawn from the volume edited by Robert Tucker, cited above.

245

1869

"On the Theory of Distances." *M.P.*

"On Syzygetic Relations among the Powers of Linear Quantics." *M.P.*

"On Syzygetic Relations Connecting the Powers of Linear Quantics." *M.P.*

"On the Umbilici of Anallagmatic Surfaces." (Title only in the British Association *Report* for this year.)

"Lectures on Geometry," given to a Class of Ladies at S. Kensington. *M.P.*

"On Boundaries in General." *Macmillan's Magazine*, August 1879; also *M.P.*

"Analysis of Cremona's Transformations." *M.P.*

1870

"On a Case of Evaporation in the Order of a Resultant." *M.P.*

"On Theories of the Physical Forces." *L. and E.*

"Proof That Every Rational Equation Has a Root." *M.P.*

"On the Space-Theory of Matter." *M.P.*

"Synthetic Proof of Miquel's Theorem." *M.P.*

"On an Unexplained Contradiction in Geometry." (Title only in the British Association *Report* of this year.)

"Lecture Notes." *M.P.*

1871

"The History of the Sun, etc." *L. and E.*

"On a Canonical Form of Spherical Harmonics." *M.P.*

"Note on the Secular Cooling and the Figure of the Earth." (Title only in British Association *Report* for this year.)

1872

"Atoms." *L. and E.*

"Ether; the Evidence for Its Existence and the Phenomena It Explains." *L. and E.*

"Remarks on a Theory of the Exponential Function Derived from the Equation $\frac{du}{dt} = pu$." *M.P.*

"On Babbage's Calculating Machines." *L. and E.*

"On the Aims and Instruments of Scientific Thought." *L. and E.*

"On the Contact of Surfaces of the Second Order with Other Surfaces." (Title only in the British Association *Report* of this year.)

"On a Theorem Relating to Polyhedra, Analogous to Mr. Cotterill's Theorem on Plane Polygons." *M.P.*

"The Dawn of the Sciences in Europe." *L. and E.*

"Geometry on an Ellipsoid." *M.P.*

1873

"The Philosophy of the Pure Sciences." *L. and E.*

"On the Hypotheses Which Lie at the Bases of Geometry." *M.P.*

"The Relations between Science and Some Modern Poetry." Recast as "Cosmic Emotion." *L. and E.*

"Preliminary Sketch of Biquaternions." *M.P.*

"On Mr. Spottiswoode's Contact Problems." *M.P.*

"On Some Curves of the Fifth Class," and "On a Surface of Zero Curvature and Finite Extent." (Titles only in the British Association *Report* for this year.)

Review of De Morgan's *Budget of Paradoxes. M.P.*

"Graphic Representation of the Harmonic Components of a Periodic Motion." *M.P.*

"Syllabus of Lectures on Motion." *M.P.*

1874

"Review of Vol. I of G. H. Lewes' 'Problems of Life and Mind.'" *L. and E.*

"The First and Last Catastrophe." *L. and E.*

"On the Education of the People." *L. and E.*

"On a Message from Prof. Sylvester," and "On the General Equations of Chemical Decomposition." (Titles only in the British Association *Report* of this year.)

"Body and Mind." *L. and E.*

"On the Nature of Things in Themselves." *L. and E.*

"Seeing and Thinking." (*Nature* Series.)

"Motion of a Solid in Elliptic Space." *M.P.*

1875

"The General Features of the History of Science." *L. and E.*

"Ultramontanism." *L. and E.*

"The Unseen Universe." *L. and E.*

"On the Scientific Basis of Morals." *L. and E.*

"On the Theory of Linear Transformations; (i) the Graphical Representation of Invariants; (ii) the Expansion of Unsymmetrical Functions in Symmetrical Functions and Determinants; (iii) the Notation of Matrices." (Title only in the British Association *Report* of this year.)

"A Fragment on Matrices." *M.P.*

"Right and Wrong; the Scientific Ground of Their Distinction." *L. and E.*

"On the Transformation of Elliptic Functions." *M.P.*

1876

"On the Free Motion under No Forces of a Rigid System in an n-fold Homaloid." *M.P.*

"Sight and What It Tells Us." *L. and E.*

"Instruments Used in Measurement." *L. and E.*

"Instruments Illustrating Kinematics, Statics and Dynamics." *L. and E.*

"The Ethics of Belief." *L. and E.*

"Notes on the Communication Entitled 'On the Transformation of Elliptic Functions.'" *M.P.*

"On the Classification of Geometric Algebras." *M.P.*

"On In-and-circumscribed Polyhedra." *M.P.*

"On the Theory of Screws in a Space of Constant Positive Curvature." *M.P.*

"On Tricircular Sextics." *M.P.*

"On the Double Theta-functions." *M.P.*

"Further Note on Biquaternions." *M.P.*

1877

"On the Types of Compound Statement Involving Four Classes." *L. and E.*

"The Ethics of Religion." *L. and E.*

"The Influence upon Morality of a Decline in Religious Belief." *L. and E.*

Review of Dr. Booth's *New Geometrical Methods. M.P.*

"On the Canonical Form and Dissection of a Riemann's Surface." *M.P.*

"Cosmic Emotion." *L. and E.*

"Notes on Vortex-motion, on the Triple-Generation of Three-bar Curves, and on the Mass-centre of an Octahedron." *M.P.*

"Enumeration of the Types of Compound Statements." *M.P.*

"Algebraic Introduction to Elliptic Functions." *M.P.*

"On Groups of Periodic Functions." *M.P.*

1878

"Remarks on the Chemico-Algebraical Theory." *M.P.*

"Virchow on the Teaching of Science." *L. and E.*

"On the Classification of Loci." *M.P.*

"Childhood and Ignorance." *L. and E.*

"Applications of Grassmann's Extensive Algebra." *M.P.*

"Elements of Dynamic: an Introduction to the Study of Motion and Rest in Solid and Fluid Bodies." Part I. Kinematic.

"Notes on Quantics of Alternate Numbers, Used as a Means for Determining the Invariants and Covariants of Quantics in General." *M.P.*

"Binary Forms of Alternate Variables." *M.P.*

"On Bessel's Functions." *M.P.*

"Theory of Marks of Multiple Theta-functions." *M.P.*

OTHER DOVER BOOKS

PRINCIPLES OF PSYCHOLOGY by William James

This one-volume edition of James' masterpiece contains *both volumes of his "long course" complete.* (It should not be confused with any of the various abridgments which omit many of the most important sections.' Here are all of his wonderfully lucid descriptions of the stream of thought, consciousness of thought, perception of time, memory, imagination, the emotions, reasoning, hypnotism, etc. "The book remains the most instructive, and easily the most absorbing summary of its subject...the keenest introspection which psychology has witnessed since the uncanny clarity of David Hume." -- *Will Durant.* Two volumes bound as one. 1408pp. Illustrations. 5 3/8 x 8.

Clothbound $7.50

SCIENCE AND HYPOTHESIS by Henri Poincaré

"Few mathematicians have had the breadth of philosophical vision that Poincaré had, and none is his superior in the gift of clear exposition." -- *E. T. Bell.* This book develops further Poincaré's views on the psychology of invention. It contains revealing discussions of Number and Magnitude, Space, Force, and Electrodynamics. 272pp. Index. 5 3/8 x 8.

Paperbound $1.25

AN INTRODUCTION
TO SYMBOLIC LOGIC by Susanne K. Langer

Even if you bogged down somewhere in the middle of high school algebra, you can learn to use mathematical logic by following the discussion given in this book. You start out with the simplest symbols and conventions and end up with a remarkable grasp of the Boole-Schroeder and Russell-Whitehead systems. New appendix on truth-value tables. Second edition, revised and expanded. 368pp. 5 3/8 x 8. Paperbound $1.60

FLATLAND by Edwin A. Abbott

An adventure in pure mathematics, a fantasy of strange spaces peopled by geometrical figures....figures that think and speak and have all-too-human emotions. Although FLATLAND is a work of fiction, it will help you understand the mysteries of two-, three-, and four-dimensional space better than most texts on the subject. Written over 70 years ago, it is a minor classic that rivals the best work of Voltaire and Swift. ix + 100pp. 5 3/8 x 8.   Paperbound $1.00

MATHEMATICAL RECREATIONS
by Maurice Kraitchik

These 250 mathematical puzzles have been collected from such diverse sources as Arabia, Egypt, France, England, Greece, India, and the United States. They provide endless hours of entertainment and instruction for both the beginner and the advanced mathematician. Among them are problems involving crypto-arithmetic, probabilities, bridge hands, chess puzzles, magic squares, problems of "difficult crossings," etc. Answers include a detailed break-down of the mathematical computations involved. Over 40 tables. 328pp. 181 illus. Second revised edition. 5 3/8 x 8.

Paperbound $1.65

THE ANALYSIS OF MATTER by Bertrand Russell

This book ranks high in the long list of contributions which Bertrand Russell has made ("One of the best that Mr. Russell has given us." -- *London Times;* "The most thorough treatment of the subject that has yet been published." -- *The Nation*). It deals with the problem of understanding the new physics through our perceptions, and covers such topics as The Logical Analysis of Physics, Pre-Relativity Physics, Causality, From Primitive Perception to Common Sense, Scientific Inference, Physics and Perception, etc. New introduction by Lester E. Denonn. Index. xiv + 408pp. 5 3/8 x 8.   Clothbound $3.95
                                            Paperbound $1.85

A BUDGET OF PARADOXES by Augustus De Morgan

Four hundred examples of scientific logic gone haywire, gleefully collected and mercilessly exposed by one of the wittiest mathematicians of the 19th Century. A fascinating survey of what Professor Ernest Nagel in his new introduction calls "the huge debris of barren intellectual labor that borders the winding path cut by modern science through the jungles of human ignorance." The book takes to task various quixotic opponents of Newtonian physics, the romantics who attempt to devise perpetual motion machines or trisect angles, and the fanatically logical objectors to the modern extension of numbers concept...among others. But it is chiefly valuable as an informal text on the scientific method in particular, and the art of thinking in general. Edited by D. E. Smith. 5 3/8 x 8. Vol. I: xxii + 402pp. Vol. II: iv + 387pp. Index. Two volumes bound as one.   Clothbound $4.95

A CONCISE HISTORY
OF MATHEMATICS by Dirk J. Struik

Here's a book that emphasizes the ideas and continuity of mathematics, rather than its anecdotal
aspects. It starts with the ancient Greek, Egyptian,
and Oriental mathematicians, and ends with the giants
of the late 19th Century. It is well illustrated, with
47 reproductions of title pages, diagrams from famous
treatises, and portraits of well known mathematicians.
"Rich in content...thoughtful in interpretation,"
wrote the *U. S. Quarterly Book List.* Two volumes
bound as one. Vol. I: xvii + 123pp. Vol. II: vi + 175pp.
Revised edition. 5 x 7 3/8.   Paperbound $1.60

SCIENCE AND METHOD by Henri Poincaré

Related to this famous mathematician's interest in the
philosophy of science was his preoccupation with the
psychology of mathematical creation. These reflections,
recorded in this book, cover many of the most signi-
ficant and interesting aspects of the germination of
ideas, their development and application. Special
chapters on Science and the Scientist, Mathematical
Reasoning, The New Mechanics, and Astronomic
Science. 288pp. 5 3/8 x 8.   Paperbound $1.25

LANGUAGE AND MYTH by Ernst Cassirer

A fascinating excursion into semantics, philosophy,
anthropology, and logic that demonstrates the importance of myth and superstition in the development
of logic. Six sections: The Place of Language and
Myth in the Pattern of Human Culture, The Evolution
of Religious Ideas, Language and Conception, Word
Magic, The Successive Phases of Religious Thought,
and The Power of Metaphor. Translated by Susanne
K. Langer. x + 103pp. Index. 5 3/8 x 8.

Clothbound $2.50
Paperbound $1.25